STECK-VAUGHN

CONNECTIONS

Life Skills & Mathematics

REVIEWERS

Rochelle Kenyon
Assistant Principal
School Board of Broward County
Fort Lauderdale, Florida

Margaret A. Rogers
Vice-Principal
San Juan Unified School District
Sacramento, California

Dee Akers Prins
Resource Specialist
Richmond Public Schools
Richmond, Virginia

Lois J. Sherard
Instructional Facilitator
New York City Board of Education
New York, New York

Danette S. Queen
Instructional Facilitator
New York City Public Schools
New York, New York

STECK-VAUGHN
COMPANY
A Subsidiary of National Education Corporation

Acknowledgments

Executive Editor: Elizabeth Strauss
Supervising Editor: Carolyn Hall
Design Director: D. Childress
Design Coordinator: Cynthia Ellis
Cover Design: D. Childress
Editorial Development: McClanahan & Company, Inc.
Project Director: Mark Moscowitz
Writers: Cathy Fillmore-Hoyt, Linda Van Hook
Editor: Doreen Stern
Design/Production: McClanahan & Company, Inc.

Photograph Credits:
p.   8   © John Griffin/Imageworks
p. 58   Van Bucher/Photo Researchers
p. 106   © Bob Daemmrich
p. 142   Rhoda Sidney/Monkmeyer Press
p. 228   David Strikler/Monkmeyer Press

Illustration Credits: Cover: Rhonda Childress
G & S Typesetters, Inc.

ISBN   0-8114-5602-1

Table of Contents

Unit 1   Whole Numbers   *Page 8*

Unit 2   Fractions   *Page 58*

Unit 3   Decimals   *Page 106*

To the Student

How to Use This Book

This book presents basic mathematics skills and concepts in the context of everyday, real-life applications. The book is divided into the following five units.

Units

Unit 1: Whole Numbers. This unit covers whole number concepts such as place value, order of operations, rounding, equations, and expressions. You will also work with the four operations: addition, subtraction, multiplication, and division of whole numbers.

Unit 2: Fractions. Fraction concepts and using the four operations with fractions are presented in this unit.

Unit 3: Decimals. This unit covers decimal concepts and using the four operations with decimals.

Unit 4: Ratio, Proportion, and Percent. In this unit you will learn the concept of ratios and how to solve proportions. You will also use the percent and interest formulas.

Unit 5: Special Topics. This unit covers the concepts of probability, circles and triangles, finding the area and circumference of a circle, and positive and negative numbers.

Inventory and Posttest

The Inventory is a self-check to see which skills you know and which skills you need to practice. After you complete all the items on the Inventory, fill out the Correlation Chart. It tells you where every skill is taught in this book. After you work through this book, you will take the Posttest. Compare your Posttest score to your Inventory score to see how much your math skills have improved.

Reviews

Each unit ends with a Unit Review. The Unit Review gives you a chance to see if you learned all the skills and concepts in that unit. Cumulative Reviews are placed after Units Two, Three, Four, and Five. Here you will review all the skills and concepts that have been presented up to that point.

Sections and Set-up Problems

All the units are divided into sections. Most of the sections begin with a real-life activity that requires little or no computation. The problems presented are set-up problems. **Set-up problems** ask you to choose the correct operation, equation, or expression that should be used to solve the problem. In the next part of the section, you will learn the computation skills needed to solve similar everyday problems. Computation is followed by instruction in problem-solving strategies. Each section ends with two pages of practice.

Real-life Applications

All skills and concepts in the sections are applied to problems in Consumer Math, Measurement and Geometry, and Data Analysis.

Consumer Math covers math that is used in personal and business situations. It includes making a purchase, selling an item, and solving problems involving money.

Measurement and Geometry includes working with both the standard and metric systems of measurement. You will solve problems that involve finding perimeter, area, volume, and circumference.

Data Analysis involves working with graphs, charts, tables, and scales as well as finding the mean and median.

Problem-Solving Strategies

You will learn many helpful strategies that are used to solve math problems. As you work with these strategies, use the following four-step plan to solve word problems.

READ Read the problem to determine what you need to find out. Identify the information you need to solve the problem.

PLAN Plan how you will solve the problem. Decide which operation or operations you will use to solve the problem.

SOLVE Solve the problem by doing all the computation necessary to find the answer.

CHECK Check your answer by reading the problem again. Ask yourself, "Does my answer make sense?" Also check your computation to make sure you did it correctly.

Answers and Explanations

Answers and Explanations to all the problems and exercises are at the back of this book beginning on page 255. The answer is given along with the worked-out problem. If you get a wrong answer, you can study the correct computation in order to find out where you made your mistake.

INVENTORY

Use this Inventory before you begin Section 1. Don't worry if you can't easily answer all the questions. The Inventory will help you determine which skills you are already strong in and which skills you need to practice further.

Read and answer the questions that follow. Check your answers on pages 255 – 257. Then enter your scores on the chart on page 7. Use the chart to figure out which skills to work on and where to find those skills in this book.

Write the value of the underlined digit in words.

1. 6,3̲02,450 _____

2. 5.347̲9 _____

Compare each pair of numbers. Write >, <, or = between the two numbers.

3. 46,023 _____ 46,203

4. 0.76 _____ 0.456

5. Round 534,103 to the nearest ten thousand.

6. Round 3.725 to the nearest hundredth.

_____

_____

7. Write the mixed number that names the shaded portion.

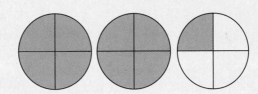

_____

Solve. Reduce answers to lowest terms.

8. 600
   − 328

9. 6.7
   − 3.846

10. 743
    × 608

11. 4)$12.28

12. $4\frac{7}{8}$
   + $2\frac{1}{3}$

13. $6\frac{2}{5}$
   − $4\frac{2}{3}$

14. $12 \div (2 + 1) \times 6 - 4 =$

15. $42 + 376 + 57 =$

Go on to the next page.

16. $3.27 + 26.4 + 8.531 =$

17. $\$5.08 - \$2.99 =$

18. $0.054 \times 0.3 =$

19. $4\frac{2}{5} \times 3\frac{3}{4} =$

20. $7{,}658 \div 42 =$

21. $31.2 \div 0.06 =$

22. $3\frac{1}{2} \div 4\frac{3}{8} =$

23. $7^2 =$

24. Change 375% to a decimal.

25. Change 0.07 to a percent.

26. Change 80% to a fraction.

27. Change $\frac{3}{4}$ to a percent.

28. What is 8% of 150?

29. What percent of $72 is $18?

30. 54 is 150% of what number?

31. $\frac{8}{20} = \frac{?}{35}$

Go on to the next page.

Circle the best answer for each item.

32. Handy Hardware had 144 gallons of interior paint and 96 gallons of exterior paint in stock. During the week, 48 gallons of interior paint were sold. Which is the correct expression to find the number of gallons of interior paint still in stock?

    (1) 96 − 48
    (2) 144 + 48
    (3) 144 − 48
    (4) 144 − 96
    (5) 144 + 96 − 48

33. Carol is building a rectangular dog kennel that is 12 feet long and 6 feet wide. What is the perimeter of the kennel in feet?

    (1) 18
    (2) 36
    (3) 72
    (4) 144
    (5) 180

34. Darius wants to carpet a living room that measures 20 feet on each side. Which is the correct expression to find the area of the room in square feet?

    (1) 20 × 9
    (2) 20 ÷ 9
    (3) 20^2
    (4) 20^2 ÷ 9
    (5) 20 + 20 + 20 + 20

35. On Friday, Village Deli sold 79 sandwiches on rye, 35 sandwiches on white, and 52 sandwiches on whole-wheat bread. Estimate the total number of sandwiches sold on Friday.

    (1) 150
    (2) 160
    (3) 170
    (4) 180
    (5) 190

36. A package contains 8 hamburger buns. Maria bought 16 packages of buns for a picnic. Which is the correct expression to find the number of buns she bought?

    (1) 8 ÷ 16
    (2) 8 + 16
    (3) 16 − 8
    (4) 16 × 8
    (5) 16 ÷ 8

37. The spinner shown has 6 equal sections. What is the probability that the wheel will stop on a 2?

    (1) $\frac{1}{6}$ or $16\frac{2}{3}\%$

    (2) $\frac{1}{3}$ or $33\frac{1}{3}\%$

    (3) $\frac{1}{2}$ or 50%

    (4) 1 or 100%

    (5) 2 or 200%

38. Jesse has a recipe that calls for $2\frac{1}{4}$ cups of chicken broth. Jesse wants to make one third of this recipe. How many cups of broth should he use?

    (1) $\frac{4}{27}$

    (2) $\frac{3}{4}$

    (3) $2\frac{1}{4}$

    (4) $5\frac{1}{4}$

    (5) $6\frac{3}{4}$

39. Joan's Market has onions on sale at 3 pounds for $1.56. A customer bought 5 pounds. Which is the correct expression to find the cost of 5 pounds of onions?

    (1) $\frac{3}{5} = \frac{?}{\$1.56}$

    (2) $\frac{3}{\$1.56} = \frac{5}{?}$

    (3) $\frac{3}{\$1.56} = \frac{?}{5}$

    (4) $\frac{5}{3} = \frac{\$1.56}{?}$

    (5) $\frac{5}{\$1.56} = \frac{3}{?}$

Go on to the next page.

40. Jermaine works 40 hours per week as a clerk at Central Auto Supply. He spends 15% of his time restocking shelves. Which is the correct expression to find the number of hours he spends restocking shelves each week?

(1) 15 × 40%
(2) 15 ÷ 40%
(3) 15% ÷ 40
(4) 40 × 15%
(5) 40 ÷ 15%

41. The vet told Andy to put his dog on a diet. During the first week of the diet, Andy's dog lost 0.2 kilogram. How many grams did the dog lose?

(1)   0.002
(2)   0.02
(3)   2
(4)   200
(5) 2,000

42. The Food Mart had ground beef on sale for $2.08 per pound. Joy bought 4 pounds of ground beef. Which is the correct expression to find the total cost of the ground beef?

(1) $2.08 × 0.4
(2) $2.08 ÷ 0.4
(3) 4 ÷ $2.08
(4) $2.08 × 4
(5) $2.08 ÷ 4

43. Ricardo's gross pay is $420.00 each week. He had $25.20 deducted for his credit union savings account. What percent of Ricardo's gross pay is deducted for savings?

(1)   0.6%
(2)   6%
(3) $16\frac{2}{3}$%
(4)   20%
(5)   25%

44. Maggie bought a jacket at Discount Fashions. The price tag is shown here.

Which is the correct expression to find the original price of the jacket?

(1) $18.60 × 30%
(2) $18.60 × 70%
(3) $18.60 ÷ 30%
(4) 30% × $18.60
(5) 30% ÷ $18.60

45. Which terms best describe this triangle?

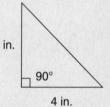

(1) acute; equilateral
(2) acute; isosceles
(3) right; acute
(4) right; equilateral
(5) right; isosceles

46. Abdul just started work at a fast-food restaurant. His current wage is $5.25 per hour. After three months, his new wage will be $5.46. What is the percent of increase in his wages?

(1)   3%
(2)   4%
(3)   20%
(4)   21%
(5)   96%

Write your answers in the blanks. Show your work.

47. What is the volume in cubic inches of the shipping carton shown?

16 in.

10 in. 12 in.

_____

48. Marcus drives a delivery truck for a bread company. His total route is $36\frac{9}{10}$ miles long. He drives $19\frac{2}{5}$ miles in the morning and finishes the route in the afternoon. Estimate the number of miles Marcus drives in the afternoon.

_____

Item 49 refers to the following table.

Fuel Economy in Miles per Gallon

	Car A	Car B	Car C
Highway	32	23	27
In town	21	14	18

49. How many miles can car B travel on the highway on 15 gallons of gas?

_____

50. Miranda needs a board that is $4\frac{1}{2}$ feet long for a shelf. She has a board that is $56\frac{1}{2}$ inches long. How many feet are in $56\frac{1}{2}$ inches?

_____

Item 51 refers to the following timecard.

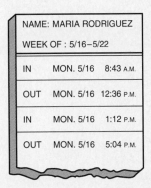

NAME: MARIA RODRIGUEZ

WEEK OF : 5/16–5/22

IN	MON. 5/16	8:43 A.M.
OUT	MON. 5/16	12:36 P.M.
IN	MON. 5/16	1:12 P.M.
OUT	MON. 5/16	5:04 P.M.

51. Approximately how many hours did Maria work before taking a lunch break?

_____

52. Find the area of this circle to the nearest square foot.

8 ft.

_____

53. Tawanna works at a gift shop. Her customer is buying a statue for $32.50 and a card for $1.75. Sales tax on this purchase is $1.71. The customer gives Tawanna $40.00 in cash. How much change should Tawanna give her customer?

_____

Item 54 refers to the following graph.

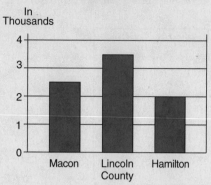

County of Residence of Woodland Mall Customers, 6/23

54. What is the approximate difference in the number of mall customers who live in Lincoln County and the number who live in Hamilton County?

_____

55. The Smiths want to put a fence around a circular flower garden. The diameter of the garden is 9 feet. To the nearest foot, how many feet of fencing will they need?

_____

Items 56 and 57 refer to the following data.

The points scored by a football team during 4 preseason games include: 37, 18, 21, 24.

56. What is the mean of these data?

_____

57. What is the median of these data?

_____

58. Of the 36 employees at Home Products, Inc., 20 work in the factory. What is the ratio in lowest terms of those who work in the factory compared to all employees?

_____

59. Mai borrowed $9,400 from her parents to buy a new car. She will pay this back in 5 years at 12% interest. How much interest will she pay?

_____

Item 60 refers to the following number line.

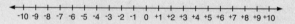

60. Before going to bed, Joe read that the temperature was 2 degrees. The next morning he heard that the temperature had dropped 7 degrees overnight. What was the temperature in the morning?

_____

Check your answers on pages 255–257.

INVENTORY
Correlation Chart

Mathematics

The chart below will help you determine your strengths and weaknesses in the math skills presented in this book. Circle the number of each item you answered correctly on the Inventory. Count the number of items you answered correctly in each row. Write the amount in the *Total Correct* space in each row. (For example, in the *Whole Number Theory* row, write the number correct in the blank before *out of 4*.) Complete this process for the remaining rows. Then add the 18 totals to get your Total Correct for the whole Inventory. If you answered fewer than 54 items correctly, refer to the page numbers in the right-hand column for further practice on these skills.

Section/Skill	Item Numbers	Total Correct	Pages
1. Whole Number Theory	1, 3, 5, 14	_____ out of 4	10–15
2. Adding and Subtracting Whole Numbers	8, 15, 17, 32 33, 35, 54	_____ out of 7	18–29
3. Multiplying and Dividing Whole Numbers	10, 11, 20 36, 49	_____ out of 5	32–43
4. Squares, Cubes, and Square Roots	23, 34, 47	_____ out of 3	46–53
5. Fraction Theory	7	_____ out of 1	60–67
6. Adding and Subtracting Fractions	12, 13, 48, 51	_____ out of 4	70–82
7. Multiplying and Dividing Fractions	19, 22, 38, 50	_____ out of 4	86–98
8. Adding and Subtracting Decimals	2, 4, 6, 9 16, 53	_____ out of 6	108–120
9. Multiplying and Dividing Decimals	18, 21, 41 42, 56, 57	_____ out of 6	124–135
10. Ratio and Proportion	31, 39, 58	_____ out of 3	144–158
11. Percent Theory	24, 25, 26, 27	_____ out of 4	162–165
12. Solving for the Part (p)	28, 40, 59	_____ out of 3	167–178
13. Solving for the Rate (r)	29, 43	_____ out of 2	182–194
14. Solving for the Base (b)	30, 44	_____ out of 2	198–206
15. Percent of Change	46	_____ out of 1	210–221
16. Probability Theory	37	_____ out of 1	230–235
17. Triangles and Circles	45, 52, 55	_____ out of 3	237–240
18. Integers	60	_____ out of 1	242–243
TOTAL CORRECT FOR INVENTORY _____ out of 60			

Unit 1

WHOLE NUMBERS

In a baseball game, numbers are used to show distance, to tell the score and player's statistics, and to identify the players.

Whole numbers are everywhere you look. You use whole numbers for counting, measuring, and putting things in order.

Imagine you are at a baseball game. Your ticket is for seat 12 in the 8th row of the bleachers. You have $4 in your pocket to buy a hot dog and a drink. In the 2nd inning, the home team scores 3 runs. In the 5th inning, they score 4 more. By the end of the 6th inning, the visiting pitcher has thrown 112 pitches. A radar gun shows the home team pitcher still throws a 94-mile-per-hour fastball. The final score is 7 to 2 for the home team. The clock on the scoreboard shows that the game took 2 hours and 35 minutes.

How were whole numbers used to count, measure, and put things in order in this example?

■ What was counted?

– the money in your pocket: $4

– the runs scored: 3 runs, 4 runs, and the final score—7 to 2

– the pitches thrown: 112 pitches

■ What was measured?

– the speed of the fastball: 94 miles per hour

– the time it took to play the game: 2 hours and 35 minutes

■ What things were put in order?

- the innings: the 2nd, 5th, and 6th innings

- the rows in the bleachers: 8th row

- the seats in the row: seat 12

You already know a lot about whole numbers. You use your knowledge of place value, comparing numbers, and rounding numbers to make decisions every day.

Would you rather win a $500 prize or a $50 prize? You would choose the $500 prize because your knowledge of **place value** tells you that $500 is much more than $50.

Would you rather pay $4 or $7 to see a movie? You would choose the $4 ticket because you know how to **compare** numbers and figure out which is less or which is greater.

Suppose you want to make a $38 purchase with cash. You decide to withdraw $40 in cash from the bank because you know that $38 is almost $40. You are **rounding** $38 to the nearest ten to figure out how much to take out of the bank.

Place value, comparing numbers, and rounding are some of the topics you will learn about in Unit 1. You will also learn more about the four whole number operations: addition, subtraction, multiplication, and division. You will learn how to do these operations and when to use them in solving problems in different situations.

Problems you might run into on the job or in everyday living are explained in the Consumer Math sections of the unit. Using whole numbers to measure is covered in the Measurement and Geometry sections.

Other parts of the unit show how to read graphs and tables. Graphs and tables are ways of organizing number information. You will need to know how to read graphs and tables to find the information you need to solve problems.

Here are a few of the problem-solving situations presented in Unit 1:

■ finding the perimeter of a yard to build a fence

■ stocking the shelves at a store

■ packaging goods in a bakery

■ making a work schedule for hotel employees

■ finding the area of a room to install carpet and tiles

■ figuring out how much a truck can hold for a shipping company

■ reading a bar graph to find information about a company's customers

Section 1

Whole Number Theory

Place Value

Which cash prize would you rather win: $50 or $500? Of course you picked $500. You know that the value of $500 is greater than the value of $50 because of the placement of the numbers or **digits**.

Our number system uses ten digits: 0, 1, 2, 3, 4, 5, 6, 7, 8, and 9. A **whole number** is formed by writing one or more digits in a row. The number 7 is a one-digit number, and the number 154 is a three-digit number. The number 5,000 is a four-digit number even though three of the digits are zeros.

The **place-value** chart at the left shows the first ten place values in our whole number system. Commas are placed every three digits counting from the right.

The value of a digit depends on its place in the number. The value of the places increases as you move to the left. The 4 in the thousands place has a greater value than the 4 in the ones place.

The number 5,214,084 is written on the place-value chart. From the chart, you can see that this whole number has 5 millions, 2 hundred thousands, 1 ten thousand, 4 thousands, 0 (or no) hundreds, 8 tens, and 4 ones.

billions	hundred millions	ten millions	millions	hundred thousands	ten thousands	thousands	hundreds	tens	ones
			5, 2	1	4, 0	8	4		

Practice ◢ Write the place value of each underlined digit. Refer to the chart above if necessary.

1. 9,6<u>5</u>0   *tens* _____

2. 97<u>2</u> _____

3. 2<u>8</u>,730 _____

4. 826,<u>1</u>10 _____

5. <u>4</u>0,059 _____

6. <u>9</u>26,420 _____

7. 2,10<u>6</u>,920 _____

8. <u>7</u>,535,000 _____

9. 57,<u>4</u>25 _____

10. 9,<u>8</u>53,483 _____

11. <u>3</u>6 _____

12. 7<u>6</u>5,999 _____

13. 28,78<u>1</u> _____

14. <u>3</u>7,654,321 _____

15. 5<u>6</u>,839 _____

16. 348,<u>6</u>53 _____

Check your answers on page 258.

Reading and Writing Whole Numbers

PAY TO THE ORDER OF	_John Bowen_	$ _150.00_
One hundred fifty & no/100		DOLLARS

To write a check, you must write the amount in words and in digits.

Use the following rules to read and write numbers.

▼ **To read a number, read each group of three digits from left to right. Then say the name of the group to the left of the comma. Don't say the word *and*.**

▼ **Example**   4,819,520 is read "four million, eight hundred nineteen thousand, five hundred twenty."

▼ **When writing big numbers in words, place a comma after the word *million* and the word *thousand*. Don't place a comma after the word *hundred*.**

▼ **Example**   5,150,425 is written "five million, one hundred fifty thousand, four hundred twenty-five."

▼ **When writing a number using digits, use zero as a place holder.**

▼ **Example**   "Two hundred four" is written 204. The zero in the tens place has no value, but it is needed to hold the tens place.

Practice ▮ Write each number in words.

1. 756   _seven hundred fifty-six_ _____

2. 43,018   _____

3. 115,200 _____

4. 5,400,012 _____

▮ Write each number using digits.

5. one thousand, seven hundred eight _1,708_ _____

6. two hundred fifty thousand, nine hundred eleven _____

7. twelve thousand, sixteen _____

8. nine million, fourteen thousand, five hundred sixty _____

Check your answers on page 258.

Comparing Numbers

Would you rather work for $7 or $5 an hour? Of course you picked $7, the greater amount. To answer the question, you compared two numbers and picked the greater one.

These three symbols are used to compare numbers. The symbols > and < are arrows that always point to the smaller number.

You can write these symbols between two numbers to show how the numbers compare.

Example

100 = 100	100 **equals** 100
$7 > $5	$7 **is greater than** $5
10 < 50	10 **is less than** 50

Use these rules to compare whole numbers:

The number that has more digits is greater.

Example   8,500 > 920 because 8,500 has more digits than 920.

If the numbers have the same number of digits, work from left to right and compare each place value.

Example   6,800 > 6,400 because 8 is greater than 4.
15,340 < 15,370 because 4 is less than 7.

Practice Compare each pair of numbers. Write >, <, or = between the two numbers.

1. 4,700 __>__ 740

2. 38,000 _____ 38,500

3. 179 _____ 179

4. 210,580 _____ 210,480

5. 1,000,000 _____ 10,000,000

6. 496 _____ 4,690

7. 13,415 _____ 13,415

8. 802,165 _____ 803,980

9. 5,000 _____ 50,000

10. 1,345 _____ 1,435

11. 10,334 _____ 10,334

12. 479 _____ 476

13. 340,635 _____ 340,835

14. 5,010 _____ 5,001

15. 682,489 _____ 682,489

16. 3,800 _____ 3,850

Rounding

Kate earns about $15,000 a year as a painter. The word *about* tells you this isn't the exact amount Kate earns. In fact, she really earns $14,965. In the first sentence, Kate's exact salary is rounded to the nearest thousand. Rounded numbers are easier to remember and use in solving problems.

Use these steps to round numbers:

Step 1: Decide to what place you want to round the number. Circle the digit.

$1④,965$

Step 2: Look at the digit to the right of the circled digit.

$1④,965$

Step 3: If this digit is 5 or more, add 1 to the circled digit. If the digit is less than 5, do not change the circled digit.

Since 9 is more than 5, add 1. 4 + 1 = 5
$1⑤,965$

Step 4: Change all the digits to the right of the circled digit to zeros.

$1⑤,000$

Example

Round 4,514 to the nearest hundred.

4,⑤14 rounds to 4,500. Since 1 is less than 5, the circled digit does not change.

Round 175,500 to the nearest ten thousand.

1⑦5,500 rounds to 180,000. Add 1 to the circled digit because the digit to the right is 5.

Practice 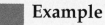 Write your answers in the blanks.

1. Round 58 to the nearest ten. ___60___

2. Round 1,723 to the nearest hundred. _____

3. Round 6,509 to the nearest thousand. _____

4. Round 861 to the nearest hundred. _____

5. Round 19,580 to the nearest thousand. _____

6. Round 209,320 to the nearest ten thousand. _____

7. Round 64,299 to the nearest thousand. _____

8. Round 5,256,000 to the nearest hundred thousand. _____

The Order of Operations

Add	+
Subtract	−
Multiply	×
Divide	÷

There are four **operations** to use with numbers to solve problems. You can add, subtract, multiply, and divide. Each operation has a special symbol.

Using numbers and operation symbols, you can write a **mathematical expression** to show how you would solve a problem. The words in the problem are changed into math symbols.

Example

"Add 5 and 1" can be written $\qquad$ 5 + 1
"Subtract 2 from 10" can be written $\qquad$ 10 − 2
"Multiply 3 by 4" can be written $\qquad$ 3 × 4
"Divide 8 by 2" can be written $\qquad$ 8 ÷ 2

An expression that has an **equal sign (=)** is called an **equation**. The equal sign shows that the amounts on both sides of the sign are equal.

Example

Equation $\qquad$ 5 + 1 = 6 $\qquad$ 3 × 4 = 12
$\qquad$ 10 − 2 = 8 $\qquad$ 8 ÷ 2 = 4

When an expression has more than one operation, the order in which you do the operations can change the answer. **Always follow this order of operations to solve an expression.**

Step 1. Do any operations in parentheses first.

Step 2. Next, multiply and divide working from left to right.

Step 3. Finally, add and subtract working from left to right.

Example

Solve: (10 + 5) ÷ 3 × 2 − 4

Step 1. Add first because 10 + 5 is in parentheses.
10 + 5 = 15

Step 2. Divide next because the division sign comes first working from left to right. 15 ÷ 3 = 5

Then multiply. 5 × 2 = 10

Step 3. Subtract. 10 − 4 = 6

(10 + 5) ÷ 3 × 2 − 4
15 ÷ 3 × 2 − 4
5 × 2 − 4
10 − 4
6

Example

Solve: 2 × 7 − 3 ÷ 3 + 4

Step 1. There are no parentheses, so go to Step 2.

Step 2. Multiply first. 2 × 7 = 14. Remember to work from left to right. Then divide. 3 ÷ 3 = 1

Step 3. Working from left to right, subtract first. 14 − 1 = 13. Then add. 13 + 4 = 17

2 × 7 − 3 ÷ 3 + 4
14 − 3 ÷ 3 + 4
14 − 1 + 4
13 + 4
17

Practice ◼ Solve each expression. Show your work.

1. $2 \times 4 - 3 + 1$
    $\quad\quad 8 - 3 + 1$
    $\quad\quad\quad 5 + 1$
    $\quad\quad\quad\quad 6$

2. $(4 + 3) \times 5$

3. $7 + 8 - 9 \div 3 + 4$

4. $8 + 6 \times (12 \div 6)$

5. $4 \times 3 - 1 + 6 \div 3$

6. $9 \div (4 - 1) + 8$

7. $6 \times 3 + 2 - 10 \div 2$

8. $(8 + 4) \div 3 + 1$

9. $35 \div 7 + 4 \times 2 - 3$

10. $3 \times (9 - 5) \div 6 \times 2$

11. $7 \times 2 + 8 - 3$

12. $10 - 7 \times 1 + 4 \div 2$

Check your answers on pages 258–259.

Using Your Math Skills

Write the place value of each underlined digit.

1. 2,8<u>3</u>4 _____
2. 3<u>2</u>8,954 _____
3. <u>7</u>,927,480 _____
4. 8,<u>0</u>51,939 _____

Write each number in words.

5. 28,302 _____
6. 1,076,500 _____

Write each number using digits.

7. forty-two thousand, fifty-seven _____
8. three million, four hundred thousand, five hundred ninety _____

Compare each pair of numbers. Write >, <, or = between the two numbers.

9. 5,680 _____ 856
10. 32,457 _____ 32,457
11. 82,346 _____ 82,546
12. 790,300 _____ 709,300

Write your answers in the blanks.

13. Round 43 to the nearest ten. _____

14. Round 2,453 to the nearest hundred. _____

15. Round 307,216 to the nearest ten thousand. _____

16. Round 4,293,785 to the nearest million. _____

Solve each expression. Show your work.

17. $5 + 4 \times 3 - 8 \div 2$

18. $32 \div (5 + 3) \times 6 - 1$

Check your answers on page 259.

Circle the best answer for each item.

Items 19 – 21 refer to the following table.

Weekly Production of Parts

Week 1	12,435
Week 2	14,526
Week 3	12,345
Week 4	14,814
Week 5	13,706

19. Which statement is false?

   (1) Fewer parts were produced during week 5 than during week 4.
   (2) Fewer parts were produced during week 1 than during week 3.
   (3) More parts were produced during week 4 than during week 2.
   (4) More parts were produced during week 5 than during week 1.
   (5) Fewer parts were produced during week 2 than during week 4.

20. During which week was the greatest number of parts produced?

   (1) week 1
   (2) week 2
   (3) week 3
   (4) week 4
   (5) week 5

21. The manager stated that about 14,000 parts were produced during one week. He had rounded the number to the nearest thousand. Which week was he talking about?

   (1) week 1
   (2) week 2
   (3) week 3
   (4) week 4
   (5) week 5

22. The number of cars sold in the state was 1,030,402. Select the expression below which shows in words the number of cars sold.

   (1) one million, three thousand, four hundred two
   (2) one million, thirty thousand, four hundred two
   (3) one hundred thirty thousand, forty-two
   (4) one hundred thirty thousand, four hundred two
   (5) one million, three thousand, four hundred twenty

23. Compare 245,306 and 245,603.

   (1) 245,306 > 245,603
   (2) 245,306 = 245,603
   (3) 245,603 < 245,306
   (4) 245,603 > 245,306
   (5) 245,306 < 245,306

24. Marsha spent $1,483 last year for day care. How much did she spend for day care rounded to the nearest hundred dollars?

   (1) $1,000
   (2) $1,400
   (3) $1,480
   (4) $1,500
   (5) $2,000

25. Four hundred ten thousand, three hundred eight race fans attended the Indianapolis 500. Select the number below which shows the attendance.

   (1)   41,038
   (2)   410,308
   (3)   4,103,008
   (4)   400,010,308
   (5) 40,010,000,308

Check your answers on page 259.

Section 2

Adding and Subtracting Whole Numbers

Perimeter

Pete and Beth need to build a fence around their yard to keep in their dog. The yard and house are shown in the diagram. They want to find out how many feet of fencing they will need to go around the yard.

▶ **The distance around the edge of something is called its perimeter.**

Pete and Beth know that the distance across the front yard is 200 feet. They know that the side of the yard next to the big tree measures 120 feet. To find the perimeter of the yard, they need to know the measurement of each side. How can they find the two missing measurements without measuring?

▶ **In a rectangle, opposite sides are equal length. Opposite sides are across from each other.**

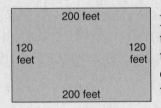

Pete and Beth's yard is a rectangle. The back yard is the same length as the front yard: 200 feet. The side near the doghouse is the same length as the side near the big tree: 120 feet. Now Pete and Beth know the length of each side of their yard. They have all the information they need to solve the problem.

Which is the correct expression to find the perimeter of the yard?

(1) 200 + 120
(2) 200 + 200 + 120 + 120
(3) 200 + 200 + 120 + 200
(4) 200 + 120 + 120 + 200 + 120
(5) 200 + 200 + 200 + 200

Answer 2 is the correct choice. They need to find the total of all the sides, so they will add all four lengths together.

200 + 200 + 120 + 120 = 640 feet

The perimeter of their yard is 640 feet.

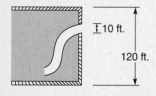

Ŧ10 ft.

120 ft.

Next, Pete and Beth decide they need a special gate in the fence for their truck. They want to put the gate on the side of the yard near the tree. The gate will measure 10 feet.

They know that the side of the yard measures 120 feet and the gate will be 10 feet. The remaining length of the side will need fencing. Which is the correct expression to find the amount of fencing they will need for this side of the yard?

(1)   120 − 10
(2)   120 + 10
(3)   10 − 120
(4)   120 + 120 + 10 + 10
(5)   120 + 120 + 120 − 10

Answer 1 is the correct choice. Pete and Beth need to find the **difference** between the two measurements, so they will subtract the smaller number from the larger one.

120 − 10 = 110 feet

They need 110 feet of fencing for the side with the gate.

Practice Circle the best answer for each item. Remember that opposite sides of a rectangle are equal in length.

1. Roger is fencing the flower bed shown in the figure. There will be a 2-foot break in the fencing on one side. Which is the correct expression to find the length of the fencing needed for the side with the break?

    ←2 ft.→
    |←———— 8 ft. ————→|

    (1)   8 − 2
    (2)   2 − 8
    (3)   8 + 2
    (4)   8 + 8 + 2 + 2
    (5)   8 + 8 + 8 + 2

2. A new exhibit at the zoo is being planned for a rectangular space that is 40 feet long and 30 feet wide. Which is the correct expression to find the perimeter of the exhibit?

    (1)   40 − 30
    (2)   40 + 30
    (3)   40 + 30 + 30
    (4)   40 + 40 + 30 + 30
    (5)   40 + 40 + 40 + 40

3. Maria is putting molding along the sides and the top of a doorway. The doorway is 3 feet wide and 7 feet high. Which is the correct expression to find the amount of molding she will need?

    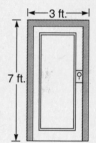

    |←—3 ft.—→|

    7 ft.

    (1)   7 − 3
    (2)   3 − 7
    (3)   7 + 3 + 3
    (4)   7 + 7 + 3
    (5)   7 + 7 + 3 + 3

4. Virgis is framing a rectangular painting. The painting is 20 inches wide and 24 inches long. Which is the correct expression to find the perimeter of the painting?

    (1)   24 − 24
    (2)   24 − 20
    (3)   20 + 20 + 24
    (4)   20 + 24 + 24
    (5)   20 + 20 + 24 + 24

5. Sandy is putting a fence across the front of her yard. The yard is 80 feet wide. She needs to leave a 3-foot opening for the sidewalk. Which is the correct expression to find how much fencing she needs?

(1) 80 + 3
(2) 80 − 3
(3) 80 + 80 + 3
(4) 80 + 80 − 3
(5) 80 + 80 + 3 + 3

6. Jane is building a rectangular dog run that is 30 feet long and 6 feet wide. Which is the correct expression to find the perimeter of the dog run?

(1) 30 + 6
(2) 30 − 6
(3) 30 + 30 + 6
(4) 30 + 30 + 6 + 6
(5) 30 + 30 − 6 − 6

7. Colin is building a railing around the edges of the deck shown in the figure. The deck is 10 feet wide and 18 feet long. Which is the correct expression to find the length of the railing?

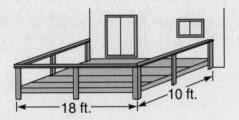

(1) 10 + 10 + 18
(2) 10 + 10 + 18 + 18
(3) 10 + 18
(4) 10 + 18 + 18
(5) 10 + 10 − 18

8. A park is in the shape of a rectangle that is 300 yards long and 200 yards wide. Which is the correct expression to find the perimeter of the park?

(1) 300 − 200
(2) 300 + 200
(3) 300 + 200 − 200
(4) 300 + 300 − 200 − 200
(5) 300 + 300 + 200 + 200

9. Jackie is planning to wallpaper her bedroom. This room is 10 feet wide and 14 feet long. The first step in finding how much paper she needs is to figure out the perimeter of the room. Which is the correct expression for her to use?

(1) 10 + 10 + 14 + 14
(2) 10 + 10 − 14
(3) 10 + 14 + 14
(4) 10 + 14
(5) 10 − 14

10. Richard is putting wood trim along two walls of his living room as shown in the figure. The room is 15 feet wide and 12 feet long. Which is the correct expression to find how long the wood trim will be?

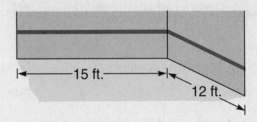

(1) 15 − 12
(2) 15 + 15 − 12
(3) 15 + 12
(4) 15 + 15 + 12
(5) 15 + 15 + 12 + 12

Adding Whole Numbers

Adding means putting numbers together to find a total. The total is also called the **sum.** An addition problem is written with a plus sign, +. Addition problems can be written in rows or in columns.

Row   Column

13 + 4 = 17   13
                    + 4
                    ——
                     17

To add whole numbers, follow these steps:

Step 1: Line up the numbers in a column. The digits in each column should have the same place value.

Step 2: Start with the ones column and add the numbers. Working to the left, add the numbers in each column.

Step 3: You need to **carry** whenever a column adds up to 10 or more. Write the number of ones in the ones place in the answer, and carry the number of tens to the tens column. Then add the tens column, place the tens in the answer, and carry the hundreds to the hundreds column. Keep working to the left until you have added the numbers in each column.

Example

Add: 238 + 12 + 125

Line up the numbers. Add the ones column (8 + 2 + 5 = 15). Write the 5 in the ones column, and carry the 1 to the tens column. Add the tens column (1 + 3 + 1 + 2 = 7). Add the hundreds column (2 + 1 = 3).

$$\begin{array}{r} \overset{1}{2}38 \\ 12 \\ +\ 125 \\ \hline 5 \end{array} \qquad \begin{array}{r} \overset{1}{2}38 \\ 12 \\ +\ 125 \\ \hline 75 \end{array} \qquad \begin{array}{r} \overset{1}{2}38 \\ 12 \\ +\ 125 \\ \hline 375 \end{array}$$

You can add numbers in a column in any order, and the answer will be the same. Adding the numbers in the reverse order is a good way to check your work. If you get the same answer twice, you can be pretty sure you have the right answer.

Check:
$$\begin{array}{r} \overset{1}{1}25 \\ 12 \\ +\ 238 \\ \hline 375 \end{array}$$

Adding money amounts is done the same way. The decimal point separates the dollars and the cents. When you write the problem, the decimal points must line up. Solve the problem as you would with whole numbers. Remember to put the decimal point and the dollar sign in the answer under the dollar sign and decimal point in the problem.

Example

Add:
$$\begin{array}{r} \$\ 4.98 \\ +\ 12.50 \end{array}$$

Solve:
$$\begin{array}{r} \overset{1}{\$}\ 4.98 \\ +\ 12.50 \\ \hline \$17.48 \end{array}$$

Check:
$$\begin{array}{r} \overset{1}{\$}12.50 \\ +\ 4.98 \\ \hline \$17.48 \end{array}$$

Practice ▶ Add and check. Show your work.

1.   254   *325*
    + 325   *+ 254*
     579   *579*

2.   476
    + 18

3.   387
    + 264

4. $4.73
    + 1.82

5.   148
    327
   + 232

6. $1.35
    4.56
   + 7.84

7.   542
    125
   + 68

8.   817
    76
   + 453

9. 38 + 157 =

10. $4.50 + $3.26 + $1.88 =

▸ ## Subtracting Whole Numbers

Subtracting is taking a smaller number away from a larger one. Subtract when you need to find the **difference** or to make a comparison.

The minus sign, –, tells you to subtract. Always subtract the smaller number from the larger one.

$$9 - 7 = 2 \qquad \begin{array}{r} 9 \\ - 7 \\ \hline 2 \end{array}$$

To subtract whole numbers, follow these steps:

Step 1: Line up the numbers so the numbers in each column have the same place value. Make sure the smaller number is on the bottom.

Step 2: Start with the ones column and subtract. Work to the left and subtract each column.

Step 3: You need to **borrow** when the digit in the bottom number is greater than the digit above it. To make the top digit greater, borrow from the column to the left.

Example ▶ Subtract 45 from 62.

Line up the numbers. The smaller number (45) is on the bottom. You can't subtract 5 from 2, so borrow 1 ten from the tens column. Cross out the 6 and write 5 above it to show there are only 5 tens left. Add the ten to the ones column, and change the 2 to 12. Now subtract each column working from right to left.

$$\begin{array}{r} 62 \\ - 45 \\ \end{array} \qquad \begin{array}{r} {}^{5\,12} \\ \cancel{62} \\ - 45 \\ \end{array} \qquad \begin{array}{r} {}^{5\,12} \\ \cancel{62} \\ - 45 \\ \hline 17 \end{array}$$

Sometimes the top number in a subtraction problem has one or more zeros in it. You can't borrow from zero, but you can borrow from the first digit to the left that isn't a zero.

Example

Subtract: 300 − 148
Borrow from the hundreds column.
Borrow from the tens column.
Subtract.

$$
\begin{array}{r} 300 \\ -\ 148 \\ \end{array}
\qquad
\begin{array}{r} \overset{2\ 10}{3\cancel{0}0} \\ -\ 148 \\ \end{array}
\qquad
\begin{array}{r} \overset{\ \ \ 9}{\overset{2\ \cancel{10}\,10}{3\cancel{0}\cancel{0}}} \\ -\ 148 \\ \hline 152 \\ \end{array}
$$

You can check subtraction by adding. Add your answer and the bottom number. The total should be the same as the top number.

$$
\begin{array}{r} \overset{1\ 1}{152} \\ +\ 148 \\ \hline 300 \\ \end{array}
$$

Subtract money amounts the same way. Subtract starting from the right. Make sure you put the decimal point and the dollar sign in the answer under the dollar sign and the decimal point in the problem.

Example

Subtract:
$$\begin{array}{r} \$9.25 \\ -\ 7.90 \\ \end{array}$$

Solve:
$$\begin{array}{r} \overset{8\ 12}{\$9.\cancel{2}5} \\ -\ 7.90 \\ \hline \$1.35 \\ \end{array}$$

Check:
$$\begin{array}{r} \overset{1}{\$1.35} \\ +\ 7.90 \\ \hline \$9.25 \\ \end{array}$$

Practice 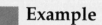 Subtract and check. Show your work.

1.
$$\begin{array}{r} 48 \\ -\ 25 \\ \hline 23 \end{array} \qquad \begin{array}{r} 23 \\ +\ 25 \\ \hline 48 \end{array}$$

2.
$$\begin{array}{r} 957 \\ -\ 304 \\ \end{array}$$

3.
$$\begin{array}{r} \$8.99 \\ -\ 4.25 \\ \end{array}$$

4.
$$\begin{array}{r} 786 \\ -\ 43 \\ \end{array}$$

5.
$$\begin{array}{r} 53 \\ -\ 28 \\ \end{array}$$

6.
$$\begin{array}{r} \$4.26 \\ -\ 2.71 \\ \end{array}$$

7.
$$\begin{array}{r} 329 \\ -\ 150 \\ \end{array}$$

8.
$$\begin{array}{r} 843 \\ -\ 376 \\ \end{array}$$

9.
$$\begin{array}{r} 500 \\ -\ 167 \\ \end{array}$$

10.
$$\begin{array}{r} \$7.15 \\ -\ 3.28 \\ \end{array}$$

11.
$$\begin{array}{r} 906 \\ -\ 29 \\ \end{array}$$

12.
$$\begin{array}{r} 520 \\ -\ 482 \\ \end{array}$$

13. 827 − 254 =

14. $8.17 − $4.99 =

15. 700 − 543 =

16. 684 − 486 =

Data Analysis

Problem-Solving Strategy: Using a Bar Graph

Tatsu is a clerk in the circulation office of the *Tilden Times*, a daily newspaper. Her office sends out bills, keeps track of payments, and makes sure the subscribers receive their papers. To make the work easier, her boss John has divided the town into six sections. John wants Tatsu to find out some information about the number of subscribers in the town.

Tatsu needs to answer these questions:

■ Which section of the town has the most subscribers?

■ About how many more subscribers live in the biggest section than in the smallest section?

■ What is the approximate total of subscribers living in the two smallest sections?

Tatsu uses this **bar graph** to find the answers. The bar graph compares the number of subscribers living in the six sections of the town.

There are three parts of the graph:

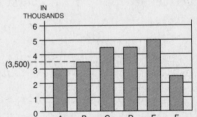

1. The **title** tells what information or **data** the graph presents.
2. The graph is built on two lines called **axis lines**. The bars of the graph rest on the horizontal axis (left to right), and the bars are labeled. The vertical axis (up and down) has a scale like a ruler. The marks on the scale represent numbers.
3. The **key** tells you any information you need to read the graph. The key on this graph, *IN THOUSANDS*, tells you information about the scale.

To read the value of a bar, follow across from the top of the bar to the marks on the scale. The number by the mark is the value of the bar.

Example   The top of the first bar labeled *A* reaches the mark labeled *3* on the scale. Since the numbers on the scale represent thousands, you know that Section A has 3,000 subscribers.

The second bar labeled *B* reaches halfway between the marks *3* and *4*. The bar represents about 3,500 subscribers. Graphs don't give exact amounts, but they are very useful for comparing numbers and making estimates.

Which section of the town has the most subscribers?

(1) Section A
(2) Section B
(3) Section C
(4) Section D
(5) Section E

Answer 5 is the correct choice. Tatsu knows the tallest bar represents the greatest number of subscribers. The bar for Section E is the tallest. It reaches the 5 mark and represents 5,000 subscribers.

About how many more subscribers live in the biggest section than in the smallest section?

(1) 2,000
(2) 2,500
(3) 3,000
(4) 3,500
(5) 4,000

Answer 2 is the correct choice. Tatsu knows the biggest section is Section E with 5,000 subscribers. The bar for Section F is the smallest. It ends between the 2 and 3 marks and represents 2,500 subscribers. She subtracts because she needs to find the difference. There are about 2,500 more subscribers living in Section E than in Section F.

$$\begin{array}{r} \overset{4\ 10}{\cancel{5},\cancel{0}00} \\ -\ 2{,}500 \\ \hline 2{,}500 \text{ subscribers} \end{array}$$

What is the approximate total of subscribers living in the two smallest sections?

(1) 4,000
(2) 4,500
(3) 5,000
(4) 5,500
(5) 6,000

Answer 4 is the correct choice. By looking at the graph, Tatsu sees the two smallest bars represent Sections A and F. There are about 3,000 subscribers in Section A and about 2,500 in Section F. Since she needs to find the total of the two sections, she adds the numbers. There are about 5,500 subscribers living in the two smallest sections.

$$\begin{array}{r} 3{,}000 \\ +\ 2{,}500 \\ \hline 5{,}500 \text{ subscribers} \end{array}$$

Tatsu reports her findings to John.

Practice ▆ Circle the best answer for each item.

Items 1–3 refer to the following graph.

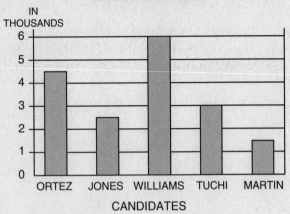

**VOTES RECEIVED BY
MAYORAL CANDIDATES**

Items 4–6 refer to the following graph.

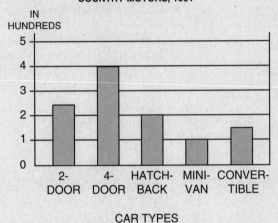

**CARS SOLD BY TOWN AND
COUNTRY MOTORS, 1991**

1. Which candidate received the most votes?

   (1) Ortez
   (2) Jones
   (3) Williams
   (4) Tuchi
   (5) Martin

2. About how many votes were received in all by the two candidates who got the most votes?

   (1) 1,000
   (2) 1,500
   (3) 3,500
   (4) 10,000
   (5) 10,500

3. What is the approximate difference in the number of votes received by the candidate who received the most votes and the candidate who received the least?

   (1) 3,500
   (2) 4,000
   (3) 4,500
   (4) 5,000
   (5) 7,500

4. Which type of car sold the least?

   (1) 2-door
   (2) 4-door
   (3) hatchback
   (4) minivan
   (5) convertible

5. About how many more 4-door cars than 2-door cars were sold by Town and Country Motors?

   (1) 100
   (2) 150
   (3) 200
   (4) 600
   (5) 650

6. What is the approximate total of the two least popular types of cars sold by Town and Country Motors?

   (1) 50
   (2) 150
   (3) 200
   (4) 250
   (5) 300

                                  Check your answers on page 261.

Consumer Math

Problem-Solving Strategy: Too Much Information/Estimating

Lila is in charge of keeping the dairy cases filled at Jons Grocery. The milk case holds 60 half-gallon cartons. When the store opens, Lila takes out any cartons that are out of date. Then she adds new cartons to fill the case. Three more times during her shift, she adds new cartons to the case. At the end of the day, Lila has to figure out how many new cartons she put in the case and write the number on a report form.

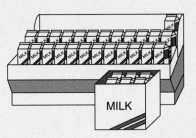

On Monday she pulled 14 outdated cartons at 8:00 A.M. and added 38 new cartons. At 10:00 A.M. she added 12 cartons. At noon she put out 19 new cartons, and at 2:00 P.M. she added 18 more.

This problem contains a lot of extra details. You don't need all of the details to solve the problem. What does Lila need to know to complete the form?

Lila needs to find the **total number of new cartons** she put in the case. You need only the numbers of **new cartons** to solve the problem. You don't need to know how many cartons the case will hold, 60, or how many cartons were outdated, 14.

During her shift she put in 38, 12, 19, and 18 new cartons. Find the <u>total</u> number of new cartons Lila put in the case on Monday.

Add the four amounts: 38 + 12 + 19 + 18

Estimate

Before she adds the numbers, Lila **estimates** the answer to the problem. The estimate gives her an idea of what the correct answer will be but it is not an exact answer. She can use the estimate to make sure her total is reasonable.

Lila quickly jots down the numbers. To estimate, she rounds each number to the nearest ten. Lila adds the rounded numbers to estimate the answer.

38	is about	40
12	is about	10
19	is about	20
+ 18	is about	+ 20
		90

The actual sum should be close to her estimate of 90 cartons. The actual sum is 87 cartons. Since 87 is close to 90, Lila is pretty sure she has found the correct total. She writes the information on the report form.

$$
\begin{array}{r}
\overset{2}{3}8 \\
12 \\
19 \\
+\ 18 \\
\hline
87 \quad \text{cartons}
\end{array}
$$

Lila has one more task to do before she goes home. She has to compare the number of cartons delivered that day with the number of cartons she put in the case. She needs to write down the number of delivered cartons that did **not** get used that day.

What information will Lila need to solve the problem? She needs to know the **number of cartons delivered** that day and the **number she put in the case**. Lila already knows she put 87 cartons in the case.

If 108 cartons were delivered on Monday, how many cartons were <u>left over</u>? She needs to subtract the cartons she put in the case from the number delivered. She subtracts because she needs to compare two numbers and find the difference.

Subtract: 108 − 87

Estimate

First, Lila estimates the difference. She rounds each number to the nearest ten and subtracts. Then she finds the actual answer.

	Estimate	Actual
108	is about 110	$\overset{0\ 10}{\cancel{1}08}$
− 87	is about − 90	− 87
	20	21

The actual number of cartons left over is 21. Since 21 is close to 20, Lila knows her answer is reasonable.

Finally, she checks her answer using addition.

$$
\begin{array}{r}
\text{Check:} \quad 21 \\
+\ 87 \\
\hline
108
\end{array}
$$

Lila had 21 cartons left over at the end of the day. She enters that number on her report form.

DAIRY REPORT

DATE	CARTONS USED	CARTONS REMAINING
9-26	87	21

Lila Hernandez

Practice ▮ Circle the best answer for each item.

1. Kunio is a driver for a recycling company. He collected 56 boxes of newspapers Monday morning and 17 more boxes that afternoon. Which is the correct expression to find the total number of boxes Kunio picked up on Monday?

   (1) 56 + 17
   (2) 56 − 17
   (3) 17 − 56
   (4) 56 + 56 + 17 + 17
   (5) 17 + 17 + 56

2. Lelia put on layaway a coat that cost $75. She put $25 down to hold the coat. Which is the correct expression to find how much she still owes for the coat?

   (1) $75 + $25
   (2) $75 + $75 + $25
   (3) $75 − $25
   (4) $25 − $75
   (5) $75 + $25 + 25

3. Tastee Burger sold 198 hamburgers on Friday. Of the hamburgers sold, 72 were sold after 7:00 P.M. Estimate the number of hamburgers sold during the rest of the day.

   (1) 110
   (2) 130
   (3) 175
   (4) 200
   (5) 210

4. Sandra is a records clerk. This week she handled requests for 67 marriage licenses, for 73 birth certificates, and for 81 death certificates. Estimate the total number of requests she handled this week.

   (1) 200
   (2) 220
   (3) 240
   (4) 260
   (5) 280

▮ Write your answers in the blanks. Show your work.

5. Carolyn sold 46 tickets for the 7:30 show at the Valley Theater. If the theater has 127 seats, how many tickets are left for the show?

_____

6. Eva works at a shoe store. At the beginning of a three-day sale, the store had 150 pairs of sandals in stock. By the end of the sale, there were 27 pairs of sandals left. The store also had 38 pairs of tennis shoes left in stock. How many pairs of sandals were sold during the sale?

_____

7. Rasheed delivers bottled water twice a week to an office building. He delivers 132 bottles of water on Tuesdays and 76 bottles on Fridays. How many fewer bottles does he deliver to the building on Fridays?

_____

8. Scott's boss told him to make one copy of a memo for each employee. There are 13 employees in the accounting office, 22 employees in sales, and 17 in service and delivery. How many copies should Scott make?

_____

Using Your Math Skills

Add or subtract.

1.
```
  237
+ 496
```

2.
```
  547
- 385
```

3.
```
  $2.95
+  4.87
```

4.
```
  600
- 321
```

5.
```
  $6.07
-  2.95
```

6.
```
  503
   58
+ 367
```

7.
```
  $2.27
   3.17
+  1.45
```

8.
```
  $9.93
-  2.94
```

9.
```
  762
- 684
```

10.
```
  836
+ 414
```

11. $3.42 + $4.58 =

12. 534 − 76 =

Write your answers in the blanks. Show your work.

13. Ed works in the mailroom of a large company. This morning he needs to make deliveries to 238 people. He makes deliveries to 149 people before his coffee break. How many people does he have to make deliveries to after his break?

_____

14. On Saturday the Perez family drove to Tall Pines Park where they will camp for 7 days. They drove 243 miles before lunch and 179 miles after lunch. The trip took 9 hours. How many miles did the Perez family drive on Saturday?

_____

15. Gloria has a motor route for delivering newspapers. She has 153 customers who receive the paper every day, 26 who get it on weekends only, and 42 who receive it on Sundays only. How many total customers does Gloria have?

_____

16. At The Lunch Counter, a hamburger costs $2.45. A hamburger platter with hamburger, fries, and coleslaw costs $3.60. Beverages cost $0.75 each. How much more does a hamburger platter cost than just a hamburger?

_____

Check your answers on pages 262–263.

Circle the best answer for each item.

17. Sue is putting a wallpaper border around her living room. The living room is 20 feet long and 14 feet wide. Which is the correct expression to find the amount of border she will need?

(1) 20 + 14
(2) 20 − 14
(3) 20 + 20
(4) 20 + 20 + 20 + 14
(5) 20 + 20 + 14 + 14

18. Last month Mark's utility bills included $53 for electricity, $28 for the phone, and $11 for water. Estimate the total of Mark's utility bills last month.

(1) $50
(2) $60
(3) $90
(4) $110
(5) $150

19. Bill weighs 208 pounds. His doctor said he should weigh only 185 pounds. Which is the correct expression to find how much weight Bill should lose?

(1) 185 − 208
(2) 208 − 185
(3) 208 + 185
(4) 208 + 208 − 185
(5) 208 − 185 + 185

20. Joshua is taking a 16-week course on office procedures. Tuition is $348 and the cost of books and supplies is $54. What is the total cost for Joshua to take this course?

(1) $294
(2) $392
(3) $402
(4) $418
(5) $888

Items 21–22 refer to the following graph.

RENTALS AT VIDEOLAND, OCT. 15

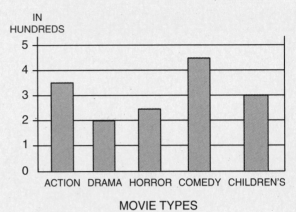

21. Which type of movie had the greatest number of rentals?

(1) action
(2) drama
(3) horror
(4) comedy
(5) children's

22. What is the approximate difference between the movie type that had the most rentals and the movie type that had the fewest rentals?

(1) 100
(2) 150
(3) 200
(4) 250
(5) 650

23. During the championship basketball game, Spike Morton scored 43 points. Of these, 17 points were made from the free throw line. Spike also fouled 4 times. Which is the correct expression to find how many points Spike scored shooting field goals?

(1) 43 − 17
(2) 43 + 17
(3) 43 − 17 − 4
(4) 43 + 4 − 17
(5) 43 + 4 + 17

Check your answers on page 263.   *Section 2: Adding and Subtracting Whole Numbers*   31

Section 3

Multiplying and Dividing Whole Numbers

Consumer Math

Dean works at a bakery. One of his jobs is putting the baked goods in packages to sell to customers. This morning he will be packing cookies in boxes. Each box holds one dozen cookies.

1 dozen = 12

Dean needs to get boxes from the storeroom. The baker tells him that there are 6 trays of cookies ready to be packaged. Dean knows each tray holds 100 cookies. He needs to figure out how many boxes he will need.

First, Dean figures out the total number of cookies that are ready. There are 6 trays with 100 cookies each. Which is the correct expression to find the total number of cookies?

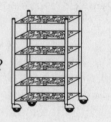

6 Trays of
100 Cookies

(1) $100 \div 6$
(2) 100×6
(3) $100 + 6$
(4) $6 - 100$
(5) $100 - 6$

Answer 2 is the correct choice. Since Dean needs to find a total, he can add 100 six times, or he can multiply 100 by 6. Multiplying is a shortcut for adding the same number more than once. Dean has to package 600 cookies.

$$
\begin{array}{r}
100 \\
100 \\
100 \\
100 \\
100 \\
+\ 100 \\
\hline
600
\end{array}
\qquad
\begin{array}{r}
100 \\
\times\ 6 \\
\hline
600
\end{array}
$$

Now Dean has to figure out how many boxes he will need to package 600 cookies. Remember, each box holds one dozen (12) cookies. To figure out how many boxes he needs, he has to know how many dozen are in 600. Which is the correct expression to find how many dozen cookies he needs to package?

(1) 600×12
(2) $600 + 12$
(3) $600 \div 12$
(4) 12×12
(5) $600 - 12$

Answer 3 is the correct choice. Dean needs to separate a large amount into groups. He can keep subtracting 12 cookies until he has used all the cookies, or he can divide. Dividing is a shortcut for subtracting the same number more than once.

$$\begin{array}{r} 50 \\ 12\overline{)600} \\ \underline{-60} \\ 00 \\ \underline{-0} \\ 0 \end{array}$$

Since 600 ÷ 12 = 50, Dean knows there are 50 dozen in 600. He gets 50 boxes from the storeroom and packages the cookies.

Practice ◢ Circle the best answer for each item.

<u>Items 1–4</u> refer to the following information.

Later that day, Ms. Loe, a teacher, calls to place an order. She wants to buy cookies for a class party. She has 36 students in her class and wants 4 cookies per student. She tells Dean to set aside enough cookies, and she will get them on her way home.

1. First, Dean needs to figure out how many cookies Ms. Loe wants to buy. She wants 4 cookies for each of her 36 students. Which is the correct expression to find the total number of cookies she needs?

   (1) 36 + 4
   (2) 36 − 4
   (3) 36 ÷ 4
   (4) 36 × 4
   (5) 4 ÷ 36

2. Dean figures out that Ms. Loe needs 144 cookies. Now he needs to know how many dozen are in 144. Which is the correct expression to find how many dozen cookies she needs?

   (1) 144 ÷ 12
   (2) 12 + 144
   (3) 12 ÷ 144
   (4) 144 − 12
   (5) 144 × 12

3. Dean figures out that Ms. Loe needs 12 dozen cookies. He has 50 dozen cookies on hand. He wants to know how many dozen cookies he will have left if he sells her 12 dozen. Which is the correct expression to find how many dozen cookies he will have left?

   (1) 50 × 12
   (2) 50 ÷ 12
   (3) 50 − 12
   (4) 12 ÷ 50
   (5) 12 + 50

4. Dean has 38 dozen left after making the sale. Later, the baker gives Dean another 8 dozen cookies to put in boxes. The baker asks Dean how many dozen cookies they now have. Which is the correct expression to find the total number of dozen they now have on hand?

   (1) 38 ÷ 8
   (2) 38 − 8
   (3) 38 ÷ 12
   (4) 38 × 12
   (5) 38 + 8

Check your answers on page 263.   *Section 3: Multiplying and Dividing Whole Numbers*

5. George bought a sofa that cost $549 including tax. He will pay for it in 3 equal payments. Which is the correct expression to find how much each payment will be?

   (1) $549 × 3
   (2) $549 − 3
   (3) $549 ÷ 3
   (4) 3 − $549
   (5) 3 + $549

6. Mrs. Wu is driving to visit her sister. It is a distance of 144 miles. After driving only 12 miles, Mrs. Wu stops for gas. Which is the correct expression to find how many miles Mrs. Wu still has to drive after getting gas?

   (1) 144 − 12
   (2) 144 ÷ 12
   (3) 144 × 12
   (4) 12 + 144
   (5) 12 ÷ 144

7. Natina makes wreaths to sell at craft fairs. She uses 6 yards of ribbon for each wreath. Which is the correct expression to find how many yards of ribbon she needs to make 48 wreaths?

   (1) 48 ÷ 6
   (2) 6 + 48
   (3) 48 − 6
   (4) 48 × 6
   (5) 6 ÷ 48

8. Marlowe bought 4 rolls of edging for his garden. Each roll is 10 feet long. Which is the correct expression to find how many feet of edging he bought?

   (1) 4 + 10
   (2) 10 ÷ 4
   (3) 4 × 10
   (4) 4 − 10
   (5) 10 + 4

9. Leon manages a service station. In the morning, he counts 18 tires on hand. He then receives a shipment of 30 tires. Which is the correct expression to find how many tires are on hand after the shipment arrives?

   (1) 18 − 30
   (2) 18 + 30
   (3) 30 × 18
   (4) 30 − 18
   (5) 30 ÷ 18

10. Van is making a fruit salad for a party. He buys 12 pounds of melon and 6 pounds of berries. Which is the correct expression to find how many pounds of fruit he buys?

    (1) 12 + 6
    (2) 12 − 6
    (3) 12 × 6
    (4) 12 ÷ 6
    (5) 6 ÷ 12

11. Valerie used 10 gallons of gas to drive 200 miles in her pickup truck. Which is the correct expression to find how far she drove on each gallon of gas?

    (1) 10 × 200
    (2) 10 + 200
    (3) 10 ÷ 200
    (4) 200 − 10
    (5) 200 ÷ 10

12. Toynette works for a toy company. She packs 18 model planes in each shipping carton. Today she packed 24 cartons of model planes. Which is the correct expression to find how many planes she packed?

    (1) 18 + 24
    (2) 24 − 18
    (3) 24 ÷ 18
    (4) 18 × 24
    (5) 18 ÷ 24

Multiplying Whole Numbers

Multiplying, like adding, helps you find a total. When you need to add the same number over and over, use **multiplication**. The times sign, ×, tells you to multiply.

$$12 \times 3 = 36$$

```
  12
×  3
  36
```

To multiply by 1-digit numbers, follow these steps:

Step 1. Write the problem so that the 1-digit number is on the bottom. It should line up with the ones place in the top number.

Step 2. Multiply the ones-place digit in the top number by the bottom number. Keep working to the left, multiplying each digit in the top number by the bottom number.

Step 3. If a result is 10 or more, you need to carry. Write the ones digit in the answer and carry the tens digit to the next column on the left. After you multiply the column on the left, add the number you carried to the result.

Example

Multiply 253 by 3.

Write the problem. Multiply the ones column
($3 \times 3 = 9$), and write the 9 in the answer.
Multiply the tens column ($5 \times 3 = 15$).
Write the 5 in the answer and carry the 1
to the hundreds column. Multiply the hundreds
column ($2 \times 3 = 6$), and add the carried 1
($6 + 1 = 7$). Write 7 in the answer.

```
 253    253    253
×  3   ×  3   ×  3
   9     59    759
```

To multiply by numbers with 2 or more digits, multiply
the top number by each digit in the bottom number. Work
from right to left. Line up each answer under the digit you
multiplied by. Finally, add the results.

```
   62       62
×  15    ×  15
  310      310
         +  62
          930
```

You can multiply numbers in any order, and the answer
will be the same. To check your work, multiply the numbers
in the reverse order. If you get the same answer twice, you
can be pretty sure you have the right answer.

```
Check:    15
        ×  62
           30
        +  90
          930
```

When the bottom number has one or more zeros, you don't need to write a
row of zeros. Just write a zero in the answer directly below the zero in the
bottom number. Then continue multiplying.

Example

```
      53          Write 00 and then         169      Multiply by 5.
   × 500          multiply by 5.         ×  205
  26,500                                      845      Write 0 and then
                                          + 3380      multiply by 2.
                                           34,645
```

Multiply money amounts by whole numbers using the same steps. Multiply as you would with whole numbers. Then put the decimal point and the dollar sign in your answer. Count the number of decimal places in both numbers in the problem. Then put the decimal point that number of places to the left in the answer.

```
    1 3
  $3.25
  ×    6
  $19.50
```

Practice ◢ Multiply. Show your work.

1. 234
    × 2
    468

2. 172
    × 4

3. 384
    × 6

4.   73
    × 18

5.   83
    × 24

6. 259
    × 47

7. $4.75
    ×   9

8.   64
    × 300

9. 837
    × 402

10. 126
    × 280

11. $3.89 × 7 =

12. 48 × 40 =

13. 527 × 63 =

14. 936 × 508 =

Computation ▶ Dividing Whole Numbers

Use **division** to figure out how many times one number goes into or divides another number. Division problems are written using the division sign, ÷. To solve the problem, write it using a division bracket, $\overline{)}$.

$$35 \div 7 = 5$$

```
      5
   7) 35
    - 35
      0
```

The examples on page 37 show the steps in dividing whole numbers.

Check your answers on page 264.

Example   Divide 348 by 6.

- How many times will 6 divide 34? $6 \times 5 = 30$ and $6 \times 6 = 36$. Choose the answer that is closer to 34 without going over 34. Write **5** in the answer space over 34. Multiply $6 \times 5 = 30$. Write 30 under 34 and subtract. Bring down the next digit.

$$\begin{array}{r} 58 \\ 6)\overline{348} \\ -30\downarrow \\ \hline 48 \\ -48 \\ \hline 0 \end{array}$$

- How many times will 6 divide 48? Write **8** in the answer space. Multiply $6 \times 8 = 48$. Write 48 under 48 and subtract.

- Check using multiplication. Multiply your answer by the number you divided by. The result should be the same as the number you divided.

$$\begin{array}{r} \overset{4}{5}8 \\ \times\ 6 \\ \hline 348 \end{array}$$

Example   Divide 2,477 by 12.

- How many times will 12 divide 24? $12 \times 2 = 24$. Write **2** in the answer space, multiply, and subtract. Bring down the next digit.

$$\begin{array}{r} 206\ r5 \\ 12)\overline{2,477} \\ -24\downarrow\downarrow \\ \hline 077 \\ -\ 72 \\ \hline 5 \end{array}$$

- Since 12 will not divide 7, write **0** in the answer space and bring down the next digit. How many times will 12 divide 77? $12 \times 6 = 72$. Write **6** in the answer space, multiply, and subtract.

- You have 5 left and there are no more digits to bring down. Write **5** in the answer space with an *r* to show 5 is the remainder.

$$\begin{array}{r} 206 \\ \times\ 12 \\ \hline 412 \\ +206 \\ \hline 2,472 \\ +\quad 5 \\ \hline 2,477 \end{array}$$

- Check your answer. Multiply 206×12, then add the remainder 5. The result should be the number you divided.

You can divide a money amount by a whole number using the same steps. Solve the problem as though the decimal point isn't there. Then put the decimal point and dollar sign in your answer above the decimal and dollar sign in the problem.

$$\begin{array}{r} \$4.20 \\ 3)\overline{\$12.60} \\ -12 \\ \hline 06 \\ -\ 6 \\ \hline 00 \\ -\ 0 \\ \hline 0 \end{array}$$

Check:
$$\begin{array}{r} \$4.20 \\ \times\ 3 \\ \hline \$12.60 \end{array}$$

Practice   Divide and check. Show your work.

1. $$\begin{array}{r} 54 \\ 8)\overline{432} \\ -40 \\ \hline 32 \\ -32 \\ \hline 0 \end{array}$$ $$\begin{array}{r} 54 \\ \times\ 8 \\ \hline 432 \end{array}$$

2. $7)\overline{\$15.05}$

3. $6)\overline{5,416}$

4. $28)\overline{475}$

5. $5)\overline{\$16.50}$

6. $42)\overline{9,714}$

7. $7,354 \div 36 =$

8. $\$12.08 \div 4 =$

Check your answers on pages 264–265.   *Section 3: Multiplying and Dividing Whole Numbers*

Data Analysis

Problem-Solving Strategy: Using a Table

Kenji works at the Westport Hotel. Today Ann, his boss, gave him a table showing the total number of rooms that have been reserved in the hotel for each day of the week. The table also shows the number of reserved rooms in the east wing and the west wing of the hotel.

WESTPORT HOTEL
Number of Rooms Reserved for the Week of October 12

	Mon.	Tues.	Wed.	Thurs.	Fri.	Sat.	Sun.
East Wing	256	305	315	212	248	240	196
West Wing	185	234	241	238	182	156	116
TOTALS	441	539	556	450	430	396	312

Tables organize number information or **data**. They have rows and columns that are labeled to help you use the information.

There are two important parts to a table:

1. The **title** tells what data the table shows. Always read the title so that you understand the limits of the table. For example, this table shows you how many rooms in the hotel have been reserved. The table doesn't show you how many rooms there are in the hotel.

2. The table is built with **rows** and **columns**. The rows go across and the columns go up and down. The rows and columns have **labels** so that you can find the information you need.

To find the number of rooms reserved on Monday in the east wing, find the box where the correct row (East Wing) and column (Mon.) come together. There are 256 rooms reserved on Monday in the east wing.

	Mon.
East Wing	256

Kenji needs the table to help him make up the work schedules for the housekeeping staff for Saturday. Kenji decides how many employees will work based on the number of rooms that are reserved.

In the east wing, 1 worker can take care of 15 rooms. How many workers will Kenji need to work in the east wing on Saturday?

(1) 15
(2) 16
(3) 17
(4) 18
(5) 19

Answer 2 is the correct choice. Kenji finds the place in the table where the row labeled *East Wing* and the column labeled *Sat.* come together. He finds there are 240 rooms reserved. Then he needs to separate 240 into groups of 15, so he divides 240 by 15. The answer, 16, is the number of workers he will need on Saturday in the east wing.

$$\begin{array}{r} 16 \\ 15\overline{)240} \\ -15 \\ \hline 90 \\ -90 \\ \hline 0 \end{array}$$

Because the rooms in the west wing are larger, 1 worker can take care of only 12 rooms. How many workers will Kenji need to work in the west wing on Saturday?

(1) 10
(2) 11
(3) 12
(4) 13
(5) 14

Answer 4 is the correct choice. Kenji finds the place in the table where the row labeled *West Wing* and the column labeled *Sat.* come together. There are 156 rooms reserved for Saturday. He needs to separate 156 into groups of 12, so he divides. The answer, 13, is the number of workers he will need on Saturday in the west wing.

$$\begin{array}{r} 13 \\ 12\overline{)156} \\ -12 \\ \hline 36 \\ -36 \\ \hline 0 \end{array}$$

Kenji needs to tell Ann the total number of workers he will need on Saturday. He knows he needs 16 workers in the east wing and 13 workers in the west wing. How many workers will he need on Saturday?

(1) 24
(2) 28
(3) 29
(4) 30
(5) 32

Answer 3 is the correct choice. He needs to find a total, so he adds the numbers. The total number of workers he needs on Saturday is 29.

$$\begin{array}{r} 16 \\ + 13 \\ \hline 29 \end{array}$$

Practice ◢ Circle the best answer for each item.

Items 1– 6 refer to the table below.

PIZZA PALACE MENU
(All prices include tax.)

	Cheese only	Any 1 topping	Any 2 toppings	Any 3 toppings	The Special (7 toppings)
Small	$3.95	$4.50	$5.05	$5.60	$7.25
Medium	$5.15	$5.80	$6.45	$7.10	$8.85
Large	$6.25	$6.95	$7.65	$8.25	$10.95

1. Jo orders 3 large special pizzas for her daughter's party. What is the total cost of these pizzas?

   (1) $3.65
   (2) $13.95
   (3) $21.75
   (4) $32.75
   (5) $32.85

2. Abdul works at Pizza Palace. A customer orders one small cheese pizza and one medium pizza with 2 toppings. How much should Abdul charge the customer?

   (1) $9.00
   (2) $9.10
   (3) $9.30
   (4) $10.40
   (5) $11.60

◢ Write your answers in the blanks. Show your work.

3. Five friends order a large pizza with 3 toppings. They split the cost equally. What is each person's share of the cost?

5. How much more does a small special pizza cost than a small pizza with 3 toppings?

4. A customer orders 2 large cheese pizzas and one medium special pizza. Find the cost of the order.

6. The cost of the ingredients for a medium pizza with one topping is $0.95. How much more than the cost of ingredients will a customer pay for this medium pizza with one topping?

Check your answers on page 265.

Area

Problem-Solving Strategy: Choose the Operation

Donna is putting wood tiling in an office building. The building manager wants her to use wood tiles that measure 1 foot on each side. Donna needs to figure out how many tiles she will need to do the job.

The first office is in the shape of a rectangle. It is 16 feet wide and 20 feet long. Donna needs to find the area of the office.

 Area is the measure of the surface of something.

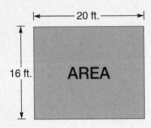

Area is measured in **square units**. Donna will find the area of the office in square feet. A square foot measures 1 foot on each side. To find the area, Donna needs to figure out how many square feet are needed to cover the surface of the floor.

Look at the diagram of the office. There are 16 rows with 20 squares in a row. You can find the area by counting all the squares, or you can add 20 sixteen times. However, the easiest way to find the area is to multiply.

You can find the area of any rectangle or square by multiplying the length by the width.

The formula for the area of a rectangle or a square is written:

 $A = l \times w$, which means *Area = length × width*.

Donna uses this formula to find the area of the office. She knows the length, 20 feet, and the width of the office, 16 feet. She multiplies 20 by 16 to find the area. The area of the office is **320 square feet**.

$$\begin{array}{r} 20 \\ \times\ 16 \\ \hline 320 \text{ square feet} \end{array}$$

Because the tiles measure 1 square foot, Donna needs 320 tiles to cover the floor. The tiles come in boxes of 50. Donna needs to figure out how many boxes of tiles she needs. She needs to separate 320 tiles into groups of 50.

Donna decides to divide 320 by 50 to solve the problem. She will need 6 full boxes and 20 tiles from another box to cover the floor. Donna needs 7 boxes of tiles to do the job.

$$\begin{array}{r} 6 \text{ r}20 \\ 50)\overline{320} \\ -300 \\ \hline 20 \end{array}$$

The building manager asks Donna how many tiles she will have left over after she finishes the job. Donna knows she will use 20 tiles from the last box of 50. She subtracts and tells her manager she will have 30 tiles left over.

$$\begin{array}{r} 50 \\ -\ 20 \\ \hline 30 \text{ tiles} \end{array}$$

The building manager is concerned about the total number of boxes of tiles on hand. He may want to order more boxes. He asks Donna to check the three storage closets and tell him the total. She finds 4 boxes in the first closet, 6 in the second, and 15 in the third. To find the total, she adds the numbers. She tells the building manager there are 25 boxes on hand.

$$\begin{array}{r} 4 \\ 6 \\ +\ 15 \\ \hline 25 \text{ boxes} \end{array}$$

To do her work, Donna had to add, subtract, multiply, and divide. Choosing the right operation is important when you are solving word problems.

STEPS TO SOLVE WORD PROBLEMS

■ Read the problem carefully.

■ Think about what you are trying to find out.

■ Ask yourself how the numbers in the problem can help you find the answer.

■ Look for clue words that tell which operation to use.

This chart will help you choose the correct operation.

You should . . .	When you need to . . .
Add	Find a **total**, find **how many in all**, put amounts together, or find the sum.
Subtract	Find a **difference**, find **how many more**, **how many less**, or **how many are left**.
Multiply	Add the same number more than once to find a total or to find a product.
Divide	Break or separate an amount into equal parts.

Practice

Items 1–8 refer to the following information.

The Juarez family is converting the garage shown in the figure into a family room. The garage is 18 feet long and 12 feet wide. Mr. Juarez is installing baseboard around all the perimeter except for the 2 door openings. The door openings are 3 feet wide and 6 feet wide. Then carpet will be installed. Carpet plus installation will cost $550. Mrs. Juarez is making 4 curtain panels. She needs 6 feet of fabric for each curtain panel.

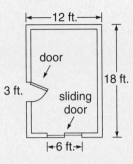

Circle the best answer for each item.

1. Which is the correct expression to find the area of the garage?

   (1) 12 × 18
   (2) 12 + 18
   (3) 12 + 12 + 18
   (4) 12 × 12 × 18 × 18
   (5) 12 + 12 + 18 + 18

2. There are 3 feet in a yard. Which is the correct expression to find the number of yards of fabric Mrs. Juarez needs?

   (1) 6 × 4 × 3
   (2) 6 + 4 + 3
   (3) 6 × 4 ÷ 3
   (4) 6 + 4
   (5) 6 ÷ 3

3. Carpet installation costs $75. Which is the correct expression to find the cost of the carpet alone?

   (1) $75 − $550
   (2) $550 ÷ $75
   (3) $550 + $75
   (4) $550 × $75
   (5) $550 − $75

4. Which is the correct expression to find the length of baseboard Mr. Juarez needs?

   (1) 12 + 12 + 18 + 18 + 3 + 6
   (2) 12 + 12 + 18 + 18 − 3 − 6
   (3) 12 + 18 − 3 − 6
   (4) 12 + 18 + 3 + 6
   (5) 12 + 12 + 18 + 18

Write your answers in the blanks. Show your work.

5. What is the area of the garage in square feet?

7. If carpet installation costs $75, what is the cost of the carpet alone?

_____

6. There are 3 feet in a yard. How many yards of fabric does Mrs. Juarez need?

8. How much baseboard does Mr. Juarez need?

_____

Check your answers on page 265.   *Section 3: Multiplying and Dividing Whole Numbers*   43

Using Your Math Skills

Multiply or divide. Show your work.

1.	456 × 3	**2.**	83 × 49	**3.**	$2.97 × 6	**4.**	178 × 702	**5.**	653 × 305

6. 4)3,293   **7.** 7)$64.40   **8.** 18)5,794   **9.** 43)8,657   **10.** 27)4,131

11. $39 \times 800 =$ **12.** $\$8.42 \times 5 =$

13. $\$16.40 \div 8 =$ **14.** $7,463 \div 52 =$

Write your answers in the blanks. Show your work.

15. Michelle ordered 8 gross of pencils. Each gross contains 144 pencils. How many pencils did Michelle order?

_____

16. Norman is replacing his kitchen floor with tiles that are 1 foot square. His kitchen is 15 feet long and 12 feet wide. How many tiles does he need?

_____

17. A shoe store has children's canvas shoes on sale for $4.97 a pair. Martin bought 4 pairs for his children. How much did Martin pay for the shoes?

_____

18. The Auto Lube Shop charges $15 for an oil change. This week the shop collected $330 for oil changes. How many customers had an oil change?

_____

Check your answers on pages 265–266.

Circle the best answer for each item.

19. A professional basketball court is 94 feet long and 50 feet wide. Which is the correct expression for finding the area of the court?

    (1) 94 + 50
    (2) 94 × 50
    (3) 94 + 50 + 50
    (4) 94 + 94 + 50 + 50
    (5) 94 × 94 × 50 × 50

20. Lena earns $6.50 an hour making deliveries for a pharmacy. She worked 7 hours on Friday. How much did Lena earn on Friday?

    (1) $6.50
    (2) $13.50
    (3) $42.35
    (4) $45.50
    (5) $52.00

21. Felecia bought 6 quarts of oil for her car. The total cost was $7.20. Which is the correct expression for finding the price of one quart of oil?

    (1) 6 × $7.20
    (2) 6 ÷ $7.20
    (3) $7.20 ÷ 6
    (4) $7.20 + 6
    (5) $7.20 × 6

22. Kelvin dug a rectangular garden in his backyard. The garden is 40 feet long and 25 feet wide. What is the area of the garden in square feet?

    (1)   15
    (2)   65
    (3)   130
    (4)   1,000
    (5) 1,000,000

23. The gas tank of Alicia's compact car holds 14 gallons of gas. Her car averages 28 miles on each gallon of gas. Which is the correct expression to find how far the car can travel on a full tank of gas?

    (1) 14 × 28
    (2) 14 + 28
    (3) 14 − 28
    (4) 28 ÷ 14
    (5) 28 − 14

Items 24 – 25 refer to the following table.

Parts Produced During the Week of March 5

	Mon.	Tue.	Wed.	Thurs.	Fri.
Total	4,238	5,416	5,324	5,672	4,890
Defective	87	73	75	64	68

24. Which is the correct expression to find the number of parts produced on Wednesday that were not defective?

    (1) 4,238 − 87
    (2) 4,238 + 87
    (3) 5,324 ÷ 75
    (4) 5,324 + 75
    (5) 5,324 − 75

25. There are 8 inspectors who check all the parts produced. If each checked an equal number of parts on Thursday, how many did each check?

    (1)   8
    (2) 79
    (3) 512
    (4) 609
    (5) 709

Check your answers on page 267.

Squares, Cubes, and Square Roots

Measurement and Geometry

Area of a Square

John works for Culver Carpets. Part of his job is to tell customers how much their carpeting will cost. John has to find the area of a room to figure the cost of the carpeting.

On Tuesday John's boss sends him to meet Sara Vega. She wants to carpet her office and asks how much it will cost. First, John measures her office. He finds that each side is 24 feet long. John knows her office is a square because all 4 sides have the same length.

> ◢ **A square is a rectangle that has four sides of equal length.**

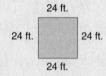

John needs to find the area of the square: On page 41, you used the formula *Area = length × width* to find the area of a rectangle. You can also multiply the length by the width to find the area of a square, but there is another way to write the formula.

> ◢ $A = s^2$, **where s is one side of the square.**

The raised 2 (s^2) tells you how many times to multiply the side by itself. Each side of Ms. Vega's office measures 24 feet. So the area of the office equals 24^2 or 24×24. John figures out that the area of the office is 576 square feet.

```
    24
 ×  24
    96
 + 48
 576 sq. ft.
```

Ms. Vega has chosen carpet that sells for $13 per square yard. John knows the number of square feet in the office. Now he needs to change the square feet to square yards.

A **square yard** is a square that measures 1 yard on each side. Also, 1 yard = 3 feet. A square that measures 3 feet on each side has 9 square feet, so 1 square yard = 9 square feet.

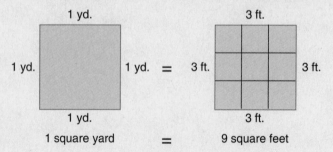

John needs to separate 576 square feet into groups of 9 to find the area of the office in square yards. Which is the correct expression to find the area in square yards?

(1) 576 + 9
(2) 576 × 9
(3) 576 ÷ 9
(4) 576 − 9
(5) 9 ÷ 576

Answer 3 is the correct choice. He needs to divide 576 by 9 to separate the square feet into groups of 9. He divides and finds that the area of the office is 64 square yards.

$$\begin{array}{r} 64 \\ 9\overline{)576} \\ \underline{-54} \\ 36 \\ \underline{-\ 36} \\ 0 \end{array}$$

Now John has all the information he needs to tell Ms. Vega the cost of the carpet. He knows the area of the office in square yards (64 sq. yd.) and the price of the carpet per square yard, $13. Which is the correct expression to find the cost of the carpet?

(1) $13 × 64
(2) $13 ÷ 64
(3) 64 ÷ $13
(4) $13 + 64
(5) 64 − $13

Answer 1 is the correct choice. The carpet costs $13 per square yard. The word *per* tells you to multiply. John multiplies the cost of 1 square yard by the number of square yards. It will cost $832 to carpet the office.

$$\begin{array}{r} 64 \\ \times\ 13 \\ 192 \\ \underline{+\ 64} \\ \$832 \end{array}$$

Practice ◢ Circle the best answer for each item.

1. Ms. Vega wants to carpet another room that measures 15 feet on each side. John needs to find the area of the room. Which is the correct expression to find the area of the room in square feet?

15 ft.
15 ft.

(1) 15 × 9
(2) 15 + 15 + 15 + 15
(3) 9 ÷ 15
(4) 15^2
(5) 15 ÷ 9

2. John figures out that the area of the room is 225 square feet. He needs to find the area in square yards. Which is the correct expression to change 225 square feet to square yards?

(1) 225 × 9
(2) 9 ÷ 225
(3) 9^2
(4) 225^2
(5) 225 ÷ 9

3. Shirley wants to carpet a dining room that measures 18 feet on each side. Which is the correct expression to find the area of the room in square feet?

   (1) 18^2
   (2) $18 + 18$
   (3) 18×9
   (4) $18 \div 9$
   (5) $18 + 18 + 18 + 18$

4. Miguel wants to order bathroom carpet from a catalog. The carpet is sold by the square yard. He finds that the area of his bathroom is 36 square feet. Which is the correct expression to change 36 square feet to square yards?

   (1) $36 \div 4$
   (2) $36 \div 9$
   (3) 36×9
   (4) 36^2
   (5) $36 \div 3$

5. John's customer wants to put a 1-foot-wide strip of contrasting color carpet around the edges of her living room. The room measures 20 feet on each side. Which is the correct expression to find the perimeter of the room?

   20 ft.
   20 ft.

   (1) 20^2
   (2) 20×1
   (3) $20 + 20$
   (4) 20^4
   (5) $20 + 20 + 20 + 20$

6. Earline bought a carpet remnant that measures 17 square yards. It was on sale for $8 per square yard. Which is the correct expression to find the total cost of the remnant?

   (1) $\$8 + 17$
   (2) $\$8 \div 17$
   (3) $\$8 \times 17$
   (4) $17 - \$8$
   (5) $17 \div \$8$

7. Mai-Ling wants to buy flooring for her kitchen. The kitchen is 10 feet long and 14 feet wide. Which is the correct expression to find the area of the room in square feet?

   (1) $10 + 10 + 14 + 14$
   (2) 10×14
   (3) 10^2
   (4) 14^2
   (5) $10^2 + 14^2$

8. Mr. McKenzie orders the same carpet for two rooms. One room measures 11 feet on each side, and the other measures 12 feet on each side. Which is the correct expression to find the area of both rooms in square feet?

   (1) $11^2 + 12^2$
   (2) $2 \times 11^2 + 12^2$
   (3) $2 \times 11^2 \times 12^2$
   (4) $2 \times (11 + 12)$
   (5) $11^2 \times 12^2$

9. Conchita wants to tile a hallway. The area of the hallway is 18 square feet. Four tiles are needed to cover one square foot. Which is the correct expression to find how many tiles Conchita needs?

   18 sq. ft.
   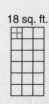

   (1) $4 \div 18$
   (2) $18^2 + 4$
   (3) $18 \div 4$
   (4) 4×18
   (5) $18 + 18$

10. The Swans want to cover their patio with indoor-outdoor carpeting. The patio measures 12 feet on each side. Which is the correct expression to find the area of the patio in square yards?

    (1) $12^2 \div 9$
    (2) $12^2 \times 9$
    (3) $12 + 12 + 12 + 12$
    (4) 12^2
    (5) $12 + 12 \div 9$

Finding Squares and Cubes

Some problems ask you to multiply the same number more than once. In the expression 7×7, you have to multiply 7 times itself. Another way to write this expression is 7^2. The 7 is the **base number** of the expression. The 2 is an **exponent**.

exponent ⌐
7^2 means 7×7

base
number

An **exponent** tells you how many times a number is to be multiplied by itself. The expression 7^2 can be read "seven to the second power" or "seven squared." The square of 7 is 49 because $7 \times 7 = 49$. The **value** of the expression 7^2 is 49.

A number is **cubed** when the number is multiplied by itself three times. Using an exponent, "4 cubed" is written 4^3. This expression means $4 \times 4 \times 4$.

To find the value of 4^3, multiply 4×4 and then multiply the answer by 4 again. The value of 4^3 is 64.

$$4 \times 4 \times 4$$
$$16 \times 4$$
$$64$$

To find the value of a number with an exponent, write the expression as a multiplication problem and multiply.

Example

Exponent	Read in Words	Multiply	Value
3^2	three squared	$3 \times 3 =$	9
10^2	ten squared	$10 \times 10 =$	100
1^3	one cubed	$1 \times 1 \times 1 =$	1
5^3	five cubed	$5 \times 5 \times 5 =$	125

Finding Square Roots

To find the square of a number, multiply that number by itself.

To find the **square root** of a number, think: "What number squared equals this number?"

Example

What is the square root of 36?

The square root of 36 is 6, because $6^2 = 6 \times 6 = 36$.

The symbol for square root is $\sqrt{\ }$. So you can write $\sqrt{36} = 6$.

The chart below shows the squares of the whole numbers 1– 20. Use the chart to find square roots.

Example

TABLE OF SQUARES

1^2 =	1	11^2 =	121
2^2 =	4	12^2 =	144
3^2 =	9	13^2 =	169
4^2 =	16	14^2 =	196
5^2 =	25	15^2 =	225
6^2 =	36	16^2 =	256
7^2 =	49	17^2 =	289
8^2 =	64	18^2 =	324
9^2 =	81	19^2 =	361
10^2 =	100	20^2 =	400

What is the square root of 225?

Find 225 on the chart.

Because 15^2 = 225, the square root of 225 is 15.

What is the value of $\sqrt{400}$?

Find 400 on the chart.

Because 20^2 = 400, the square root of 400 is 20.

The value of $\sqrt{400}$ is 20.

Practice ▸ Write each expression as a multiplication problem and multiply.

1. 6^3 $6 \times 6 \times 6$
             36×6
                216

2. 5^2

3. 1^2

4. 7^3

▸ Use the chart above to find the value of each expression.

5. 8^2

6. 11^2

7. 18^2

8. 16^2

9. $\sqrt{121}$

10. $\sqrt{16}$

11. $\sqrt{289}$

12. $\sqrt{196}$

Check your answers on page 267.

Volume of a Rectangular Container

Problem-Solving Strategy: Use a Formula

Gail works for a shipping company. She keeps records on the loads the company trucks carry. She records what each shipment contains and its weight and value. She also has to figure out how much space the shipment takes in the truck.

The trucking company earns more money when its trucks are full. But sometimes a shipment fills only part of the truck. Gail figures out how many cubic feet each shipment will take and how much space is left in the truck.

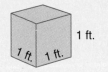

1 ft.

A **cubic foot** is shaped like a box that measures 1 foot on each side. The box is 1 foot long, 1 foot wide, and 1 foot high. The volume of the box is 1 cubic foot.

Volume measures the space inside an object. The space is measured in cubic units such as cubic inches and cubic feet. Think of these cubic units as boxes that are the same size on every side. The boxes are neatly stacked to fill the space, and the number of boxes is the volume of the space.

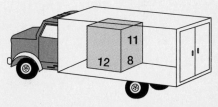

The company's trucks have a rectangular shape. The items to be shipped are packed in boxes and arranged to fit into a space shaped like a box. In the diagram, the shipment fills a space that is 12 feet long, 8 feet wide, and 11 feet high.

Gail uses a formula to find the volume of the shipment. The formula for the volume of a rectangular box is written:

 $V = l \times w \times h$, **which means**
<u>V</u>olume = <u>l</u>ength x <u>w</u>idth x <u>h</u>eight.

Follow these steps to use a formula:

Step 1: Substitute the numbers you know for the letters in the formula.

Step 2: Do the operations shown in the formula. Always follow the order of operations rules.

■ Do any operations in parentheses first.

■ Next, multiply and divide working from left to right.

■ Finally, add and subtract working from left to right.

Gail knows the shipment has a rectangular box shape. She knows the shipment is 12 feet long, 8 feet wide, and 11 feet high. What is the volume of the shipment in cubic feet?

(1)   968
(2)   1,056
(3)   1,152
(4)   1,331
(5)   1,728

Answer 2 is the correct choice. To use the formula, Gail substitutes the numbers she knows for the letters in the formula. Then she multiplies the first two numbers, the length (12) and the width (8). Next she multiplies the result (96) by the height (11). She finds that the volume of the shipment is 1,056 cubic feet.

$$V = l \times w \times h$$
$$V = 12 \times 8 \times 11$$

```
  12          96
×  8        × 11
  96          96
            + 96
           1,056
```

Gail also needs to figure out how much space will be left on the truck after the shipment is loaded. She needs to compare the volume of the shipment with the volume of the truck and find the difference. First, she needs to find the volume of the truck.

The truck has a box shape, and the inside of the truck measures 16 feet long, 8 feet wide, and 14 feet high. What is the volume of the truck in cubic feet?

(1)   1,024
(2)   1,456
(3)   1,654
(4)   1,792
(5)   2,048

Answer 4 is the correct choice. Gail substitutes the numbers for the letters in the formula. Then she multiplies the length (16) by the width (8). Finally, she multiplies the result (128) by the height (14). The truck has a volume of 1,792 cubic feet.

$$V = l \times w \times h$$
$$V = 16 \times 8 \times 14$$

```
  16         128
×  8        × 14
 128         512
            +128
           1,792
```

Now Gail is ready to find the space left on the truck. She subtracts the volume of the shipment from the volume of the truck.

```
      1,792        Check:      736
     −1,056                 +1,056
        736  cu. ft.          1,792
```

There are 736 cubic feet of space left on the truck.

Practice ◢ Write your answers in the blanks. Show your work.

1. What is the volume of the rectangular container shown in cubic inches?

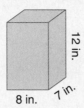
12 in.
8 in. 7 in.

_____

2. The food compartment of a refrigerator is 3 feet long, 2 feet wide, and 5 feet high. What is the volume of the food compartment in cubic feet?

_____

3. A rectangular shipping carton is 28 inches long, 40 inches wide, and 20 inches high. What is the volume of the carton in cubic inches?

_____

4. Tony is going to buy sand for his children's sandbox. The sandbox is 6 feet long, 4 feet wide, and 1 foot high. What is the volume of the sandbox in cubic feet?

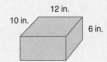
6 ft.
4 ft. 1 ft.

_____

◢ Circle the best answer for each item.

<u>Items 5–7</u> refer to the following information.

Mabel works for a packing and mailing service. A customer brings in a gift-wrapped box that is 9 inches long, 7 inches wide, and 5 inches high. Mabel places the box in a shipping carton that is 12 inches long, 10 inches wide, and 6 inches high. She fills the rest of the carton with foam pieces.

5. What is the volume of the gift-wrapped box in cubic inches?

7 in. 9 in. 5 in.

   (1)   21
   (2)   45
   (3)   63
   (4)   315
   (5)   720

6. What is the volume of the shipping carton in cubic inches?

12 in.
10 in. 6 in.

   (1)   72
   (2)   120
   (3)   315
   (4)   620
   (5)   720

7. What is the volume in cubic inches that Mabel fills with foam pieces?

   (1)   315
   (2)   405
   (3)   415
   (4)   720
   (5) 1,035

Using Your Math Skills

Write each expression as a multiplication problem and multiply.

1. 8^2

2. 1^3

3. 3^3

4. 9^2

Use the chart on page 50 to find the value of each expression.

5. 17^2

6. 15^2

7. $\sqrt{25}$

8. $\sqrt{324}$

Write your answers in the blanks. Show your work.

9. The Mahers' living room measures 20 feet on each side. What is its area in square feet?

12. Marsha bought 9 square yards of carpet for her bedroom. The carpet cost $14 per square yard. What was the total cost of the carpet?

10. A rectangular storage bin is 15 feet long, 12 feet wide, and 10 feet deep. What is the volume of the bin in cubic feet?

10 ft.
12 ft.
15 ft.

13. Viola is a carpet salesperson. She measures a customer's family room and finds its area is 576 square feet. What is the area in square yards?

11. Willis installs pools. Today he is installing an inground pool that is 30 feet long, 6 feet wide, and 4 feet deep. What is the volume in cubic feet of the dirt that he must remove before he installs the pool?

14. A trash hauler places large trash bins at apartment complexes. Each bin is 12 feet long, 8 feet wide, and 6 feet high. What is the volume of each bin in cubic feet?

Check your answers on page 268.

Circle the best answer for each item.

15. Which is the correct expression to find the volume of the rectangular container shown in cubic inches?

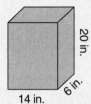

14 in.   20 in.   6 in.

  (1) $14 + 6 + 20$
  (2) $14 \times 6 \times 20$
  (3) $14 \times 6 + 20$
  (4) $14 \times 6 \times 20 \div 9$
  (5) $14 + 6 + 20 \div 12$

16. Dave orders linoleum for his kitchen, which measures 15 feet on each side. Which is the correct expression to find the area of the kitchen in square feet?

  (1) $15 + 15$
  (2) $15^2 \div 9$
  (3) $15 \times 15 \times 15$
  (4) $15 + 15 + 15 + 15$
  (5) 15^2

17. Dennis drives a delivery van. The cargo area of the van is 8 feet long, 5 feet wide, and 4 feet high. What is the volume of the cargo area in cubic feet?

8 ft.   5 ft.   4 ft.

  (1)   17
  (2)   40
  (3)   52
  (4)   105
  (5)   160

18. Dwayne measures the conference room of his office building and finds it measures 42 feet on each side. Which is the correct expression to find the area in square yards?

  (1) 42^2
  (2) $42^2 \times 9$
  (3) $42^2 \div 9$
  (4) $42 \div 9$
  (5) 42×4

19. Marcus needs to buy bricks for a patio he is building. The patio will measure 10 feet on each side. What will be the area of the patio in square feet?

  (1)   20
  (2)   40
  (3)   100
  (4)   200
  (5) 1,000

20. Joan needs to fill a rectangular carton with foam pieces. The carton is 18 inches long, 12 inches wide, and 3 inches high. Which is the correct expression to find the volume of the carton in cubic inches?

  (1) $18 \times 12 \times 3$
  (2) $18 + 12 + 3$
  (3) $18 \times 12 + 3$
  (4) $(18 + 12) \times 3$
  (5) $18 \times 12 \div 3$

21. What is the volume in cubic inches of a shipping carton that is 18 inches wide, 18 inches long, and 20 inches tall?

  (1)   324
  (2)   360
  (3)   720
  (4)   5,832
  (5)   6,480

22. Pat measures the hallways and bathroom in her house so she can buy new linoleum. She finds a total area of 108 square feet. What is the area in square yards?

  (1)   9
  (2)   12
  (3)   36
  (4)   108
  (5)   972

Check your answers on page 268.   *Section 4: Squares, Cubes, and Square Roots*   55

Unit 1 Review:
Whole Numbers

Write the place value of each underlined digit.

1. 2<u>3</u>4,957 _____

2. <u>6</u>,030,495 _____

Compare each pair of numbers. Write >, <, or = between the two numbers.

3. 417 _____ 1,740

4. 54,972 _____ 54,927

Solve. Show your work.

5. $4 + 2 \times 6 - 12 \div 2$

6. $3 \times (1 + 3) \div 4 - 1$

7.
```
  426
   84
+ 253
```

8.
```
$2.48
×    4
```

9.
```
$9.54
- 3.78
```

10. $27 \overline{)\ 785}$

11.
```
  726
× 308
```

12. $4^3 =$

13.
```
  500
- 243
```

14. $32 + 847 + 309 =$

15. $436 \times 60 =$

16. $\$25.04 \div 8 =$

17. $3,976 \div 13 =$

Write your answers in the blanks.

18. Round 4,375,429 to the nearest ten thousand.

_____

19. Use the chart on page 50. What is the value of $\sqrt{169}$?

_____

Circle the best answer for each item.

20. Martin is building a fence around his rectangular vegetable garden. The garden is 48 feet long and 20 feet wide. Which is the correct expression to find the perimeter of the garden?

    (1) 48×20
    (2) 48^2
    (3) $48^2 + 20^2$
    (4) $48 + 20$
    (5) $48 + 48 + 20 + 20$

21. On Friday Lorene spent $57 for groceries, $13 for dry cleaning, and $21 for an oil change. Estimate the total amount of money Lorene spent on Friday.

    (1) $70
    (2) $80
    (3) $90
    (4) $100
    (5) $110

Item 22 refers to the following graph.

Sweat Shirt Sales, Sept.–Jan.

22. Find the approximate difference between the number of sweat shirts sold during the month with the greatest number of sales and the number of sweat shirts sold during the month with the least number of sales.

    (1)   100
    (2)   250
    (3)   300
    (4)   350
    (5)   400

23. Ramon earns $6 an hour as a cook. He worked 38 hours last week and 43 hours this week. Which is the correct expression to find how much Ramon earned this week?

    (1) 6×38
    (2) 6×43
    (3) $38 + 43$
    (4) $6 \times (38 + 43)$
    (5) $6 + 38 + 43$

24. Carol is a carpet salesperson. She measures a bedroom and finds each side is 14 feet long. What is the area of this room in square feet?

    (1)   18
    (2)   28
    (3)   56
    (4)   196
    (5)   38,416

Item 25 refers to the following table.

CINEMA PLUS TICKET PRICES

	Before 6:00	After 6:00
Children	$3.50	$3.50
Adults	$3.50	$7.00
Senior Citizens (over 55)	$3.50	$5.00

25. Raphael is taking his 2 children and his mother to the 7:30 show. His mother is 65. How much will it cost for all 4 tickets?

    (1) $10.50
    (2) $12.00
    (3) $14.00
    (4) $15.50
    (5) $19.00

FRACTIONS

Fractions are used to show part of a whole. Here the sign shows that there is less than 1 mile to the next exit.

A **fraction** is a way to show part of a whole amount. Fractions are most often used when you are measuring something.

Imagine you are going on a 900-mile trip. You plan to drive for three days. You decide to drive $\frac{1}{3}$ of the distance on the first day. After driving $3\frac{1}{2}$ hours the first day, you need to stop for gas. A sign tells you that the next exit is $2\frac{1}{4}$ miles away. After the exit, you read on a billboard that a gas station is $\frac{3}{4}$ of a mile down the road. You buy $10\frac{1}{2}$ gallons of gas and then go on your way again.

In this example, fractions are used to measure things. Fractions represent part of a whole amount.

- You decide to drive $\frac{1}{3}$ of the total distance on the first day.

- The gas station is $\frac{3}{4}$ of a mile down the road.

Mixed numbers are also used in the example. Mixed numbers show values greater than one. A mixed number is a whole number and a fraction.

- You drive $3\frac{1}{2}$ hours.

- The exit is $2\frac{1}{4}$ miles away.

- You put $10\frac{1}{2}$ gallons of gas in the car.

You already know a lot about fractions. You round and compare fractions to make decisions every day.

A recipe calls for 11 ounces of chicken broth. At the store you have a choice of three sizes of cans: $6\frac{1}{2}$ ounces, $10\frac{7}{8}$ ounces, or 16 ounces. You buy the can that holds $10\frac{7}{8}$ ounces because you know $10\frac{7}{8}$ is almost 11 ounces.

Two shirts are on sale. Both shirts were originally $25.00. Now one shirt is marked $\frac{1}{4}$ off, and the other is marked $\frac{1}{2}$ off. Which is the better buy? You compare the two fractions and decide that the shirt marked $\frac{1}{2}$ off is the better buy because $\frac{1}{2}$ is greater than $\frac{1}{4}$.

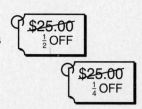

You can also tell when two fractions are equal. You know that 1 quarter is $\frac{1}{4}$ of a dollar. You know that 2 quarters ($\frac{2}{4}$ of a dollar) equal $\frac{1}{2}$ of a dollar.

$$\frac{2}{4} = \frac{1}{2}$$

In Unit 2, you will learn more about comparing and rounding fractions. You will also learn about adding, subtracting, multiplying, and dividing fractions. Actually, you do the four operations with fractions every day. Think about these examples.

Yesterday you worked $\frac{1}{2}$ hour of overtime. If you work another $\frac{1}{2}$ hour of overtime today, you know you will have worked 1 hour of overtime. You know that $\frac{1}{2} + \frac{1}{2} = 1$.

You have been at work for $7\frac{1}{2}$ hours. You know you need to work $\frac{1}{2}$ hour more to make 8 hours. You know that $8 - 7\frac{1}{2} = \frac{1}{2}$.

You want to make four hamburgers. If you use $\frac{1}{4}$ pound of ground meat for each hamburger, you will have to buy 1 pound of ground meat. You know that $\frac{1}{4} \times 4 = 1$.

You need $2 to pay for parking. If the four people in the car each chip in fifty cents or $\frac{1}{2}$ dollar, you will have $2. You know that $2 \div 4 = \frac{1}{2}$.

Here are a few of the problem-solving situations presented in Unit 2:

- ■ reading a pattern to make clothing

- ■ finding distances using a map

- ■ figuring out an employee's hours using a timecard

- ■ adjusting a recipe to serve more or fewer people

- ■ measuring with a ruler

- ■ cutting boards to certain lengths

- ■ planning a large dinner

Section 5

Fraction Theory

Facts About Fractions

A **fraction** is part of a whole. When a whole is broken into parts, the parts are fractions of the whole.

A fraction is written with one number over another number. The top number is called the **numerator**. The bottom number is called the **denominator**.

$$\frac{1}{8} \begin{array}{l} \leftarrow \text{ numerator} \\ \leftarrow \text{ denominator} \end{array}$$

The denominator tells how many equal parts the whole is divided into. The numerator tells how many of those parts you are working with.

Example   A pizza is cut into 8 equal pieces. After dinner, only 1 piece is left. So $\frac{1}{8}$ of the pizza is left, and $\frac{7}{8}$ of the pizza is gone.

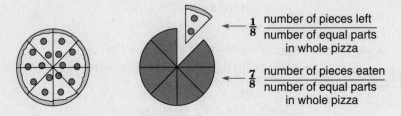

In the example above, the fractions $\frac{1}{8}$ and $\frac{7}{8}$ show part of one whole thing—the pizza. A fraction can also show part of a group.

Example   Margo bought 4 apples. She ate 3 apples. In other words, she ate $\frac{3}{4}$ of the apples. She saved $\frac{1}{4}$ of the apples.

$$\frac{3}{4} \begin{array}{l} \text{number of apples eaten} \\ \text{number of apples in group} \end{array}$$

There are three kinds of fractions: proper fractions, improper fractions, and mixed numbers.

In a **proper fraction**, the numerator (top number) is less than the denominator (bottom number). A proper fraction has a value less than 1. Fractions such as $\frac{3}{4}$, $\frac{1}{5}$, and $\frac{7}{10}$ are proper fractions.

▼ **Example**   This rectangle has been divided into 8 parts. Three parts are shaded. So $\frac{3}{8}$ of the rectangle is shaded. In the proper fraction, $\frac{3}{8}$, the numerator, 3, is less than the denominator, 8. The value of $\frac{3}{8}$ is less than 1 because the shaded part is less than the whole rectangle.

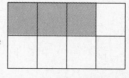

The value of an **improper fraction** is equal to 1 or greater than 1. The numerator is the same as or greater than the denominator. Fractions such as $\frac{5}{4}$, $\frac{4}{3}$, and $\frac{3}{2}$ are examples of improper fractions.

▼ **Example**   This circle has been divided into 2 parts. Both parts are shaded. The fraction $\frac{2}{2}$ shows how much of the circle is shaded. In other words, the value of $\frac{2}{2}$ is 1. Any fraction with the same numerator and denominator equals 1.

▼ **Example**   Each of two squares has been divided into 4 parts. Five parts are shaded. The fraction $\frac{5}{4}$ names the shaded parts. $\frac{5}{4}$ is an improper fraction because the numerator, 5, is greater than the denominator, 4. The value of $\frac{5}{4}$ is greater than 1.

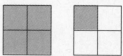

A **mixed number** is another way to show a value greater than 1. In a mixed number, a whole number is written next to a fraction. A mixed number is the sum of a whole number and a proper fraction.

▼ **Example**   Each of the three circles below has been divided into two parts. Five parts are shaded. The two circles that are completely shaded are named by the whole number 2. The shaded part of the third circle is named by the fraction $\frac{1}{2}$. The mixed number $2\frac{1}{2}$ tells what part of the circles is shaded.

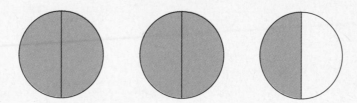

Practice Write the fraction that names the shaded part.

1.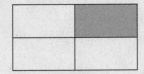

$$\frac{1}{4}$$

2.

_____

3.

_____

4.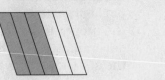

_____

5.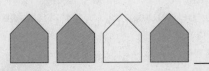

_____

6.

_____

Write the improper fraction that names the shaded part.

7.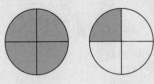

$$\frac{5}{4}$$

8.

_____

9.

_____

Write the mixed number that names the shaded part.

10.

$$1\frac{2}{3}$$

11.

_____

12.

_____

Check your answers on page 270.

Changing Improper Fractions and Mixed Numbers

Improper fractions and mixed numbers can both name values greater than 1. Each of the 4 squares below has been divided into 4 parts. The shaded part can be called $\frac{13}{4}$ (an improper fraction) or $3\frac{1}{4}$ (a mixed number).

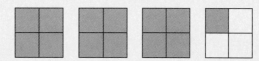

To solve problems with fractions, you will change improper fractions to mixed numbers and mixed numbers to improper fractions. An improper fraction can be written as either a mixed number or a whole number.

To change an improper fraction to a mixed number, follow these steps:

Example

Write $\frac{9}{5}$ as a mixed number.

Step 1. Divide the numerator by the denominator.

Step 2. If there is a remainder, write the remainder over the original denominator.

$$5 \overline{)\begin{array}{c} 1 \\ 9 \\ -5 \\ \hline 4 \end{array}} \qquad \frac{9}{5} = 1\frac{4}{5}$$

When there is no remainder, the improper fraction equals a whole number.

Example

Write $\frac{12}{4}$ as a whole number. Divide the numerator by the denominator.

$$4 \overline{)\begin{array}{c} 3 \\ 12 \\ -12 \\ \hline 0 \end{array}} \qquad \frac{12}{4} = 3$$

A mixed number can always be written as an improper fraction because both numbers name a value greater than 1.

To change a mixed number to an improper fraction, follow these steps:

Example

Write $2\frac{3}{8}$ as an improper fraction.

Step 1. Multiply the denominator of the fraction by the whole number part of the mixed number.

$$2\frac{3}{8} = \frac{(8 \times 2) + 3}{8}$$

Step 2. Add the numerator of the fraction to the result.

$$= \frac{16 + 3}{8}$$

Step 3. Write the total over the original denominator.

$$= \frac{19}{8}$$

You can also change a whole number to an improper fraction. Write the whole number as the numerator with 1 as the denominator.

$$4 = \frac{4}{1} \qquad 10 = \frac{10}{1}$$

Practice ▆ Change each improper fraction to a whole or mixed number. Show your work.

1. $\frac{7}{4}$
$$4\overline{)7} \quad 1\frac{3}{4}$$
$$\underline{-4}$$
$$3$$

2. $\frac{18}{6}$

3. $\frac{14}{5}$

4. $\frac{10}{3}$

5. $\frac{20}{4}$

6. $\frac{15}{8}$

▆ Change each whole or mixed number to an improper fraction. Show your work.

7. $1\frac{5}{6}$ $\quad \frac{(6 \times 1) + 5}{6} = \frac{6 + 5}{6}$
$$= \frac{11}{6}$$

8. $2\frac{1}{2}$

9. 7

10. $3\frac{4}{5}$

11. 12

12. $10\frac{3}{4}$

Equal Fractions

Different fractions can represent the same value. The shaded parts of the two rectangles below are equal. So $\frac{1}{2}$ and $\frac{4}{8}$ are different names for the same value.

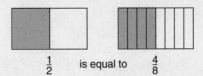

$\frac{1}{2}$ is equal to $\frac{4}{8}$

Cross-multiply to find if two fractions are equal. Multiply the numerator of each fraction by the denominator of the other. If the results are equal, the fractions are equal.

$$\frac{1}{2} \times \frac{4}{8} = \frac{1}{2} \diagdown\!\!\!\!\diagup \frac{4}{8} \qquad \begin{array}{l} 2 \times 4 = 8 \\ 1 \times 8 = 8 \end{array}$$

▆ **Example** Are $\frac{6}{8}$ and $\frac{3}{4}$ equal fractions?

Cross–multiply: $\frac{6}{8} \diagdown\!\!\!\!\diagup \frac{3}{4}$ $\qquad \begin{array}{l} 6 \times 4 = 24 \\ 8 \times 3 = 24 \end{array}$

Because the results are the same, $\frac{6}{8}$ and $\frac{3}{4}$ are equal.

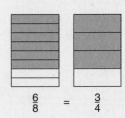

$\frac{6}{8} = \frac{3}{4}$

Check your answers on page 270.

Reducing a Fraction to Lower Terms

Reducing a fraction to lower terms means finding an equal fraction with a smaller numerator and denominator. The numerator and denominator of a fraction are sometimes called **terms**.

To reduce a fraction, divide the numerator and the denominator by the same number. The fraction has been reduced to lowest terms when no number except 1 will divide evenly into the numerator and the denominator.

Example

Reduce $\frac{8}{10}$ to lowest terms.

The number 2 will divide evenly into both the numerator and the denominator.

$$\frac{8}{10} = \frac{8 \div 2}{10 \div 2} = \frac{4}{5}$$

The fraction $\frac{4}{5}$ is in lowest terms because no number except 1 will divide evenly into both 4 and 5.

Check your work by cross-multiplying.

$$\frac{8}{10} \diagdown\diagup \frac{4}{5} \qquad \begin{array}{l} 8 \times 5 = 40 \\ 10 \times 4 = 40 \end{array} \qquad \text{The fractions } \frac{8}{10} \text{ and } \frac{4}{5} \text{ are equal fractions.}$$

You may need to divide more than once to reduce a fraction to lowest terms.

Example

Reduce $\frac{4}{8}$ to lowest terms.

The number 2 will divide evenly into both 4 and 8. But $\frac{2}{4}$ is not in lowest terms. Both 2 and 4 can be divided evenly by 2.

$$\frac{4}{8} = \frac{4 \div 2}{8 \div 2} = \frac{2}{4} = \frac{2 \div 2}{4 \div 2} = \frac{1}{2}$$

The fraction $\frac{1}{2}$ is in lowest terms because no number except 1 will divide evenly into both 1 and 2. The fraction $\frac{4}{8}$ equals $\frac{1}{2}$.

Notice that dividing both the numerator and the denominator by 4 would have reduced $\frac{4}{8}$ to lowest terms in one step. However, the answer is the same either way.

$$\frac{4}{8} = \frac{4 \div 4}{8 \div 4} = \frac{1}{2}$$

Check your work by cross-multiplying.

$$\frac{4}{8} \diagdown\diagup \frac{1}{2} \qquad \begin{array}{l} 4 \times 2 = 8 \\ 8 \times 1 = 8 \end{array} \qquad \text{The fractions } \frac{4}{8} \text{ and } \frac{1}{2} \text{ are equal fractions.}$$

Practice ■ Reduce each fraction to lowest terms. Show your work.

1. $\dfrac{3 \div 3}{6 \div 3} = \dfrac{1}{2}$

2. $\dfrac{8}{12}$

3. $\dfrac{4}{10}$

4. $\dfrac{6}{8}$

5. $\dfrac{20}{25}$

6. $\dfrac{12}{36}$

7. $\dfrac{6}{9}$

8. $\dfrac{8}{16}$

9. $\dfrac{16}{20}$

10. $\dfrac{10}{14}$

11. $\dfrac{5}{15}$

12. $\dfrac{20}{24}$

Raising a Fraction to Higher Terms

Raising a fraction to higher terms means finding an equal fraction with a greater numerator and denominator.

To raise a fraction to higher terms, multiply the numerator and the denominator by the same number.

■ **Example** Raise $\frac{2}{5}$ to an equal fraction with higher terms. Multiply both the numerator and the denominator by 2.

$$\dfrac{2}{5} = \dfrac{2 \times 2}{5 \times 2} = \dfrac{4}{10}$$

Check your work by cross-multiplying.

$$\frac{2}{5} \diagdown \frac{4}{10}$$

$$2 \times 10 = 20$$
$$5 \times 4 = 20$$

The fractions $\frac{2}{5}$ and $\frac{4}{10}$ are equal fractions.

Sometimes you need to raise a fraction so that it will have a certain denominator.

Example

Raise $\frac{1}{4}$ to an equal fraction with a denominator of 20.

$$\frac{1}{4} = \frac{?}{20}$$

Think, "What number should be multiplied by 4 to get 20?" To answer the question, divide 4 into 20. The result is 5. Multiply both the numerator and the denominator by 5.

$$\frac{1}{4} = \frac{1 \times 5}{4 \times 5} = \frac{5}{20}$$

Check your work by cross-multiplying.

$$\frac{1}{4} \diagdown \frac{5}{20}$$

$$1 \times 20 = 20$$
$$4 \times 5 = 20$$

The fractions $\frac{1}{4}$ and $\frac{5}{20}$ are equal fractions.

Practice Find an equal fraction with the given denominator. Show your work.

1. $\frac{3}{4} = \frac{?}{8}$ $\frac{3 \times 2}{4 \times 2} = \frac{6}{8}$

2. $\frac{2}{3} = \frac{?}{12}$

3. $\frac{1}{6} = \frac{?}{18}$

4. $\frac{7}{10} = \frac{?}{20}$

5. $\frac{5}{8} = \frac{?}{24}$

6. $\frac{2}{5} = \frac{?}{30}$

7. $\frac{4}{9} = \frac{?}{18}$

8. $\frac{1}{4} = \frac{?}{12}$

9. $\frac{7}{8} = \frac{?}{32}$

10. $\frac{3}{5} = \frac{?}{25}$

11. $\frac{7}{12} = \frac{?}{36}$

12. $\frac{3}{10} = \frac{?}{40}$

Using Your Math Skills

Write the proper or improper fraction that names the shaded part.

1. _____

2.  _____

3. 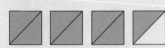 _____

4. 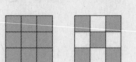 _____

Write the mixed number that names the shaded part.

5. 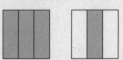 _____

6. 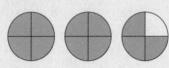 _____

Change each fraction to a whole or mixed number.

7. $\frac{11}{6}$

8. $\frac{25}{5}$

9. $\frac{19}{8}$

Change each whole or mixed number to an improper fraction.

10. 7

11. $1\frac{7}{8}$

12. $4\frac{3}{5}$

Reduce each fraction to lowest terms.

13. $\frac{5}{10}$

14. $\frac{9}{12}$

15. $\frac{16}{24}$

Find an equal fraction with the given denominator.

16. $\frac{1}{2} = \frac{?}{18}$

17. $\frac{5}{6} = \frac{?}{24}$

18. $\frac{3}{4} = \frac{?}{32}$

Check your answers on page 271.

Write your answers in the blanks.

19. Ace Wholesale employs 25 people. Seven employees work in the warehouse. What fraction of the employees works in the warehouse?

    _____

20. Martha's softball team won 9 out of 16 games this season. What fraction of the games did her team win?

    _____

21. Of the 40 children who come to a day-care center, 13 come only for the after-school program. What fraction of the children comes only after school?

    _____

22. Elmer baked 36 muffins for a bake sale. His children ate 5 muffins. What fraction of the muffins did his children eat?

    _____

Circle the best answer for each item.

23. Juan completed $\frac{6}{8}$ of his workday before taking a break. In lowest terms, how much of his workday did Juan complete?

    (1) $\frac{2}{2}$

    (2) $\frac{3}{2}$

    (3) $\frac{3}{4}$

    (4) $\frac{4}{6}$

    (5) $\frac{12}{16}$

24. In the garage, Val found $\frac{15}{4}$ gallons of paint. Which whole or mixed number describes the number of gallons of paint she found?

    (1) $1\frac{5}{4}$

    (2) 3

    (3) $3\frac{3}{4}$

    (4) 4

    (5) $4\frac{1}{4}$

25. Betty lives 7 miles from town. Which improper fraction describes this distance?

    (1) $\frac{7}{1}$

    (2) $\frac{1}{7}$

    (3) $\frac{7}{7}$

    (4) $\frac{10}{7}$

    (5) $\frac{7}{10}$

26. Lupe needs $\frac{2}{3}$ of a dozen eggs to bake a cake. Which fraction also describes the part of a dozen eggs Lupe needs?

    (1) $\frac{12}{9}$

    (2) $\frac{12}{8}$

    (3) $\frac{5}{12}$

    (4) $\frac{8}{12}$

    (5) $\frac{9}{12}$

27. Tom works at an electronics store. His sales this month were $\frac{10}{5}$ as much as his sales last month. Which whole or mixed number describes how much greater his sales were this month?

    (1) $\frac{1}{2}$

    (2) 2

    (3) $2\frac{1}{5}$

    (4) $2\frac{5}{5}$

    (5) 5

28. Tonya's baby gained $1\frac{5}{16}$ pounds last month. Which improper fraction describes how many pounds the baby gained?

    (1) $\frac{15}{16}$

    (2) $\frac{21}{16}$

    (3) $\frac{51}{16}$

    (4) $\frac{81}{16}$

    (5) $\frac{16}{21}$

Check your answers on page 271.

Section 5: Fraction Theory   69

Adding and Subtracting Fractions

Data Analysis ## Reading a Table

David, a tailor, is sewing bridesmaid dresses for Jan and Sue. The dress pattern he is going to use has a table of information on the back. David will use the table to find how much fabric to buy.

Yardage Requirements

	Sizes	10	12	14
Dress A		$2\frac{7}{8}$	3	$3\frac{1}{8}$
Dress B		3	$3\frac{1}{8}$	$3\frac{1}{4}$
Dress C		$3\frac{1}{4}$	$3\frac{3}{8}$	$3\frac{5}{8}$

The table has labels across the top and down the left side. This pattern can be used to make a dress in three sizes. The sizes are shown across the top of the table. The pattern can also be used to make a dress in three styles. The styles, labeled *A*, *B*, and *C*, are shown down the left side of the table.

Using the table, David can find how many yards of fabric he will need to make the dresses in the styles and sizes he needs.

David decides to make dress style C in size 10 for Jan and in size 14 for Sue. He needs to buy enough fabric for the two dresses. He finds the row labeled *Dress C* and reads across to the column labeled *10*. He needs $3\frac{1}{4}$ yards of fabric to make Jan's dress. Then David finds the row labeled *Dress C*. He reads across to the column labeled *14* and finds he needs $3\frac{5}{8}$ yards of fabric for Sue's dress.

Which is the correct expression to find the total number of yards of fabric he will need?

(1) $10 - 3\frac{1}{4}$

(2) $3\frac{1}{4} + 3\frac{5}{8}$

(3) $3\frac{1}{4} - 3\frac{5}{8}$

(4) $10 + 3\frac{1}{4}$

(5) $3\frac{5}{8} - 3\frac{1}{4}$

70 *Unit 2: Fractions*

Answer 2 is the correct choice. David needs to find the total yardage for the two dresses. He adds $3\frac{1}{4}$ (the yardage for Jan's dress) and $3\frac{5}{8}$ (the yardage for Sue's dress) to find the total yardage. He needs to buy $6\frac{7}{8}$ yards of fabric to make the dresses.

$$3\frac{1}{4} = 3\frac{2}{8}$$
$$+\ 3\frac{5}{8} = +\ 3\frac{5}{8}$$
$$\overline{6\frac{7}{8}\ \text{yards}}$$

Jan and Sue may want David to use dress style B instead. David knows he needs $6\frac{7}{8}$ yards for the dresses in style C. He wants to know if he would need more fabric for style B.

Yardage Requirements

Sizes	10	12	14
Dress A	$2\frac{7}{8}$	3	$3\frac{1}{8}$
Dress B	③	$3\frac{1}{8}$	$3\frac{1}{4}$
Dress C	$3\frac{1}{4}$	$3\frac{3}{8}$	$3\frac{5}{8}$

Using the table, David finds that he will need 3 yards for Jan's dress and $3\frac{1}{4}$ yards for Sue's dress. He finds the total number of yards needed for style B and compares it to $6\frac{7}{8}$, the number of yards needed for style C. There are two steps to solving the problem: finding a total and comparing the two amounts.

Which is the correct expression to find the total of 3 and $3\frac{1}{4}$ and to compare the result to $6\frac{7}{8}$?

(1) $6\frac{7}{8} + (3 - 3\frac{1}{4})$

(2) $6\frac{7}{8} - (3 - 3\frac{1}{4})$

(3) $6\frac{7}{8} + (3 + 3\frac{1}{4})$

(4) $6\frac{7}{8} - (3 + 3\frac{1}{4})$

(5) $(3 + 6\frac{7}{8}) - 3\frac{1}{4}$

Answer 4 is the correct choice. David adds 3 and $3\frac{1}{4}$ to find the total yardage for the dresses in style B. Then he subtracts this total from $6\frac{7}{8}$ (the total yardage for the dresses in style C) to find the difference.

$$3$$
$$+\ 3\frac{1}{4}$$
$$\overline{6\frac{1}{4}}$$

David adds first. He needs $6\frac{1}{4}$ yards for the dresses in style B. Then he subtracts. The difference is $\frac{5}{8}$ of a yard. He will need $\frac{5}{8}$ of a yard more fabric to make the dresses in style C.

$$6\frac{7}{8} = 6\frac{7}{8}$$
$$-\ 6\frac{1}{4} = -\ 6\frac{2}{8}$$
$$\overline{\frac{5}{8}\ \text{yard}}$$

Practice ◼ Circle the best answer for each item.

Items 1–3 refer to the table below.

Yardage Requirements:
Woman's Jacket and Skirt

Sizes	10	12	14
Jacket A	$2\frac{1}{4}$	$2\frac{3}{8}$	$2\frac{1}{2}$
Jacket B	$1\frac{7}{8}$	$1\frac{7}{8}$	$2\frac{1}{8}$
Skirt	$2\frac{5}{8}$	$2\frac{5}{8}$	$2\frac{5}{8}$

1. A tailor is making a skirt and jacket B in size 12. Which is the correct expression to find the total number of yards of fabric he needs for the jacket and the skirt?

    (1) $1\frac{7}{8} - 2\frac{5}{8}$

    (2) $1\frac{7}{8} + 2\frac{5}{8}$

    (3) $2\frac{3}{8} + 1\frac{5}{8}$

    (4) $2\frac{3}{8} - 1\frac{5}{8}$

    (5) $2\frac{3}{8} + 1\frac{5}{8}$

2. Ruby is trying to decide whether to make a skirt and jacket A or a skirt and jacket B in size 10. Which is the correct expression to find how many more yards of fabric she needs to make a skirt and jacket A instead of a skirt and jacket B?

    (1) $2\frac{1}{4} - 1\frac{7}{8} - 2\frac{5}{8}$

    (2) $(1\frac{7}{8} + 2\frac{5}{8}) - (2\frac{1}{4} + 2\frac{5}{8})$

    (3) $2\frac{1}{4} + 2\frac{5}{8} - 1\frac{7}{8} + 2\frac{5}{8}$

    (4) $(2\frac{1}{4} + 2\frac{5}{8}) - (1\frac{7}{8} + 2\frac{5}{8})$

    (5) $(2\frac{1}{4} + 1\frac{7}{8}) - 2\frac{5}{8}$

3. Carlos was hired to make jacket A and the skirt in size 14. Which is the correct expression to find how many yards he needs for the jacket and skirt?

    (1) $2\frac{1}{8} + 2\frac{5}{8}$

    (2) $2\frac{1}{4} - 2\frac{5}{8}$

    (3) $2\frac{3}{8} + 2\frac{5}{8}$

    (4) $2\frac{1}{4} + 2\frac{5}{8}$

    (5) $2\frac{1}{2} + 2\frac{5}{8}$

Items 4–6 refer to the table below.

Yardage Requirements:
Child's Jumper and Blouse

Sizes	4	5	6
Jumper	$1\frac{3}{4}$	$1\frac{7}{8}$	2
Blouse A	$1\frac{1}{8}$	$1\frac{1}{4}$	$1\frac{3}{8}$
Blouse B	$1\frac{1}{8}$	$1\frac{1}{8}$	$1\frac{1}{4}$
Facing, Blouse B	$\frac{3}{4}$	$\frac{3}{4}$	$\frac{7}{8}$

4. Charnelle decides to make matching jumpers for her two daughters. One daughter wears size 4 and the other wears size 6. Which is the correct expression to find how many yards of fabric she needs?

    (1) $1\frac{3}{4} + 1\frac{7}{8}$

    (2) $1\frac{1}{4} - 2$

    (3) $1\frac{3}{4} + 2$

    (4) $2 - 1\frac{1}{3}$

    (5) $2 \times (1\frac{3}{4} + 2)$

5. Misha decides to make blouse B and a jumper for her daughter in size 5. Which is the correct expression to find how many yards of fabric and facing she needs?

    (1) $1\frac{3}{4} + 1\frac{1}{8} + \frac{3}{4}$

    (2) $1\frac{7}{8} + 1\frac{1}{8} + \frac{3}{4}$

    (3) $1\frac{7}{8} - 1\frac{1}{8} + \frac{3}{4}$

    (4) $1\frac{7}{8} + 1\frac{1}{4} - \frac{3}{4}$

    (5) $1\frac{7}{8} + 1\frac{1}{4} + \frac{5}{8}$

6. Russ has a fabric remnant that is 5 yards long. The remnant will be used to make a jumper and blouse A in size 4. Which is the correct expression to find how many yards of fabric will be left?

    (1) $5 - 1\frac{3}{4} + 1\frac{1}{8}$

    (2) $5 + 1\frac{3}{4} + 1\frac{1}{8}$

    (3) $5 + 1\frac{3}{4} - 1\frac{1}{8}$

    (4) $5 - (1\frac{3}{4} + 1\frac{1}{8})$

    (5) $(5 - 1\frac{3}{4}) + 1\frac{1}{8}$

Check your answers on page 271.

Adding Fractions

Like fractions have the same denominator. In other words, like fractions have a **common denominator**. The fractions $\frac{1}{4}$ and $\frac{3}{4}$ have the common denominator 4. The fractions $\frac{1}{6}$ and $\frac{2}{3}$ have different denominators, and they are called **unlike fractions**.

Use these steps to add like fractions:

Step 1. Add the numerators (the top numbers).

Step 2. Write the sum over the common denominator.

Step 3. If the answer is an improper fraction, change it to a mixed number. Reduce the answer to lowest terms.

Example

Add: $\frac{5}{8} + \frac{7}{8}$

$$\frac{5}{8} + \frac{7}{8} = \frac{12}{8} = 1\frac{4}{8} = 1\frac{1}{2}$$

You can add fractions only if the fractions have the same denominator. To add unlike fractions, find a common denominator for the fractions and change to like fractions. A **common denominator** is a number that each denominator will divide evenly.

Example

Add: $\frac{1}{3} + \frac{3}{4}$

Since $\frac{1}{3}$ and $\frac{3}{4}$ are unlike fractions, find a common denominator for 3 and 4. Think, "What number will both 3 and 4 divide evenly?" You know that 3 and 4 will divide 12 evenly because $12 \div 3 = 4$ and $12 \div 4 = 3$.

Now change $\frac{2}{3}$ and $\frac{3}{4}$ to equal fractions with a denominator of 12.

$$\frac{1}{3} = \frac{1 \times 4}{3 \times 4} = \frac{4}{12} \qquad \frac{3}{4} = \frac{3 \times 3}{4 \times 3} = \frac{9}{12}$$

Since $\frac{4}{12}$ and $\frac{9}{12}$ are like fractions, add the numerators. The answer, $\frac{13}{12}$, is an improper fraction. Change it to a mixed number.

$$\frac{4}{12} + \frac{9}{12} = \frac{13}{12} = 1\frac{1}{12}$$

Use these steps to add mixed numbers:

Step 1. Add the fractions, changing unlike fractions to like fractions.

Step 2. Add the whole numbers.

Step 3. If the sum of the fractions is an improper fraction, change it to a mixed number. Add the fraction total to the whole number total.

Step 4. Reduce your answer to lowest terms.

Example   Add: $2\frac{5}{6} + 3\frac{1}{2}$

$$2\frac{5}{6} \;=\; 2\frac{5}{6}$$
$$+\,3\frac{1}{2} \;=\; +\,3\frac{3}{6}$$
$$\overline{\phantom{+\,3\frac{1}{2}}}$$
$$5\frac{8}{6} \;=\; 5 + 1\frac{2}{6} \;=\; 6\frac{2}{6} \;=\; 6\frac{1}{3}$$

Practice   Add. Reduce your answers to lowest terms.

1. $\dfrac{2}{9} + \dfrac{5}{9} = \dfrac{7}{9}$

2. $\dfrac{7}{10} + \dfrac{9}{10} =$

3. $\dfrac{1}{4} + \dfrac{3}{5} =$

4. $\dfrac{5}{6} + \dfrac{2}{3} =$

5. $\quad 2\frac{1}{5}$
    $+\ 3\frac{2}{5}$

6. $\quad 4\frac{5}{12}$
    $+\ 2\frac{7}{12}$

7. $\quad 1\frac{1}{4}$
    $+\ 3\frac{2}{3}$

8. $\quad 5\frac{2}{3}$
    $+\ 2\frac{2}{5}$

9. $\quad 6\frac{5}{8}$
    $+\ \ \frac{1}{6}$

10. $\quad 3\frac{2}{3}$
    $+\ 2\frac{3}{4}$

Subtracting Fractions

Subtracting fractions is a lot like adding fractions. You can only subtract like fractions. To subtract unlike fractions, you must find a common denominator before you can subtract. Subtract only the numerators; then write the difference over the common denominator. Reduce your answer to lowest terms.

The following examples show the steps in subtracting fractions.

Example Subtract: $\frac{7}{8} - \frac{1}{8}$

Subtract the numerators ($7 - 1 = 6$). Write 6 over the common denominator, 8. Reduce $\frac{6}{8}$ to lowest terms.

$$\frac{7}{8} - \frac{1}{8} = \frac{6}{8} = \frac{3}{4}$$

Example Subtract: $\frac{4}{5} - \frac{3}{10}$

Change the unlike fractions to like fractions. First, find a common denominator. Think, "What number will both 5 and 10 divide evenly?" Both 5 and 10 will divide 10 evenly. Change $\frac{4}{5}$ to a like fraction with a denominator of 10.

$$\frac{4}{5} = \frac{4 \times 2}{5 \times 2} = \frac{8}{10}$$

Then subtract the numerators, and reduce the answer to lowest terms.

$$\frac{8}{10} - \frac{3}{10} = \frac{5}{10} = \frac{1}{2}$$

To subtract a fraction or mixed number from a whole number, borrow 1 from the whole number and rewrite it as a fraction. Any fraction with the same number in both the numerator and denominator has a value of 1. So $\frac{3}{3}$, $\frac{5}{5}$, and $\frac{100}{100}$ each have a value of 1. Change the 1 borrowed from the whole number column to a fraction with a value of 1. Use the common denominator, and write a fraction that has a value of 1.

Example Subtract: $5 - 2\frac{3}{8}$

Borrow 1 from the whole number 5 and rewrite as a fraction with a common denominator of 8. The fraction, $\frac{8}{8}$, is equal to 1. Subtract. The answer $2\frac{5}{8}$ is in lowest terms.

$$5 = \overset{4}{\cancel{5}}\frac{8}{8}$$
$$- 2\frac{3}{8} = - 2\frac{3}{8}$$
$$\overline{\qquad 2\frac{5}{8}}$$

When you subtract with mixed numbers, the fraction part of the top number is sometimes smaller than the fraction part of the bottom number. If so, borrow 1 from the whole number column, rewrite it as a fraction, and **add** it to the fraction in the fraction column.

Example

Subtract: $3\frac{1}{4} - 1\frac{5}{6}$

Find a common denominator and write equal fractions. You can't subtract $\frac{10}{12}$ from $\frac{3}{12}$. Borrow 1 from the whole number column. Think of the borrowed 1 as $\frac{12}{12}$ and add it to $\frac{3}{12}$ in the fraction column. You now have $\frac{15}{12}$ in the fraction column ($\frac{12}{12} + \frac{3}{12} = \frac{15}{12}$). Subtract the fractions and then the whole numbers. The answer, $1\frac{5}{12}$, is in lowest terms.

$$3\frac{1}{4} = \quad 3\frac{3}{12} = \quad \overset{2\ 15}{\cancel{3}\frac{\cancel{3}}{12}}$$
$$-\ 1\frac{5}{6} = \quad -\ 1\frac{10}{12} = \quad -\ 1\frac{10}{12}$$
$$\overline{1\frac{5}{12}}$$

Practice Subtract. Reduce your answers to lowest terms.

1. $\frac{11}{12} - \frac{5}{12} = \frac{6}{12} = \frac{1}{2}$

2. $\frac{5}{6} - \frac{3}{8} =$

3. $\frac{9}{16} - \frac{1}{4} =$

4. $6 - 2\frac{3}{5} =$

5. $\quad 4\frac{7}{8}$
   $- 1\frac{3}{8}$

6. $\quad 7\frac{3}{4}$
   $- 2\frac{2}{3}$

7. $\quad 8$
   $- 5\frac{2}{9}$

8. $\quad 6\frac{1}{6}$
   $- 3\frac{5}{6}$

9. $\quad 9\frac{1}{4}$
   $- 8\frac{5}{8}$

10. $\quad 7\frac{2}{5}$
    $- 1\frac{2}{3}$

Check your answers on page 272.

Using a Map

Problem Solving Strategy: Estimating

Kim drives a delivery truck for a laundry service. She delivers clean linens and picks up used linens at restaurants.

The map below shows her route for Monday of each week. Kim begins at point A on the map, drives east to point B, and heads north to point C. Next she works her way west and south through points D, E, and F. Finally, Kim drives south to point A.

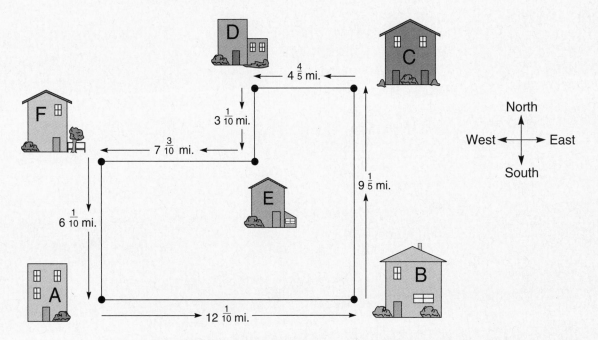

The distance between points is marked on the map in miles. The points show each time Kim changes direction along her route. She makes many stops between the points on the map.

Kim's boss, Miguel, wants her to be at point D on the map by noon. Miguel asks Kim to figure out how many miles she drives from point A to point D. He also wants to know how many miles she will drive in the afternoon from point D back to point A.

Kim covers three distances to get from point A to point D. She drives $12\frac{1}{10}$ miles from A to B, then $9\frac{1}{5}$ miles from B to C, and finally $4\frac{4}{5}$ miles from C to D. To find the total miles driven from A to D, she adds the three numbers.

First, Kim estimates the distance. Instead of adding the fractions, she works with simpler numbers. She rounds the mixed numbers to whole numbers. If the fraction part is less than $\frac{1}{2}$, she doesn't change the whole number. If the fraction part is $\frac{1}{2}$ or greater, she adds 1 to the whole number.

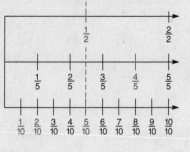

Kim is working with fifths and tenths on her map. She knows that $\frac{5}{10}$ equals $\frac{1}{2}$. She also knows that $\frac{1}{10}$ is less than $\frac{1}{2}$ and that $\frac{4}{5}$ is greater than $\frac{1}{2}$. She uses these facts to round the distances.

Estimate

After rounding, she adds the whole numbers and finds that the estimated distance on her route between points A and D is about 26 miles.

$$\begin{array}{rl} 12\frac{1}{10} & \text{is about} \quad 12 \\ 9\frac{1}{5} & \text{is about} \quad 9 \\ + \ 4\frac{4}{5} & \text{is about} \ + \ 5 \\ \hline & \phantom{\text{is about} \ +} 26 \end{array}$$

Next she adds the mixed numbers to find the exact distance.

$$\begin{array}{rcl} 12\frac{1}{10} & = & 12\frac{1}{10} \\ 9\frac{1}{5} & = & 9\frac{2}{10} \\ + \ 4\frac{4}{5} & = & + \ 4\frac{8}{10} \\ \hline & & 25\frac{11}{10} \ = \ 25 \ + \ 1\frac{1}{10} \ = \ 26\frac{1}{10} \text{ miles} \end{array}$$

Because $26\frac{1}{10}$ miles is close to her estimate of 26 miles, Kim knows her answer is reasonable.

Now Kim needs to find the distance she will drive in the afternoon. She knows that her total route is $42\frac{3}{5}$ miles long. She knows she drives $26\frac{1}{10}$ miles in the morning. She needs to figure out how many miles she drives in the afternoon. Kim can subtract to solve the problem.

Estimate

First, she estimates an answer. She rounds to the nearest whole number and subtracts. Kim finds the distance she drives in the afternoon is about 17 miles.

$$\begin{array}{rl} 42\frac{3}{5} & \text{is about} \quad 43 \\ - \ 26\frac{1}{10} & \text{is about} \ - \ 26 \\ \hline & \phantom{\text{is about} \ -} 17 \end{array}$$

Next Kim subtracts the mixed numbers to find the exact distance she drives in the afternoon.

$$\begin{array}{rcl} 42\frac{3}{5} & = & 42\frac{6}{10} \\ - \ 26\frac{1}{10} & = & - \ 26\frac{1}{10} \\ \hline & & 16\frac{5}{10} \ = \ 16\frac{1}{2} \end{array}$$

Because $16\frac{1}{2}$ miles is close to her estimate of 17 miles, Kim knows her answer is reasonable. Kim tells Miguel that she drives $26\frac{1}{10}$ miles in the morning and $16\frac{1}{2}$ miles in the afternoon.

Practice ▪ Circle the best answer for each item.

Items 1–5 refer to the following information.

Jose restocks soda machines for a vending company. The map below shows the route Jose follows each day.

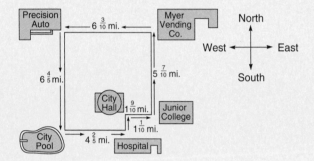

1. During the morning Jose restocks machines for all the customers between Myer Vending Company and the hospital. Estimate how many miles Jose drives during the morning.

    (1) 8
    (2) 9
    (3) 16
    (4) 17
    (5) 19

2. During the morning Jose drives from Myer Vending Company to the hospital. Exactly how many miles does he drive during the morning?

    (1) $13\frac{1}{10}$

    (2) $16\frac{1}{2}$

    (3) $16\frac{4}{5}$

    (4) $16\frac{9}{10}$

    (5) $17\frac{1}{2}$

▪ Write your answers in the blanks. Show your work.

3. One-Stop Gas and Food is $3\frac{3}{10}$ miles past the city pool. Exactly how many miles must Jose drive to get from One-Stop Gas and Food to the hospital?

    _____

4. After lunch in the hospital cafeteria, Jose completes his route. Estimate how many miles Jose drives during the afternoon.

    _____

5. During the afternoon, Jose drives from the hospital back to Myer Vending Company. Exactly how many miles does he drive during the afternoon?

    _____

Timecards

Problem-Solving Strategy: Using a Table

Kareem is an office clerk in a grocery store. Part of his job is to complete the timecards for the employees of the store. Timecards are used to keep a record of the times employees start and stop working. The employees push their cards into a machine that is attached to a clock. The machine stamps the time of day on the card.

After the employees punch in and out, Kareem figures out how many hours the employees were at work. He needs to know the following facts about measuring time.

■ There are 24 hours in one day.

■ There are 60 minutes in one hour.

■ The clock shows a 12-hour period of time. The clock goes through the 12-hour cycle twice in one day.

■ The abbreviations A.M. and P.M. refer to a 12-hour cycle. A.M. starts at midnight and goes through the morning. P.M. starts at noon and goes through the evening.

The employees punch in and out twice each day. They punch in when they come to work in the morning and out when they go to lunch. They punch in when they come back from lunch and punch out when they finish working for the day. Kareem is working on the timecard of Jan Lopez. He is computing the hours Jan worked on Monday, March 4. The card shows she worked from 8:15 A.M. to 12:36 P.M., when she went to lunch. Jan came back at 1:28 P.M. and worked until 5:17 P.M.

NAME:	Jan Lopez		
WEEK OF:	3/4 – 3/11		
IN	MON.	3/4	8:15 A.M.
OUT	MON.	3/4	12:36 P.M.
IN	MON.	3/4	1:28 P.M.
OUT	MON.	3/4	5:17 P.M.
IN	TUES.	3/5	8:05 A.M.

Came to work

Went to lunch

Returned from lunch

Left work

First, Kareem finds the number of hours Jan worked in the morning. His boss, Carol, wants time recorded to the nearest quarter hour. For each part of an hour an employee works, Kareem figures out whether the number of minutes is closest to the hour, or closest to 15, 30, or 45 minutes past the hour. Then he changes the minutes to a fractional part of a whole hour.

15 minutes $= \frac{1}{4}$ hour, because $\frac{15}{60} = \frac{15 \div 15}{60 \div 15} = \frac{1}{4}$

30 minutes $= \frac{1}{2}$ hour, because $\frac{30}{60} = \frac{30 \div 15}{60 \div 15} = \frac{2}{4} = \frac{1}{2}$

45 minutes $= \frac{3}{4}$ hour, because $\frac{45}{60} = \frac{45 \div 15}{60 \div 15} = \frac{3}{4}$

Kareem uses fractions to figure the hours worked. First, he changes the times to mixed numbers. Jan came in to work at 8:15 A.M. Since 15 minutes is $\frac{1}{4}$ of an hour, Kareem thinks of 8:15 as $8\frac{1}{4}$. She went to lunch at 12:36 P.M. Since 36 is close to 30 minutes, Kareem changes 12:36 to $12\frac{1}{2}$. Then he subtracts the smaller mixed number from the larger one. Jan worked $4\frac{1}{4}$ hours in the morning.

$$
\begin{aligned}
12\frac{1}{2} &= 12\frac{2}{4} \\
- 8\frac{1}{4} &= - 8\frac{1}{4} \\
\hline
&\quad\; 4\frac{1}{4} \text{ hours}
\end{aligned}
$$

Now Kareem finds how many hours Jan worked after lunch. She came back from lunch at 1:28 P.M. Since 28 is about 30 minutes, Kareem changes 1:28 to $1\frac{1}{2}$. Jan left work for the day at 5:17 P.M. Since 17 minutes is close to 15, Kareem changes 5:17 to $5\frac{1}{4}$. Then he subtracts the smaller mixed number from the larger one. Jan worked $3\frac{3}{4}$ hours in the afternoon.

$$
\begin{aligned}
&&& 4\frac{5}{4} \\
5\frac{1}{4} &= 5\frac{1}{4} &=& \;\cancel{5}\frac{1}{4} \\
- 1\frac{1}{2} &= - 1\frac{2}{4} &=& - 1\frac{2}{4} \\
\hline
&&& 3\frac{3}{4} \text{ hours}
\end{aligned}
$$

Kareem knows Jan worked $4\frac{1}{4}$ hours in the morning and $3\frac{3}{4}$ hours in the afternoon. What was the total number of hours Jan worked during the day?

(1) 7

(2) $7\frac{3}{4}$

(3) 8

(4) $8\frac{1}{4}$

(5) $8\frac{1}{2}$

Answer 3 is the correct choice. Kareem adds $4\frac{1}{4}$ and $3\frac{3}{4}$ hours to find the total. The total of the fraction part of the mixed numbers is $\frac{4}{4}$, an improper fraction. So, $\frac{4}{4}$ is changed to the whole number, 1, and added to the sum of the whole numbers. Jan worked 8 hours on Monday.

$$
\begin{aligned}
&\;\; 4\frac{1}{4} \\
+&\;\; 3\frac{3}{4} \\
\hline
&\;\; 7\frac{4}{4} = 7 + 1 = 8 \text{ hours}
\end{aligned}
$$

Practice ◼ Write your answers in the blanks. Show your work.

<u>Items 1– 3</u> refer to the timecard below.

```
NAME:      Vlady Krislov
WEEK OF:    3/12 – 3/19

IN    MON.  3/12   9:00 A.M.
OUT   MON.  3/12  12:42 P.M.
IN    MON.  3/12   1:48 P.M.
OUT   MON.  3/12   6:02 P.M.
```

1. How many hours to the nearest quarter hour did Vlady work in the morning?

_____

2. How many hours to the nearest quarter hour did Vlady work in the afternoon?

_____

3. How many total hours to the nearest quarter hour did Vlady work on Monday?

_____

◼ Circle the best answer for each item.

<u>Items 4– 6</u> refer to the timecard below.

```
NAME:      Paul Wagner
WEEK OF:    3/12 – 3/19

IN    TUES.  3/13   8:50 A.M.
OUT   TUES.  3/13  12:32 P.M.
IN    TUES.  3/13   1:24 P.M.
OUT   TUES.  3/13   5:10 P.M.
```

4. How many hours to the nearest quarter hour did Paul work in the morning?

(1) $3\frac{1}{4}$

(2) $3\frac{1}{2}$

(3) $3\frac{3}{4}$

(4) $4\frac{1}{4}$

(5) $5\frac{1}{4}$

5. How many hours to the nearest quarter hour did Paul work in the afternoon?

(1) $3\frac{3}{4}$

(2) 4

(3) $4\frac{1}{2}$

(4) $4\frac{3}{4}$

(5) $6\frac{3}{4}$

6. How many total hours to the nearest quarter hour did Paul work on Tuesday?

(1) $7\frac{1}{2}$

(2) 8

(3) $8\frac{1}{4}$

(4) 9

(5) $9\frac{1}{2}$

Check your answers on page 273.

Using Your Math Skills

Add or subtract. Reduce your answers to lowest terms.

1. $\frac{15}{16} - \frac{9}{16} =$

2. $\frac{1}{5} + \frac{7}{10} =$

3. $8 - 2\frac{1}{6} =$

4. $\frac{5}{6} + \frac{3}{8} =$

5. $\begin{array}{r} 3\frac{7}{9} \\ + \ 4\frac{2}{9} \\ \hline \end{array}$

6. $\begin{array}{r} 4\frac{9}{10} \\ - \ 2\frac{3}{10} \\ \hline \end{array}$

7. $\begin{array}{r} 2\frac{5}{8} \\ + \ 2\frac{3}{4} \\ \hline \end{array}$

8. $\begin{array}{r} 9\frac{1}{5} \\ - \ 8\frac{3}{5} \\ \hline \end{array}$

9. $\begin{array}{r} 3 \\ - \ \frac{7}{8} \\ \hline \end{array}$

10. $\begin{array}{r} 6\frac{1}{3} \\ - \ 2\frac{3}{4} \\ \hline \end{array}$

Write your answers in the blanks. Show your work.

11. Ray and Donna's baby weighed $7\frac{1}{4}$ pounds at birth. During the first week, the baby lost $\frac{1}{2}$ pound. How much did the baby weigh at the end of the first week?

_____

12. To make rye bread, Tony uses $2\frac{3}{4}$ cups of rye flour and $3\frac{1}{2}$ cups of white flour. How much flour does Tony use to make bread?

_____

13. Last summer, Plainview received $13\frac{7}{10}$ inches of rain. This summer, Plainview received $19\frac{1}{10}$ inches of rain. How much more rain did Plainview receive this summer than last summer?

_____

14. Tyrone needs a piece of wood that is $4\frac{7}{12}$ feet long for a shelf. He has a board that is 6 feet long. If he cuts the shelf from this board, how much of the board will be left over?

_____

Circle the best answer for each item.

15. A recycling center collected $2\frac{1}{2}$ tons of paper, $1\frac{1}{2}$ tons of glass, and $\frac{3}{4}$ ton of aluminum last month. Which is the correct expression to find how many tons the center collected last month?

(1) $1\frac{1}{2} + \frac{3}{4}$

(2) $2\frac{1}{2} + 1\frac{1}{2}$

(3) $2\frac{1}{2} + 1\frac{1}{2} + \frac{3}{4}$

(4) $2\frac{1}{2} + 1\frac{1}{2} - \frac{3}{4}$

(5) $2\frac{1}{2} - 1\frac{1}{2} - \frac{3}{4}$

16. Jo bought $2\frac{7}{8}$ pounds of peanuts and $\frac{3}{4}$ of a pound of cashews for a party. How many pounds of nuts did Jo buy?

(1) $2\frac{1}{8}$

(2) $2\frac{5}{8}$

(3) $2\frac{5}{6}$

(4) $3\frac{3}{8}$

(5) $3\frac{5}{8}$

17. Willa's goal is to jog $17\frac{1}{2}$ miles a week. So far this week she has jogged $9\frac{1}{4}$ miles. Choose the correct expression to find the number of miles she needs to jog to reach her goal.

(1) $9\frac{1}{4} - 17\frac{1}{2}$

(2) $17\frac{1}{2} - 9\frac{1}{4}$

(3) $17\frac{1}{2} + 9\frac{1}{4}$

(4) $17\frac{1}{2} \times 9\frac{1}{4}$

(5) $17\frac{1}{2} \div 9\frac{1}{4}$

18. Sal worked $5\frac{1}{4}$ hours cleaning two offices. It took $1\frac{1}{2}$ hours to clean one. How many hours did he spend cleaning the other?

(1) $3\frac{3}{4}$

(2) $4\frac{1}{2}$

(3) $4\frac{3}{4}$

(4) $5\frac{1}{4}$

(5) $6\frac{3}{4}$

Items 19 – 21 refer to the table below.

Yardage Requirements: Prom Dress

Sizes	8	10	12
Dress A	$5\frac{3}{4}$	$5\frac{7}{8}$	$6\frac{3}{8}$
Dress B			
Main Color	$5\frac{1}{8}$	$5\frac{1}{4}$	$5\frac{5}{8}$
Contrasting Color	$1\frac{3}{8}$	$1\frac{3}{8}$	$1\frac{1}{2}$
Lace A	$2\frac{1}{2}$	$2\frac{5}{8}$	$2\frac{3}{4}$
Lace B	$2\frac{1}{8}$	$2\frac{1}{8}$	$2\frac{1}{4}$

19. Jenny would like to make dress B in size 12. How many yards of fabric will she need?

(1) $3\frac{1}{4}$

(2) $6\frac{5}{8}$

(3) $7\frac{1}{8}$

(4) $8\frac{1}{2}$

(5) $9\frac{1}{8}$

20. Caryn is trying to decide whether she wants to make dress A or dress B. How many more yards of lace are needed if she chooses dress A in size 8 rather than dress B in size 8?

(1) $\frac{1}{8}$

(2) $\frac{1}{6}$

(3) $\frac{3}{8}$

(4) $\frac{5}{8}$

(5) $4\frac{5}{8}$

21. Marcia is planning to sew a prom dress for her daughter in size 12. Which is the correct expression to find how many more yards of fabric she would need for dress B than for dress A?

(1) $(5\frac{1}{8} + 1\frac{3}{8}) - 5\frac{3}{4}$

(2) $5\frac{5}{8} - 1\frac{1}{2} - 6\frac{3}{8}$

(3) $(5\frac{5}{8} + 1\frac{1}{2}) - 6\frac{3}{8}$

(4) $6\frac{3}{8} - (5\frac{5}{8} + 1\frac{1}{2})$

(5) $6\frac{3}{8} - 5\frac{5}{8} - 1\frac{1}{2}$

Check your answers on page 274.

Write your answers in the blanks. Show your work.

Items 22–24 refer to the following information.

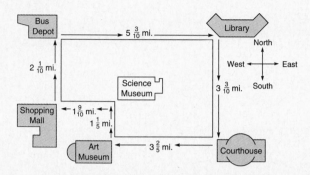

Sundra is a city bus driver. The map above shows the route she drives starting at the bus depot.

22. The busiest part of Sundra's route is between the courthouse and the shopping mall. About how many miles is this part of the route?

_____

23. Exactly how many miles is the part of Sundra's route between the courthouse and the shopping mall?

_____

24. Sundra's entire route is $17\frac{1}{5}$ miles long. Estimate how many miles she has left to drive after she has reached the library.

_____

Items 25–27 refer to the timecard below.

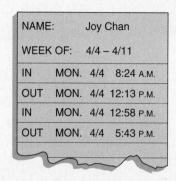

25. How many hours to the nearest quarter hour did Joy work in the morning?

_____

26. How many hours to the nearest quarter hour did Joy work in the afternoon?

_____

27. How many total hours to the nearest quarter hour did Joy work on Monday?

_____

Check your answers on pages 274–275.

Multiplying and Dividing Fractions

Consumer Math

Mike is cooking baked beans for a company picnic. He has a recipe that serves 5 people, but he wants to make enough for 15 people. Since 3 times 5 is 15, he knows he needs to make three times the amount in the recipe. He decides to triple the recipe.

The ingredients in the recipe are measured using whole numbers, mixed numbers, and fractions. For instance, the recipe calls for $1\frac{1}{3}$ cups of catsup. Which is the correct expression to find the number of cups of catsup Mike should use?

(1) $1 \times 1\frac{1}{3}$

(2) $1\frac{1}{3} \times 3$

(3) $1\frac{1}{3} \div 3$

(4) $1\frac{1}{3} \times \frac{1}{3}$

(5) $3 \div 1\frac{1}{3}$

Answer 2 is the correct choice. Since Mike wants to make 3 times the amount of the recipe, he must multiply the amount of catsup in the recipe, $1\frac{1}{3}$ cups, by 3.

He multiplies and finds he needs 4 cups of catsup.

$$1\frac{1}{3} \times 3 = \frac{4}{3} \times \frac{3}{1} = \frac{12}{3} = 4 \text{ cups}$$

Mike multiplies the amount of each ingredient by 3 to triple the recipe.

Jenny is making chili for the same picnic. She has a recipe that serves 20 people. She wants to make enough for 10 people. Since 10 is one half of 20, she decides to make only half of the recipe.

$$\frac{10}{20} = \frac{10 \div 10}{20 \div 10} = \frac{1}{2}$$

Her recipe calls for $3\frac{1}{2}$ pounds of ground beef. Which is the correct expression to find how much ground beef she will need to make half of the recipe?

(1) $\frac{1}{2} \times 3 \times 2$

(2) $3\frac{1}{2} \times 2$

(3) $3\frac{1}{2} \div \frac{1}{2}$

(4) $3\frac{1}{2} \times \frac{1}{2}$

(5) $\frac{1}{2} \div 3\frac{1}{2}$

Answer 4 is the correct choice. Jenny wants to find half **of** $3\frac{1}{2}$ pounds. The word *of* often means multiply. Multiplying by $\frac{1}{2}$ separates the amount into 2 equal parts.

$$3\frac{1}{2} \times \frac{1}{2} = \frac{7}{2} \times \frac{1}{2} = \frac{7}{4} = 1\frac{3}{4} \text{ pounds}$$

Jenny should use $1\frac{3}{4}$ pounds of ground beef to make half of the recipe.

Another way to solve the problem is to divide $3\frac{1}{2}$ by 2. Multiplying by $\frac{1}{2}$ is the same as dividing by 2. Dividing by 2 also separates the whole amount into 2 equal parts.

$$3\frac{1}{2} \div 2 = \frac{7}{2} \div \frac{2}{1} = \frac{7}{2} \times \frac{1}{2} = \frac{7}{4} = 1\frac{3}{4} \text{ pounds}$$

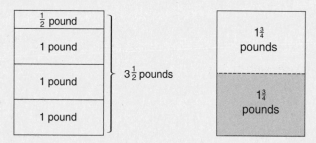

When the whole is separated into two parts, each part is $\frac{1}{2}$ of the whole.

To make half of the recipe, Jenny can either multiply the amount of each ingredient by $\frac{1}{2}$, or she can divide each amount by 2.

Practice ◆ Circle the best answer for each item.

1. Vince has a recipe for scalloped potatoes that serves 12 people. The recipe calls for $5\frac{1}{2}$ pounds of potatoes. He decides to make a third of this recipe for his family. Which is the correct expression to find the amount of potatoes he should use?

   (1) $\frac{1}{3} \div 5\frac{1}{2}$

   (2) $5\frac{1}{2} \div \frac{1}{3}$

   (3) $5\frac{1}{2} \times 1$

   (4) $5\frac{1}{2} \times 3$

   (5) $5\frac{1}{2} \div 3$

2. Kasia wants to make one loaf of bread. Her recipe makes 2 loaves and calls for $7\frac{1}{4}$ cups of flour. Which is the correct expression to find the number of cups of flour Kasia should use?

   (1) $\frac{1}{2} \div 7\frac{1}{4}$

   (2) $2 \div 7\frac{1}{4}$

   (3) $7\frac{1}{4} \times \frac{1}{2}$

   (4) $7\frac{1}{4} \div \frac{1}{2}$

   (5) $7\frac{1}{4} \times 2$

3. Ginny is making fudge to sell at a fair. To make 1 pound of fudge, she needs $\frac{1}{3}$ cup of cocoa. She has $4\frac{2}{3}$ cups of cocoa. Which is the correct expression to find the number of pounds of fudge Ginny can make with the cocoa she has?

   (1) $\frac{1}{3} \div 4\frac{2}{3}$

   (2) $3 \div 4\frac{2}{3}$

   (3) $4\frac{2}{3} \times \frac{1}{3}$

   (4) $4\frac{2}{3} \div \frac{1}{3}$

   (5) $4\frac{2}{3} \div 1$

4. Karl is making macaroni and cheese to take to a potluck supper. His recipe calls for $1\frac{1}{4}$ cups of milk, but he plans to double the recipe. Which is the correct expression to find the number of cups of milk he should use?

   (1) $\frac{1}{2} \div 1\frac{1}{4}$

   (2) $2 \div 1\frac{1}{4}$

   (3) $1\frac{1}{4} \times \frac{1}{2}$

   (4) $1\frac{1}{4} \div 2$

   (5) $1\frac{1}{4} \times 2$

5. Rosa is making chile rellenos for a family reunion. Her recipe serves 6 people and calls for $\frac{1}{2}$ cup diced green chilies. She needs to make enough to serve 18 people. Which is the correct expression to find the number of cups of chilies she should use?

   (1) $\frac{1}{2} \times \frac{1}{3}$

   (2) $\frac{1}{2} \times 3$

   (3) $\frac{1}{2} \div 3$

   (4) $\frac{1}{2} \times 18$

   (5) $6 \div \frac{1}{2}$

6. Luis has a recipe for lasagna that serves 24 people. The recipe calls for $1\frac{1}{2}$ pounds of mozzarella cheese. Luis wants to make enough lasagna for 12 people. Which is the correct expression to find the number of pounds of mozzarella cheese he should use?

   (1) $1\frac{1}{2} \div 2$

   (2) $1\frac{1}{2} \times 2$

   (3) $1\frac{1}{2} \div 12$

   (4) $1\frac{1}{2} \times 24$

   (5) $2 \div 1\frac{1}{2}$

Check your answers on page 275.

Multiplying Fractions

You do not need to find a common denominator to multiply and divide fractions. To multiply one fraction by another, follow these steps.

Example Multiply: $\frac{2}{3} \times \frac{3}{8}$

Step 1. Multiply the numerators (top numbers).

$$\frac{2}{3} \quad \frac{3}{8} = 6$$

Step 2. Multiply the denominators (bottom numbers).

$$\frac{2 \times 3}{3 \times 8} = \frac{6}{24}$$

Step 3. Reduce the answer to lowest terms.

$$\frac{6}{24} = \frac{6 \div 6}{24 \div 6} = \frac{1}{4}$$

A shortcut called **canceling** will make your work easier. **Canceling** is a way to reduce both fractions before you multiply. Let's work the same problem again using the shortcut.

Step 1. Look at the first numerator and the second denominator. Think of a number that will divide both evenly. Divide both by 2. Cross out the 2 and write 1 to show 2 ÷ 2 = 1. Cross out the 8 and write 4 to show 8 ÷ 2 = 4.

$$\frac{\overset{1}{\cancel{2}}}{3} \times \frac{3}{\underset{4}{\cancel{8}}}$$

Step 2. Look at the second numerator and the first denominator and repeat the process. Since both numbers are 3, you can divide each by 3.

$$\frac{\overset{1}{\cancel{2}}}{\underset{1}{\cancel{3}}} \times \frac{\cancel{3}}{\underset{4}{\cancel{8}}}$$

Step 3. Now multiply.

$$\frac{\overset{1}{\cancel{2}}}{\underset{1}{\cancel{3}}} \times \frac{\overset{1}{\cancel{3}}}{\underset{4}{\cancel{8}}} = \frac{1}{4}$$

You can also multiply fractions by mixed numbers and whole numbers. Change the mixed and whole numbers to improper fractions first. Then follow the steps for multiplying fractions. If your answer is an improper fraction, simplify it by changing the improper fraction to a mixed or whole number.

Example Multiply: $4\frac{1}{2} \times \frac{1}{3}$

Change. Cancel. Multiply. Simplify.

$$4\frac{1}{2} \times \frac{1}{3} = \frac{9}{2} \times \frac{1}{3} = \frac{\overset{3}{\cancel{9}}}{2} \times \frac{1}{\underset{1}{\cancel{3}}} = \frac{3}{2} = 1\frac{1}{2}$$

Example

Multiply: $6 \times 1\frac{4}{9}$

Change.   Cancel.   Multiply.   Simplify.

$$6 \times 1\frac{4}{9} = \frac{6}{1} \times \frac{13}{9} = \frac{\overset{2}{\cancel{6}}}{1} \times \frac{13}{\underset{3}{\cancel{9}}} = \frac{26}{3} = 8\frac{2}{3}$$

Practice   Multiply. Reduce your answers to lowest terms.

1. $\frac{2}{3} \times \frac{1}{5} = \frac{2}{15}$

2. $\frac{5}{6} \times \frac{5}{8} =$

3. $3 \times \frac{4}{5} =$

4. $\frac{3}{7} \times \frac{2}{9} =$

5. $\frac{3}{8} \times 6 =$

6. $5 \times 2\frac{3}{10} =$

7. $\frac{5}{8} \times 2\frac{2}{5} =$

8. $3\frac{1}{2} \times \frac{8}{9} =$

9. $2\frac{1}{3} \times 1\frac{1}{2} =$

10. $1\frac{4}{5} \times 6\frac{2}{3} =$

Computation

Dividing Fractions

Dividing fractions is the same as multiplying fractions — with one important exception. You must **invert** the fraction you are dividing by. *Invert* means to turn over or to switch the numerator and the denominator. The top number becomes the bottom number, and the bottom number becomes the top number. When you invert the fraction you are dividing by, also change the division sign to a multiplication sign.

Follow these steps to divide fractions.

Divide: $\frac{3}{8} \div \frac{1}{2}$

Step 1. Invert the fraction you are dividing by, and change the ÷ sign to ×.

$$\frac{3}{8} \div \frac{1}{2} = \frac{3}{8} \times \frac{2}{1}$$

Step 2. Multiply the fractions. Cancel.

If you are dividing by a mixed number or a whole number, change it to an improper fraction before you invert.

$$\frac{3}{8} \times \frac{2}{1} = \frac{3}{\overset{}{\underset{4}{\cancel{8}}}} \times \frac{\overset{1}{\cancel{2}}}{1} = \frac{3}{4}$$

◗ Example

Divide: $6 \div 2\frac{2}{5}$

$$6 \div 2\frac{2}{5} = \frac{6}{1} \div \frac{12}{5} = \frac{6}{1} \times \frac{5}{12} = \frac{\cancel{6}}{1} \times \frac{5}{\underset{2}{\cancel{12}}} = \frac{5}{2} = 2\frac{1}{2}$$

◗ Example

Divide: $5\frac{1}{3} \div 4$

$$5\frac{1}{3} \div 4 = \frac{16}{3} \div \frac{4}{1} = \frac{16}{3} \times \frac{1}{4} = \frac{\overset{4}{\cancel{16}}}{3} \times \frac{1}{\underset{1}{\cancel{4}}} = \frac{4}{3} = 1\frac{1}{3}$$

Practice ◗ Divide. Reduce your answers to lowest terms.

1. $\frac{4}{5} \div \frac{1}{3} = \frac{4}{5} \times \frac{3}{1} = \frac{12}{5} = 2\frac{2}{5}$

2. $\frac{2}{7} \div \frac{3}{4} =$

3. $4 \div \frac{4}{5} =$

4. $\frac{2}{3} \div \frac{5}{6} =$

5. $\frac{7}{12} \div 3 =$

6. $2 \div 1\frac{1}{7} =$

7. $\frac{5}{8} \div 1\frac{5}{6} =$

8. $3\frac{3}{4} \div \frac{3}{10} =$

9. $1\frac{2}{5} \div 2\frac{1}{4} =$

10. $4\frac{1}{4} \div 1\frac{1}{2} =$

Check your answers on page 275.

Measuring Length

Problem-Solving Strategy: Draw a Diagram

Tien works for a company that makes and repairs furniture. Today she is cutting boards into lengths needed to make sofas. Tien has an order form that tells her how long to cut the boards.

The first job on the form calls for three $8\frac{1}{2}$-inch lengths. Because the pieces are short, Tien wants to cut them from scrap wood.

Tien has a scrap of wood that is $2\frac{1}{2}$ feet long. She needs to figure out if the scrap is long enough to cut three $8\frac{1}{2}$-inch pieces.

The order form gives the measurements in inches. The scrap wood is measured in feet. To solve the problem, Tien needs to express both lengths in the same unit of length. She also needs to know the total length of the three $8\frac{1}{2}$-inch boards.

This chart shows the relationship between the units used to measure length. You can tell from the chart that a yard is longer than a foot, and a foot is longer than an inch.

1 yard	= 3 feet
1 yard	= 36 inches
1 foot	= 12 inches

YARD

FOOT

← INCH

Tien decides to change $2\frac{1}{2}$ feet to inches. To change a larger unit to a smaller unit, multiply. To change $2\frac{1}{2}$ feet to inches, Tien multiplies the number of feet, $2\frac{1}{2}$, by the number of inches in one foot, 12.

The scrap wood is $2\frac{1}{2}$ feet long. How long is the wood in inches?

(1) $24\frac{1}{2}$

(2) 26

(3) $28\frac{1}{2}$

(4) 30

(5) 32

Answer 4 is the correct choice. Tien multiplies $2\frac{1}{2}$ by 12 to find the number of inches. The scrap wood is 30 inches long.

$$2\frac{1}{2} \ \times \ 12 \ = \ \frac{5}{2} \times \frac{12}{1} \ = \ \frac{5}{2} \times \frac{\overset{6}{\cancel{12}}}{\underset{1}{1}} \ = \ \frac{30}{1} \ = \ 30 \text{ inches}$$

Now she needs to know the total length of three $8\frac{1}{2}$-inch boards. Tien multiplies $8\frac{1}{2}$ by 3 to find the total length she will need to cut the pieces.

$$8\frac{1}{2} \ \times \ 3 \ = \ \frac{17}{2} \times \frac{3}{1} \ = \ \frac{51}{2} \ = \ 25\frac{1}{2} \text{ inches}$$

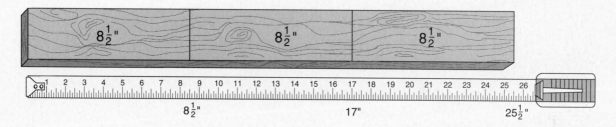

Now both measurements are in inches, so Tien can compare the lengths. Since 30 inches is longer than $25\frac{1}{2}$ inches, she knows she can cut the three pieces from the scrap wood.

Next Tien uses a tape measure to mark the cuts on the board. A tape measure is a ruler printed on metal tape.

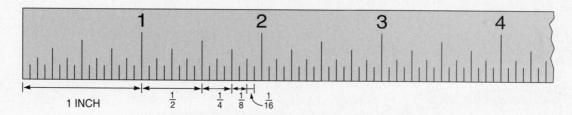

A ruler is divided into inches. The inches are numbered from left to right. Each inch is divided into halves, fourths, eighths, and sixteenths. The markings that show fractions of an inch are different heights to make it easier to read the ruler.

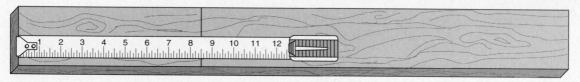

Tien lines up the tape measure with the end of the board. She reads to the right to find the $\frac{1}{2}$-inch mark to the right of 8. Then she draws a line across the board to mark the cut. She checks her measurement again and makes the cut.

The next job on the order form is to cut 4 pieces of lumber measuring $16\frac{1}{8}$ inches each. Tien multiplies $16\frac{1}{8}$ by 4 to figure out what length board she will need.

$$16\frac{1}{8} \times 4 = \frac{129}{\overset{8}{\underset{2}{8}}} \times \frac{\overset{1}{4}}{1} = \frac{129}{2} = 64\frac{1}{2} \text{ inches}$$

The scrap wood is arranged in bins by length in feet. Tien needs to change $64\frac{1}{2}$ inches to feet to find the best piece of scrap wood for the job. To change a smaller unit to a larger unit, divide. Tien divides $64\frac{1}{2}$ inches by 12, the number of inches in one foot.

How many feet are in $64\frac{1}{2}$ inches?

(1) $4\frac{3}{4}$

(2) 5

(3) $5\frac{1}{4}$

(4) $5\frac{3}{8}$

(5) $5\frac{5}{8}$

Answer 4 is the correct choice. Tien divides $64\frac{1}{2}$ by 12. Tien needs a board that is at least $5\frac{3}{8}$ feet long.

$$64\frac{1}{2} \div 12 = \frac{129}{2} \div \frac{12}{1} = \frac{129}{2} \times \frac{1}{12} = \frac{129}{24} = 5\frac{9}{24} = 5\frac{3}{8}$$

Tien gets a board from the 5-foot bin and measures it. It is exactly $64\frac{7}{8}$ inches long. Tien knows that each cut she makes will waste $\frac{1}{8}$ inch of the board. She wants to make sure the board is long enough to cut the 4 pieces of wood. She needs to figure out how many cuts she will make.

Tien draws a diagram to figure out how many cuts she will need to make. From the diagram, she can see that she will have to make 3 cuts to get 4 pieces of wood. Drawing a diagram is a good way to make sure you understand the problem.

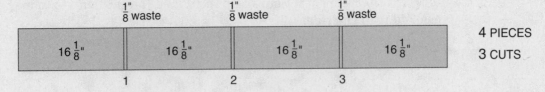

Tien will make 3 cuts, and each cut will waste $\frac{1}{8}$ inch of wood. She multiplies 3 cuts by $\frac{1}{8}$ inch and finds that $\frac{3}{8}$ inch will be wasted in the cutting.

$$3 \times \frac{1}{8} = \frac{3}{1} \times \frac{1}{8} = \frac{3}{8} \text{ inch}$$

Tien needs $64\frac{1}{2}$ inches for the 4 lengths of wood and $\frac{3}{8}$ inch for the waste. The $64\frac{7}{8}$-inch board is exactly the right length for the job.

$$
\begin{aligned}
64\frac{1}{2} &= 64\frac{4}{8} \\
+ \ \frac{3}{8} &= + \ \frac{3}{8} \\
\hline
&\ 64\frac{7}{8}
\end{aligned}
$$

Practice ▪ Circle the best answer for each item.

1. Tien needs to put a piece of wood that is $45\frac{1}{2}$ inches long into the correct scrap bin. How long is the piece of wood in feet?

    (1) $1\frac{1}{4}$

    (2) $3\frac{19}{24}$

    (3) $4\frac{1}{2}$

    (4) 135

    (5) 540

2. After cutting upholstery fabric for a chair, Tien has $\frac{2}{3}$ yard of fabric left. How long is the fabric in inches?

    (1) 2
    (2) 9
    (3) 20
    (4) 24
    (5) 54

3. Tien needs a piece of upholstery fabric to tack along the bottom of a $7\frac{1}{2}$-foot couch. How many yards of fabric does she need?

    (1) $\frac{5}{24}$

    (2) $\frac{5}{8}$

    (3) $2\frac{1}{2}$

    (4) $10\frac{1}{2}$

    (5) $22\frac{1}{2}$

4. Tien also needs to cut a piece of wood to a length of $26\frac{1}{4}$ inches. How many feet are in $26\frac{1}{4}$ inches?

    (1) $\frac{9}{10}$

    (2) $2\frac{3}{16}$

    (3) $3\frac{1}{3}$

    (4) 4

    (5) $13\frac{1}{3}$

▪ Write your answers in the blanks. Show your work.

Items 5–8 refer to the following information.

Tien needs to cut 5 shelves for a cabinet. Each shelf is to be $1\frac{2}{3}$ feet long. She would like to cut the shelves from one piece of board and not have any wood left over. Each cut will waste $\frac{3}{16}$ inch of wood.

5. How many inches of wood are needed for 5 shelves?

    _____

6. How many cuts are needed to make 5 shelves from one board? Draw a diagram to prove your answer.

    _____

7. What is the total amount of waste Tien will have from cutting the shelves?

    _____

8. What is the length in inches of the board that Tien should use?

    _____

Check your answers on pages 275–276.

Completing a Table of Information

Tom is making dinner for 24 people. He has planned the menu. Now he is making a shopping list for the ingredients he will need.

A list is actually a table of information. There are two columns on the table. The first column lists the ingredients Tom needs for the dinner. The second column shows how much of each ingredient Tom needs to buy.

Grocery List	
Sweet Potatoes	8 lb.
Turkey	
Potatoes	
Onions	6 med.

Tom has completed most of the table. He still needs to figure out the amounts for two items.

First, Tom needs to figure out what size turkey to buy. Turkeys are sold by the pound. Tom needs to know how many pounds of turkey he should buy to serve 24 people. In a cookbook, Tom reads that he should buy $\frac{3}{4}$ pound per person.

There will be 24 people at the dinner. If Tom needs $\frac{3}{4}$ pound of turkey per person, how many pounds of turkey should he buy?

(1)   16
(2)   18
(3)   20
(4)   22
(5)   24

Answer 2 is the correct choice. Tom multiplies $\frac{3}{4}$ by 24 to find the answer.

$$\frac{3}{4} \times 24 = \frac{3}{4} \times \frac{24}{1} = \frac{3}{\underset{1}{\cancel{4}}} \times \frac{\overset{6}{\cancel{24}}}{1} = \frac{18}{1} = 18 \text{ pounds}$$

Tom writes 18 pounds on the list.

Tom also needs to buy potatoes. In the same cookbook, Tom reads that he should buy $\frac{1}{2}$ pound of potatoes for each person. Tom knows that the store sells potatoes individually by the pound or in 10-pound bags. The large bags usually cost less money. Tom would like to buy one 10-pound bag of potatoes. He needs to know if a 10-pound bag of potatoes is enough to serve 24 people.

Grocery List	
Sweet Potatoes	8 lb.
Turkey	18 lb.
Potatoes	
Onions	6 med.

If he needs $\frac{1}{2}$ pound for each person, how many people would a 10-pound bag of potatoes serve?

(1) 10
(2) 18
(3) 20
(4) 24
(5) 25

Answer 3 is the correct choice. Tom divides 10 pounds by $\frac{1}{2}$ pound to find the answer. A 10-pound bag of potatoes will serve 20 people.

$$10 \div \frac{1}{2} = \frac{10}{1} \div \frac{1}{2} = \frac{10}{1} \times \frac{2}{1} = \frac{20}{1} = 20 \text{ people}$$

The 10-pound bag isn't enough for 24 people. Tom needs to figure out how many more pounds of potatoes he will need if he buys the 10-pound bag. He knows the 10-pound bag will serve 20 people, so he subtracts to find how many more people he needs to serve.

$$\begin{array}{r} 24 \\ -\ 20 \\ \hline 4 \text{ people} \end{array}$$

He needs to serve 4 more people. If he plans $\frac{1}{2}$ pound for each person, how many more pounds of potatoes does he need to buy?

(1) 2

(2) $2\frac{1}{2}$

(3) 3

(4) $3\frac{1}{2}$

(5) 4

Answer 1 is the correct choice. He multiplies the number of people, 4, by the amount for each person, $\frac{1}{2}$ pound, to find the number of pounds he needs to buy.

$$4 \times \frac{1}{2} = \frac{4}{1} \times \frac{1}{2} = \frac{\overset{2}{\cancel{4}}}{1} \times \frac{1}{\underset{1}{\cancel{2}}} = \frac{2}{1} = 2 \text{ pounds}$$

He can buy one 10-pound bag and 2 additional pounds of potatoes. Altogether he needs 12 pounds of potatoes (10 + 2 = 12). Tom writes 12 pounds on his grocery list.

Grocery List	
Sweet Potatoes	8 lb.
Turkey	18 lb.
Potatoes	12 lb.
Onions	6 med.

Practice ◾ Complete each table. Write your answers in the blanks. Show your work.

Items 1– 4 refer to the following information.

Monroe is cooking dinner for 12 people. His cookbook gives the following serving information:

$\frac{1}{2}$ pound of pot roast per person

$\frac{3}{8}$ pound of potatoes per person

$\frac{1}{4}$ pound of beets per person

$\frac{3}{4}$ cup of peas per person

Grocery List	
Rolls	2 doz.
Pot roast	1. _____
Potatoes	2. _____
Beets	3. _____
Peas	4. _____

1. How many pounds of pot roast should Monroe buy?

2. How many pounds of potatoes should Monroe buy?

3. How many pounds of beets should Monroe buy?

4. How many cups of peas should Monroe buy?

Items 5– 8 refer to the following information.

At a craft fair, Tamara received orders for 16 dolls. Each doll requires the following materials:

$\frac{1}{2}$ yard of brown fabric

$\frac{5}{8}$ yard of calico fabric

$1\frac{1}{2}$ yards of eyelet ruffle

$\frac{3}{4}$ pound of fiberfill

Materials List	
Fabric – brown	5. _____
Fabric – calico	6. _____
Eyelet ruffle	7. _____
Fiberfill	8. _____
Brown yarn	4 skeins

5. How many yards of brown fabric are needed to fill the orders?

6. How many yards of calico fabric are needed to fill the orders?

7. How many yards of eyelet ruffle does Tamara need?

8. How many pounds of fiberfill are needed to stuff the dolls?

Check your answers on page 276.

Using Your Math Skills

Multiply or divide. Reduce your answers to lowest terms.

1. $\frac{4}{5} \times \frac{1}{3} =$

2. $\frac{4}{9} \div \frac{1}{6} =$

3. $\frac{5}{8} \div \frac{3}{5} =$

4. $\frac{2}{7} \times \frac{5}{12} =$

5. $7 \div \frac{7}{8} =$

6. $6 \times \frac{3}{4} =$

7. $\frac{4}{15} \times \frac{9}{10} =$

8. $\frac{2}{5} \div \frac{4}{9} =$

9. $\frac{11}{12} \times 8 =$

10. $4 \times 2\frac{5}{6} =$

11. $\frac{3}{8} \div 4 =$

12. $5 \div 1\frac{1}{9} =$

13. $\frac{7}{12} \times 3\frac{3}{5} =$

14. $\frac{5}{6} \div 2\frac{1}{2} =$

15. $2\frac{3}{4} \times \frac{2}{3} =$

16. $4\frac{1}{2} \div 1\frac{1}{5} =$

17. $3\frac{1}{5} \div 2\frac{2}{5} =$

18. $2\frac{5}{12} \times 1\frac{5}{7} =$

19. $2\frac{6}{7} \times 1\frac{5}{16} =$

20. $3\frac{1}{3} \div 4\frac{1}{6} =$

Check your answers on page 276.   *Section 7: Multiplying and Dividing Fractions*

Write your answers in the blanks. Show your work.

21. The 15 acres of vacant land across the street from Dominic's house are being developed as building lots. Each lot is to be $\frac{5}{8}$ acre. How many building lots will there be?

_____

22. Sharla bought $5\frac{1}{2}$ pounds of ground beef. Before freezing the ground beef, she plans to make it into hamburger patties that weigh $\frac{1}{4}$ pound each. How many patties can Sharla make?

_____

23. Delia is a secretary at Auto Insurance Agency. She works $7\frac{1}{2}$ hours a day. Delia answers the phone $\frac{1}{3}$ of each day. How many hours does Delia spend answering the phone each day?

_____

24. On Saturday, 24 people bought cars at Best Car Sales. Of the 24 customers, $\frac{3}{4}$ bought new cars. How many people bought new cars?

_____

25. Mahmud planted $4\frac{2}{3}$ dozen flowering plants in his garden. During the drought, he lost $\frac{1}{7}$ of his plants. How many dozen plants survived?

_____

26. Miguel's recipe for jelly calls for $1\frac{3}{4}$ ounces of pectin. He has 14 ounces of pectin. How many batches of jelly could he make with this?

_____

27. Donna can walk at the rate of $3\frac{1}{2}$ miles per hour. If she keeps up this pace, how far can she walk in $1\frac{1}{2}$ hours?

_____

28. Maggie makes braided rugs. She needs to cut strips of fabric $1\frac{1}{8}$ inches wide for the rugs. How many strips can she cut from a piece of fabric 45 inches wide?

_____

Check your answers on page 277.

Circle the best answer for each item.

29. Richard is making meatballs for a party. His recipe calls for $\frac{3}{4}$ cup of bread crumbs. He plans to double the recipe. Which is the correct expression to find the number of cups of bread crumbs he should use?

(1) $\frac{3}{4} \times \frac{1}{2}$

(2) $\frac{3}{4} \times 1$

(3) $\frac{3}{4} \times 2$

(4) $\frac{3}{4} \div 2$

(5) $2 \div \frac{3}{4}$

30. Carla's recipe for potato salad serves 18 people and calls for $1\frac{7}{8}$ cups of mayonnaise. Carla wants to make enough salad to serve 6 people. How many cups of mayonnaise should she use?

(1) $\frac{5}{16}$

(2) $\frac{5}{8}$

(3) $\frac{15}{16}$

(4) $3\frac{3}{4}$

(5) $5\frac{5}{8}$

31. John needs a 56-inch piece of linoleum for his bathroom floor. Which is the correct expression to find how long the linoleum is in feet?

(1) $56 \div 3$
(2) 56×10
(3) 56×12
(4) $56 \div 12$
(5) $56 \div 36$

32. Brenda is making throw pillows. She bought a fabric remnant that is $3\frac{1}{2}$ yards long. How long is the remnant in inches?

(1) $10\frac{2}{7}$

(2) 35

(3) 42

(4) 108

(5) 126

Write your answers in the blanks to complete the table. Show your work.

Items 33–36 refer to the following information.

Henry is cooking dinner for 20 people. His cookbook gives the following serving guide:

$\frac{3}{4}$ pound of chicken per person

$\frac{1}{4}$ cup of uncooked rice per person

$\frac{1}{2}$ pound of cauliflower per person

$\frac{3}{8}$ pound of broccoli per person

Grocery List	
Chicken	**33.** _____
Uncooked rice	**34.** _____
Cauliflower	**35.** _____
Broccoli	**36.** _____

33. How many pounds of chicken will Henry need to buy?

34. How many cups of rice are needed to serve 20 people?

35. How many pounds of cauliflower are needed?

36. How many pounds of broccoli does Henry need to buy?

Check your answers on page 277.

Unit 2 Review:
Fractions

Solve. Show your work. Reduce answers to lowest terms.

1. $\frac{5}{6} + \frac{3}{4} =$

2. $\frac{9}{10} - \frac{2}{3} =$

3. $\begin{aligned} & 4\frac{7}{8} \\ + \ & 2\frac{1}{3} \end{aligned}$

4. $\begin{aligned} & 3\frac{2}{5} \\ - \ & 1\frac{3}{4} \end{aligned}$

5. $\frac{7}{12} \div \frac{5}{8} =$

6. $\frac{15}{16} \times \frac{8}{9} =$

7. $3\frac{1}{3} \times 2\frac{1}{2} =$

8. $3\frac{3}{8} \div 3\frac{3}{5} =$

Write your answers in the blanks. Show your work.

9. The Rockets lost 3 of the 20 games played this season. What fraction of the games did the Rockets lose?

    _____

10. Raul works at a garden supply store. The store receives flower seeds in 30-ounce boxes. Raul repackages the seeds in $\frac{3}{4}$-ounce packets. How many packets can Raul fill from each box?

    _____

11. Keiko needs a piece of wood that is $55\frac{1}{2}$ inches long to trim a window. How many feet of wood does she need?

    _____

12. Bob bought a jumbo roll of wrapping paper. The paper on the roll is $8\frac{1}{3}$ yards long. How many feet of paper are on the roll?

    _____

Check your answers on pages 277–278.

Item 13 refers to the following map.

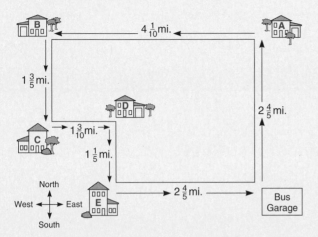

North
West ← → East
South

13. Henry drives a school bus. He completes his route at point C. Estimate how many miles he must drive to get from the end of his route to the bus garage.

_____

Item 14 refers to the following timecard.

```
NAME: GERI D' ANGELO
WEEK OF: 6/21–6/27

IN      MON. 6/21    8:51 A.M.

OUT     MON. 6/21   12:24 P.M.

IN      MON. 6/21    1:08 P.M.

OUT     MON. 6/21    5:03 P.M.
```

14. How many hours to the nearest quarter hour did Geri work on Monday?

_____

Circle the best answer for each item.

Items 15 and 16 refer to the following table.

Yardage Requirements: Skirt and Blouse

Sizes	10	12	14
Blouse A	$2\frac{3}{4}$	$2\frac{7}{8}$	3
Blouse B	$2\frac{7}{8}$	3	$3\frac{1}{4}$
Skirt A, B	$1\frac{1}{4}$	$1\frac{1}{4}$	$1\frac{5}{8}$

15. Gloria is making a skirt and blouse A in size 12. How many yards of fabric does she need for the skirt and blouse?

(1) $1\frac{3}{4}$

(2) $3\frac{1}{8}$

(3) $4\frac{1}{8}$

(4) $4\frac{1}{4}$

(5) $4\frac{5}{8}$

16. Pearl is trying to decide whether to make a skirt and blouse A or a skirt and blouse B in size 14. Which is the correct expression to find how many more yards of fabric she will need for the skirt and blouse B than for the skirt and blouse A?

(1) $(3 + 1\frac{5}{8}) - (3\frac{1}{4} + 1\frac{1}{4})$

(2) $(3 + 1\frac{5}{8}) - (3\frac{1}{4} - 1\frac{1}{4})$

(3) $(3\frac{1}{4} + 1\frac{5}{8}) + (3\frac{1}{4} + 1\frac{5}{8})$

(4) $(3\frac{1}{4} + 1\frac{5}{8}) - (3 + 1\frac{5}{8})$

(5) $(3 + 1\frac{1}{4}) - (3\frac{1}{4} + 1\frac{5}{8})$

17. Clara has a recipe for bread pudding that serves 8 people. The recipe calls for $2\frac{1}{3}$ cups of milk. Clara wants to make enough bread pudding to serve 16 people. Which is the correct expression to find the number of cups of milk she should use?

(1) $2\frac{1}{3} \times \frac{1}{2}$

(2) $2\frac{1}{3} \times 2$

(3) $2\frac{1}{3} \div 2$

(4) $2\frac{1}{3} \times 16$

(5) $16 \div 2\frac{1}{3}$

Check your answers on page 278.

Cumulative Review

Compare each pair of numbers. Write >, <, or = between the two numbers.

1. 32,774 _____ 3,274

2. 948,526 _____ 948,256

Solve. Show your work.

3. $8 - 3 \times 2 + 9 \div 3$

4. $6 \times (7 - 2) \div 10 + 1$

5. $\begin{array}{r} \$8.52 \\ -\ 3.98 \\ \hline \end{array}$

6. $\begin{array}{r} 594 \\ \times\ 607 \\ \hline \end{array}$

7. $\begin{array}{r} 900 \\ -\ 417 \\ \hline \end{array}$

8. $38\overline{)7,843}$

9. $684 + 35 + 257 =$

10. $\$38.07 \div 9 =$

11. $\frac{2}{3} + \frac{5}{8} =$

12. $\frac{5}{9} \div \frac{5}{6} =$

13. $\begin{array}{r} 3\frac{4}{5} \\ +\ 5\frac{1}{3} \\ \hline \end{array}$

14. $\begin{array}{r} 6\frac{2}{3} \\ -\ 2\frac{3}{4} \\ \hline \end{array}$

15. $6\frac{2}{3} \div 1\frac{7}{9} =$

16. $2\frac{5}{8} \times 1\frac{5}{7} =$

Check your answers on pages 278–279.

**Write your answers in the blanks.
Show your work.**

17. Use the chart on page 50 to find the value of $\sqrt{324}$.

_____

18. Round 5,648,312 to the nearest hundred thousand.

_____

<u>Item 19</u> refers to the following graph.

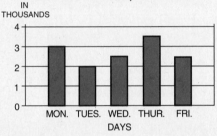

19. What is the approximate difference in the number of parts produced on the day with the highest production and the day with the lowest production?

_____

20. Eric is putting a wallpaper border around his dining room. The room is 12 feet wide and 18 feet long. How many feet of border does he need?

_____

21. What is the volume in cubic inches of a packing carton that is 18 inches long, 12 inches wide, and 15 inches high?

_____

Circle the best answer for each item.

22. On Friday, Lupe bought a pair of overalls for $36. He also put on layaway a jacket that costs $85. He paid $15 to hold the jacket. Which is the correct expression to find how much Lupe spent on Friday?

  (1) $36 + $85 + $15
  (2) $36 + $85 − $15
  (3) $36 + $85
  (4) $36 + $15
  (5) $85 − $15

23. Sally is a cook at The Corner Deli. On Monday, she made 63 sandwiches on wheat bread, 89 sandwiches on rye bread, and 45 sandwiches on white bread. Estimate the total number of sandwiches she made.

  (1) 185
  (2) 190
  (3) 200
  (4) 215
  (5) 225

24. Tawanna is making a picture frame. She needs $54\frac{3}{4}$ inches of wood. Which is the correct expression to find the number of feet of wood she needs?

  (1) $54\frac{3}{4} \div 3$

  (2) $54\frac{3}{4} \div 12$

  (3) $54\frac{3}{4} \times 12$

  (4) $54\frac{3}{4} \div 36$

  (5) $54\frac{3}{4} \times 36$

Check your answers on page 279.

DECIMALS

In a supermarket, decimals are used for prices and to measure weight and capacity.

A **decimal** is a type of fraction. Decimals show parts of whole numbers. In a decimal number, the decimal point separates the whole number from the fraction. You already know that $3.50 means 3 whole dollars plus ½ of a dollar. The fraction part of $3.50, $0.50, is also a decimal.

Imagine you are stopping at the grocery store on your way home from work. You think of the things you need and guess they will cost about $25.00. Then you check your wallet to see if you have enough money. You add the bills and coins and find you have $27.75. You should have enough. Two of the things you buy are a bunch of bananas priced at $0.79 per pound and a 1.5-liter bottle of soda. When you get to the cashier, a scale built into the counter shows that the bananas weigh 3.76 pounds. The computerized cash register figures the cost of the bananas and adds it to your total. The final total is $26.18. You give the cashier $27.00 and receive $0.82 in change.

In what ways were decimals used to show a fractional part of a whole? Some things were counted and some were measured.

What was counted?

- the money in your wallet: $27.75

- the cost of each item: the bananas—$0.79 per pound

- the total cost of your purchases: $26.18

- your change: $0.82

What was measured?

- the weight of the bananas: 3.76 pounds

- the volume of the soda bottle: 1.5 liters

You already know a lot about decimals. You use decimals every day to make decisions about money. You also use the concepts of place value, comparing, and rounding with decimals in many other areas of life.

You are using what you know about place value when you write an amount of money on a check. You know a money amount has two decimal places to show the cents.

1665

$ _49.55_

DOLLARS

Is a price of $12.98 closer to $12.00 or to $13.00? You know $12.98 is almost $13.00. You are rounding $12.98 to the nearest whole number to find the answer.

SALE $12.98

Suppose that two athletes run 100 meters in the Olympics. One finishes in 10.25 seconds; the other takes 10.06 seconds. Which is the faster time? Since 10.06 seconds is less than 10.25 seconds, 10.06 is the faster time. You are comparing decimals to solve the problem.

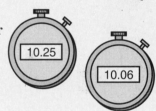

10.25

10.06

Place value, comparing decimals, and rounding are a few of the topics covered in Unit 3. You will also add, subtract, multiply, and divide decimals. Finally, you will use decimals in real-life situations in the Consumer Math and Measurement and Geometry parts of the unit.

Here are a few of the problem-solving situations presented in Unit 3:

- using the metric system to measure length, weight, and volume

- filling out a sales slip

- giving correct change to a customer

- ordering supplies

- finding the total cost when you make a purchase

- reading a line graph to find information

- finding the average (mean) of a set of numbers

- finding the median of a set of numbers

- using mean and median to find information about a store's customers

Section 8

Adding and Subtracting Decimals

Place Value

Suppose you stop to put gas in your car at the local gas station. You look at the pump and find you owe $9.75 for 8.2 gallons of gasoline. These two numbers, $9.75 and 8.2, are decimal numbers.

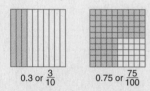

0.3 or $\frac{3}{10}$ 0.75 or $\frac{75}{100}$

A **decimal,** like a fraction, shows part of a whole number. In fact, decimals are fractions that use a place-value system. The decimal 0.3 means three tenths. It is equal to the fraction $\frac{3}{10}$. The decimal 0.75 means seventy-five hundredths. It is equal to the fraction $\frac{75}{100}$ or $\frac{3}{4}$.

Decimal numbers always have a decimal point. The decimal point is read as "and." The value of each digit is determined by the place of the digit. The chart shows the names of several whole number and decimal place values. The numbers to the left of the decimal point are whole numbers. The numbers to the right of the decimal point stand for part of a whole number.

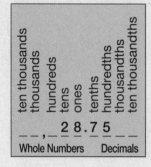

Reading Decimals

Follow these steps to read a decimal number.

Step 1. Say the whole number part. If there is a single zero before the decimal point, go to Step 3.

Step 2. Say the word *and* for the decimal point.

Step 3. Say the number to the right of the decimal point as though it were a whole number.

Step 4. Say the place name for the last digit.

Example

3.8 means $3\frac{8}{10}$, and it is read "three and eight tenths."

0.12 means $\frac{12}{100}$, and it is read "twelve hundredths."

Practice ■ Write the value of the underlined digit in words.

1. 24.3<u>5</u>6 ___*five hundredths*___   2. 3.<u>7</u>8 _____

3. 0.49<u>1</u> _____   4. 267.<u>3</u>259 _____

5. 14.173<u>6</u> _____   6. 5.7<u>0</u>84 _____

■ Write each number in word form.

7. 4.17 ___*four and seventeen hundredths*___

8. 0.256 _____

9. 2.09 _____

10. 6.805 _____

Using Zeros in Decimals

Use the following guidelines to help you understand the use of zeros in decimals.

■ A single zero before the decimal point shows that the decimal does not have a whole number part. For example, 0.75 is less than one.

■ Zeros immediately to the right of the decimal point are **place holders**. These zeros have no value and are not read as part of the number. 0.005 is read "five thousandths."

■ You can add zeros after the last digit in a decimal without changing the value of the decimal. For example, 1.200 = 1.2.

Comparing Decimals

Would you rather pay $0.79 or $0.99 per pound for apples? Of course, you picked $0.79 per pound, the smaller amount. To answer the question, you had to compare two decimals and find the smaller one.

To compare two decimals, line up the decimal points. If the two decimals have the same number of places, compare each place value from left to right as you did with whole numbers.

■ **Example**   0.<u>1</u>5   0.15 < 0.25   <u>4</u>.198   4.198 > 3.199
0.<u>2</u>5   <u>3</u>.199

If the two decimals have a different number of digits, write zeros after the last digit of the decimal with fewer digits so that the two decimals have the same number of digits. Then compare as you did with whole numbers.

Example

	Add zeros.	Compare.
0.325	0.<u>3</u>25	0.325 < 0.500
0.5	0.<u>5</u>00	

Rounding

Follow the same steps to round decimals as you did to round whole numbers.

Step 1. Circle the digit to which you need to round.

Step 2. Look at the digit to the right of the circled digit.

Step 3. If this digit is 5 or more, add 1 to the circled digit. If the digit is less than 5, do not change the circled digit.

Step 4. Drop the digits to the right of the circled digit.

Example

Round 5.1628 to the nearest hundredth.

5.1⑥28 rounds to 5.16. Since 2 is less than 5, the circled digit does not change. Drop the remaining digits.

Round 6.57 to the nearest whole number (the ones place).

⑥.57 rounds to 7. Since the digit to the right of 6 is 5, add 1 to the circled digit. Drop the remaining digits.

Practice ▪ Compare each pair of numbers. Write >, <, or = between the two numbers.

1. 0.27 __<__ 0.72   2. 0.43 _____ 0.09   3. 0.73 _____ 0.542

4. 8.058 _____ 8.58   5. 2.58 _____ 2.580   6. 53.005 _____ 52.008

▪ Write your answers in the blanks.

7. Round 6.3782 to the nearest hundredth. __6.38__

8. Round 8.276 to the nearest whole number. _____

9. Round 46.3518 to the nearest tenth. _____

10. Round 71.0483 to the nearest thousandth. _____

Check your answers on page 280.

Measurement and Geometry / Using Metrics

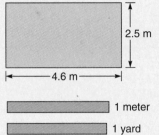

2.5 m

4.6 m

1 meter

1 yard

Charlie is building fences around flower beds that are in front of an office building. The measurements on the landscaping plans are in meters. The plan for one of the flower beds is shown here.

A **meter** (m) is a measure of length in the metric system. A meter is a little longer than a yard.

Things that are measured in feet or yards can also be measured in meters. A part or fraction of a meter is shown with a decimal. Instead of writing $1\frac{1}{2}$ meters, write 1.5 meters.

Charlie needs to buy fencing materials for the flower bed in the plan. He needs to calculate (figure out) the perimeter of the bed. Remember, the perimeter is the distance around the edge of something.

From the diagram, Charlie sees the flower bed is a rectangle that measures 4.6 meters long and 2.5 meters wide. Which is the correct expression to find the perimeter of the flower bed in meters?

(1) 4.6 + 2.5
(2) 4.6 + 4.6 + 2.5 + 2.5 + 2.5
(3) 2.5 + 2.5 + 2.5 + 4.6
(4) 4.6 + 4.6 + 2.5 + 2.5
(5) 4.6 + 4.6 + 4.6 + 4.6

Answer 4 is the correct choice. Charlie needs to find the total of all the sides, so he adds all four lengths. He will need 14.2 meters of fencing.

$$\begin{array}{r} 4.6 \\ 4.6 \\ 2.5 \\ + \ 2.5 \\ \hline 14.2 \ \text{meters} \end{array}$$

Charlie decides to leave a 0.8-meter opening in the center of one of the 4.6-meter sides. He wants to find how much fencing he will need for the side with the opening. Which is the correct expression to find how much fencing Charlie will need for this side?

(1) 4.6 + 0.8
(2) 4.6 − 0.8
(3) 0.8 − 4.6
(4) 4.6 + 4.6 + 0.8 + 0.8
(5) 4.6 + 4.6 + 4.6 − 0.8

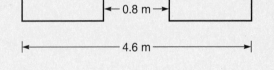

←0.8 m→

4.6 m

Answer 2 is the correct choice. Charlie needs to find the difference between the length of the side and the opening, so he subtracts. He will need 3.8 meters of fencing for the side.

$$\begin{array}{r} {}^{3}\!\!\!\!{}^{1}\\ \cancel{4}.6 \\ - \ 0.8 \\ \hline 3.8 \ \text{meters} \end{array}$$

Practice ▮ Circle the best answer for each item.

Items 1–2 refer to the following diagram of a flower bed.

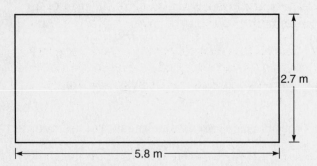

2.7 m

5.8 m

1. Shauna is fencing the flower bed shown. Which is the correct expression to find the perimeter of the flower bed in meters?

   (1) 5.8 + 2.7
   (2) 5.8 + 2.7 + 2.7
   (3) 5.8 + 5.8 + 2.7
   (4) 5.8 + 5.8 + 2.7 + 2.7
   (5) 5.8 + 5.8 + 5.8 + 5.8

2. Shauna decides to leave a 0.7-meter opening in the center of one of the 2.7-meter sides. Which is the correct expression to find how many meters of fencing Shauna will need for this side?

   (1) 2.7 + 0.7
   (2) 2.7 − 0.7
   (3) 2.7 + 2.7 + 0.7 + 0.7
   (4) 5.8 + 5.8 + 2.7 + 0.7
   (5) 5.8 + 5.8 + 2.7 − 0.7

Items 3–4 refer to the following diagram of a flower bed.

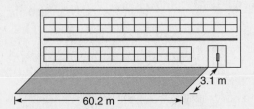

3.1 m

60.2 m

3. Stan is fencing three sides of this flower bed. Which is the correct expression to find how many meters of fencing Stan will need?

   (1) 60.2 + 3.1
   (2) 60.2 − 3.1
   (3) 60.2 + 3.1 + 3.1
   (4) 60.2 + 60.2 + 3.1
   (5) 60.2 + 60.2 + 3.1 + 3.1

4. Stan decides to put an ornamental piece of fencing that is 15.8 meters long in the center of the 60.2-meter side. Which is the correct expression to find how many meters of regular fencing Stan will need for the 60.2-meter side?

   (1) 15.8 + 60.2
   (2) 15.8 − 60.2
   (3) 60.2 − 15.8
   (4) 60.2 + 3.1 + 3.1 + 15.8
   (5) 60.2 + 3.1 + 3.1 − 15.8

5. Write the expression to find the perimeter of the garden shown.

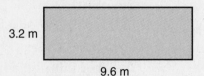

3.2 m

9.6 m

Check your answers on page 280.

Adding and Subtracting Decimals

You have learned to add and subtract money. Adding and subtracting money is much like working with whole numbers. The only difference is that you have to put a decimal point in the answer.

In problems about money, the decimal numbers always have two decimal places to show the number of cents. In other kinds of problems, the decimal numbers may have different numbers of places. You have to set up the problem correctly before you add or subtract.

Follow these steps to add or subtract decimals.

Step 1. Write the numbers in a column so that the decimal points are in a line under each other.

Step 2. If necessary, add zeros so that all the numbers have the same number of decimal digits. Remember, you can add zeros after the last digit in a decimal without changing the value.

Step 3. Add or subtract as you would with whole numbers.

Step 4. Put the decimal point in the answer directly under the decimal points in the problem. Check your answer.

Example

Add: 4.6 + 14 + 3.38 + 0.125

Write the problem. Line up the decimal points.	Put zeros to the right of the last decimal digit.	Add. Put the decimal point in the answer.
4.6	4.600	$\overset{1\ 1\ 1}{4.600}$
14	14.000	14.000
3.38	3.380	3.380
+ 0.125	+ 0.125	+ 0.125
		22.105

Example

Subtract: 15.2 − 9.75

Write the problem. Line up the decimal points.	Put zeros to the right of the last decimal digit.	Subtract. Put the decimal point in the answer.
15.2	15.20	$\overset{4\ 11}{15.20}$
− 9.75	− 9.75	− 9.75
		5.45

Practice ▪ Add or subtract. Show your work.

1.   3.726
   + 4.915
   8.641

2.   17.368
   − 8.415

3.   24.28
   − 13.7

4.   28.467
   + 37.29

5.   12.05
   − 6.8

6.   35.2
   + 41.84

7.   74.3
   − 51.42

8.   93.26
   − 14.336

9.   15.93
   + 4.895

10.   8.45
   + 15.316

11.   3.7
   14.24
   + 2.3

12.   24.81
   35.7
   + 28.274

13.   8.4
   − 0.31

14.   14.8
   − 6.753

15.   12
   + 5.88

16. 2.43 + 0.57 + 3.18 =

17. 67.31 − 49.826 =

18. 57.43 − 29.5 =

19. 0.3 + 21.508 + 3.4 =

20. 4.26 + 5.1 + 8.39 =

21. 12.6 − 8.897 =

22. 14.56 + 3.8 + 12.277 =

23. 2.8 + 34.337 + 5.68 =

24. 36.4 − 16.04 =

25. 0.7 − 0.512 =

Check your answers on pages 280–281.

Consumer Math

Problem-Solving Strategy: Multi-Step Problems

Eva works at a flower shop. She records each sale on a sales slip. The sales slip has lines to write a description of the purchase and the price of the item purchased.

Ms. Morris is buying two flower arrangements. The first arrangement costs $19.95. The second arrangement is much larger and costs $52.75. Eva writes the items and prices on the sales slip. To complete the sales slip, Eva must write amounts next to the words *SUBTOTAL*, *TAX*, and *TOTAL*.

A **subtotal** is a total of part of a group of numbers. In this case, the subtotal is the total of only the two flower arrangements. The subtotal does not include the tax. **Tax** is money that people must pay to support the government.

Compton Floral 444 W. Orange Grove Margate, FL 33063		
Sm. Arrangement	*$19*	*95*
Large Arrangement	*52*	*75*
SUBTOTAL		
TAX		
TOTAL	$	

The **total** is the complete cost of the order. The total on the sales slip includes the cost of both flower arrangements and the sales tax.

Completing the sale involves several steps. Eva must find how much Ms. Morris owes for the flowers. Then Eva collects the money from the customer. If Ms. Morris gives her more than the amount owed, Eva will also have to give her the correct change.

The key to solving a problem with more than one step is to think through the problem and decide what to do on each step **before** you solve the problem.

Eva needs to find three numbers: the subtotal, the total, and the amount of change to give to Ms. Morris.

She can solve the problem in three steps:

Step 1. Find the subtotal by adding $19.95 and $52.75.

Step 2. Find the total by adding the sales tax to the subtotal.

Step 3. Find the change by subtracting the total from the amount that Ms. Morris gives her.

First, Eva finds the subtotal and writes it on the sales slip. She adds the two amounts to find the subtotal.

$19.95
+ 52.75

Before she adds, Eva estimates the answer to the problem. She rounds the numbers to the nearest whole number. Then she adds the rounded amounts.

$$
\begin{array}{r}
\$19.95 \text{ is about} \quad \$20 \\
+\ 52.75 \text{ is about} \quad +\ 53 \\
\hline
\$73
\end{array}
$$

She knows the actual sum should be close to $73. She adds the amounts and gets an answer of $72.70. Since $72.70 is close to $73, Eva is pretty sure she has found the correct subtotal.

$$
\begin{array}{r}
\overset{11\ 1}{\$19.95} \\
+\ 52.75 \\
\hline
\$72.70
\end{array}
$$

She writes $72.70 on the sales slip on the line marked *SUBTOTAL*.

SUBTOTAL	72	70
TAX		
TOTAL	$	

Next Eva adds the sales tax to the subtotal. She looks on a tax chart on the counter and finds that Ms. Morris owes $4.91 in sales tax. She writes the amount on the sales slip on the line marked *TAX*. Then she needs to find the total of $72.70 and $4.91. She estimates first and then adds.

Estimate
$$
\begin{array}{r}
\$72.70 \\
+\ 4.91 \\
\end{array}
$$
is about
is about
$$
\begin{array}{r}
\$73 \\
+\ 5 \\
\hline
\$78
\end{array}
$$
Add
$$
\begin{array}{r}
\overset{1}{\$72.70} \\
+\ 4.91 \\
\hline
\$77.61
\end{array}
$$

Since $77.61 is close to $78, Eva is pretty sure her answer is correct. She writes $77.61 on the sales slip on the line marked *TOTAL*.

Eva tells Ms. Morris that she owes $77.61 for the two arrangements. Ms. Morris gives her $80.00 in cash. Since $80.00 is greater than $77.61, Eva must give Ms. Morris the correct change. To find the difference between the two amounts, she subtracts. She estimates first and then subtracts.

Compton Floral
444 W. Orange Grove
Margate, FL 33063

Sm. Arrangement	$19	95
Large Arrangement	52	75
SUBTOTAL	72	70
TAX	4	91
TOTAL	$77	61

Estimate
$$
\begin{array}{r}
\$80.00 \\
-\ 77.61 \\
\end{array}
$$
is about
is about
$$
\begin{array}{r}
\$80 \\
-\ 78 \\
\hline
\$\ 2
\end{array}
$$
Subtract
$$
\begin{array}{r}
\overset{9\ \ 9}{\$\cancel{80}.\cancel{00}} \\
-\ 77.61 \\
\hline
\$\ 2.39
\end{array}
$$

The difference, $2.39, is close to $2.00, so Eva is pretty sure her answer is correct. She gives Ms. Morris $2.39 in change and a copy of the sales slip.

Practice   Write your answers in the blanks. Show your work.

Items 1–4 refer to the following information.

Ervin works at a clothing store. His customer, Mr. Simon, is buying a pair of jeans that costs $34.95 and a sweat shirt that costs $24.50. Sales tax on this purchase is $2.97. Mr. Simon gives Ervin $70.00 in cash.

1. Estimate the subtotal before tax of this sale.

   _____

2. What is the exact subtotal before tax of this sale?

   _____

3. What is the total including tax of this sale?

   _____

4. How much change should Ervin give Mr. Simon?

   _____

  Circle the best answer for each item.

Items 5–8 refer to the following information.

Mrs. Wilson wants to buy two winter coats for her children. One coat costs $76.50, and the other costs $81.75. Sales tax on the coats is $9.49. Mrs. Wilson decides to put the coats on layaway and pays $45.00 to hold them.

5. What is the subtotal before tax of this sale?

   (1) $91.24
   (2) $130.99
   (3) $147.75
   (4) $157.25
   (5) $158.25

6. What is the total including tax of this sale?

   (1) $140.00
   (2) $148.76
   (3) $167.74
   (4) $197.74
   (5) $203.25

7. Estimate how much Mrs. Wilson still owes on the coats.

   (1) $116
   (2) $118
   (3) $120
   (4) $123
   (5) $126

8. Exactly how much does Mrs. Wilson still owe on the coats?

   (1) $122.74
   (2) $125.00
   (3) $132.75
   (4) $147.25
   (5) $150.49

Data Analysis

Problem Solving Strategy: Using a Line Graph

Dennis Stone works for the Department of Water and Power for the City of Los Angeles. He is helping his boss put together a flier that will encourage people to save water. His boss, Lupe Navarro, wants to include the 2-page flier with this month's utility bills. She asks Dennis to find the levels of rainfall for Los Angeles this year.

She wants to know:

■ How many inches of rainfall did the city receive in March this year?

■ How many more inches of rainfall did the city receive in February than in March?

■ What was the total amount of rainfall for February and March this year?

Dennis goes to the library and finds the line graph to the right. The graph shows the rainfall for the first six months of the year.

A line graph contains lines called **axes.** Each axis is labeled. In the graph to the right, the vertical (up and down) axis is marked with a scale. The scale represents the number of inches of rainfall in Los Angeles. The longest marks on the scale represent whole numbers. The smaller marks divide each inch into tenths.

The horizontal (left to right) axis is marked with letters representing the first six months of the year: **J**anuary, **F**ebruary, **M**arch, **A**pril, **M**ay, and **J**une.

The points on the graph show the number of inches of rainfall for each month. You can tell how many inches of rainfall fell each month by following across from the point to the mark on the scale. The points are connected by a line. The line shows the increase or decrease in the amount of rainfall for the six-month period.

Example   The point for January (above the first letter *J*) is between *2* and *3* on the scale. By counting the small lines, you can see the point represents 2.6 inches of rainfall.

Dennis uses the graph to answer his boss's questions.

How many inches of rainfall did the city receive in March of this year?

(1) 0.2
(2) 1.2
(3) 1.9
(4) 2.1
(5) 2.9

Answer 3 is the correct choice. Dennis finds the point for March above the first *M* on the bottom scale. He reads across to the scale. The point represents 1.9 inches of rainfall.

How many more inches of rainfall did the city receive in February than in March of this year?

(1) 0.2
(2) 0.4
(3) 0.8
(4) 0.9
(5) 1.1

Answer 4 is the correct choice. Dennis finds the point for February and reads across to the scale. There were 2.8 inches of rainfall in February. He subtracts to find the difference between 2.8 inches and 1.9 inches, the rainfall for March. There was 0.9 inch more rainfall in February than in March.

$$\begin{array}{r} \overset{1}{2}\llap{\,}8 \\ -\ 1.9 \\ \hline 0.9 \text{ inch} \end{array}$$

What was the total amount of rainfall for February and March of this year?

(1) 4.4
(2) 4.7
(3) 4.9
(4) 5.0
(5) 5.2

Answer 2 is the correct choice. To find the total rainfall for the two months, Dennis adds 2.8, the rainfall for February, and 1.9, the rainfall for March. There were 4.7 inches of rainfall during the two-month period.

$$\begin{array}{r} \overset{1}{}2.8 \\ +\ 1.9 \\ \hline 4.7 \text{ inches} \end{array}$$

Practice ◤ Circle the best answer for each item.

◤ Write your answers in the blanks. Show your work.

Items 1–3 refer to the following line graph.

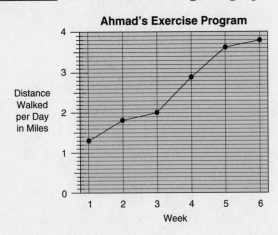

Items 4–6 refer to the following line graph.

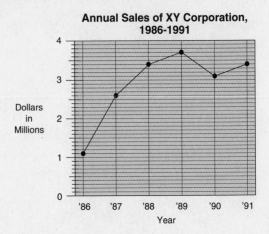

1. How many miles did Ahmad walk each day during week 4 of his exercise program?

   (1) 2.4
   (2) 2.9
   (3) 3.1
   (4) 3.9
   (5) 29

2. During which time period did Ahmad have the greatest increase in the distance he walked per day?

   (1) from week 1 to week 2
   (2) from week 2 to week 3
   (3) from week 3 to week 4
   (4) from week 4 to week 5
   (5) from week 5 to week 6

3. How many miles farther did Ahmad walk each day during week 6 of his program than during week 1?

   (1) 0.5
   (2) 2.5
   (3) 2.9
   (4) 3.0
   (5) 5.1

4. What were the annual sales of XY Corporation in 1987?

   _____

5. What were the total sales for 1990 and 1991?

   _____

6. What is the difference in sales between the year with the greatest sales and the year with the lowest sales?

   _____

Using Your Math Skills

Write the value of the underlined digit in words.

1. 3.2<u>7</u>5 _____

2. 14.078<u>2</u> _____

Compare each pair of numbers. Write >, <, or = between the two numbers.

3. 0.759 _____ 0.795

4. 0.326 _____ 0.54

Write your answers in the blanks.

5. Round 3.196 to the nearest hundredth. _____

6. Round 6.453 to the nearest tenth. _____

7. Round 0.724 to the nearest whole number. _____

Add or subtract. Show your work.

8. 4.26
  + 3.947

9. 7.389
  − 0.49

10. 5.9
   − 4.78

11. 3.81
   12.463
   + 5.4

12. 12.372 − 9.473 =

13. 7.37 − 5.893 =

14. 8.25 + 9.47 + 3.06 =

15. 15.43 + 2.9 + 3.816 =

16. 4.245 + 1.97 + 2.8 =

17. 3.8 − 1.924 =

Circle the best answer for each item.

18. Julio's doctor prescribed sixteen thousandths of a gram of a medicine for him. Which is the correct number of grams the doctor prescribed?

    (1)   0.0016
    (2)   0.016
    (3)   0.16
    (4)   1,600
    (5)   16,000

19. Lucinda is fencing her vegetable garden. The garden is a rectangle that measures 5.2 meters long and 3.4 meters wide. Which is the correct expression to find the perimeter of the garden?

    (1) 5.2 + 3.4
    (2) 5.2 + 3.4 + 3.4
    (3) 5.2 + 5.2 + 3.4
    (4) 5.2 + 5.2 + 3.4 + 3.4
    (5) 5.2 + 5.2 + 5.2 + 3.4

20. Calvin had 4.2 meters of upholstery fabric. He used 2.7 meters of fabric to recover a chair. How many meters of fabric did Calvin have left?

    (1)   1.5
    (2)   2.5
    (3)   6.9
    (4)   13.8
    (5)   15

21. The Auto Mart sells a car battery for $65.49. At Highway Auto, the same battery sells for $53.99. Estimate how much you will save if you buy at Highway Auto.

    (1) $8
    (2) $9
    (3) $11
    (4) $13
    (5) $16

Write your answers in the blanks.
Show your work.

22. The average rainfall in June in Valley City is 14.3 centimeters. This June, Valley City received 12.76 centimeters of rain. How many centimeters below average was this June's rainfall?

    _____

23. A box of Brand A laundry detergent weighs 3.42 kilograms. A box of Brand B laundry detergent weighs 3.059 kilograms. Both boxes cost the same. Which is the better buy?

    _____

24. Chiang needed scrap lumber to build shelves in her garage. She found one piece 2.9 meters long and another 3.16 meters long. How many meters of lumber did Chiang find altogether?

    _____

25. Lenora is making a rectangular frame for a picture that is 0.6 meter long and 0.46 meter wide. What is the perimeter of the inside of the frame?

    _____

Items 26 – 29 refer to the following information.

George works in the electronics department of a large store. His customer, Mrs. McDonald, is buying a portable tape player for $36.90 and a cassette tape for $7.49. Sales tax on this purchase is $2.67. Mrs. McDonald gives George $50.00 in cash.

26. Estimate the subtotal before tax of this sale.

_____

27. What is the exact subtotal before tax of this sale?

_____

28. What is the total including tax of this sale?

_____

29. How much change should George give Mrs. McDonald?

_____

Circle the best answer for each item.

Items 30 – 32 refer to the following graph.

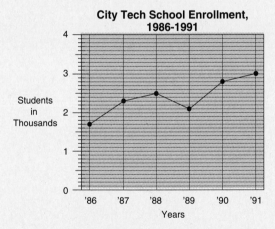

30. How many students were enrolled in 1987?

   (1)   1.6 thousand
   (2)   2.3 thousand
   (3)   2.5 thousand
   (4)   3.7 thousand
   (5)   23 thousand

31. Which was the greatest change in enrollment?

   (1)   decrease from 1986 to 1987
   (2)   increase from 1986 to 1987
   (3)   decrease from 1988 to 1989
   (4)   decrease from 1989 to 1990
   (5)   increase from 1989 to 1990

32. How many more students were enrolled in 1991 than in 1986?

   (1)   1.3 thousand
   (2)   2.3 thousand
   (3)   2.7 thousand
   (4)   3.0 thousand
   (5)   4.7 thousand

Section 9

Multiplying and Dividing Decimals

Consumer Math

Victor orders the supplies in the county clerk's office. He needs to order some office supplies.

Victor needs to find the cost of buying 3 packages of computer paper. He also needs to order 10 typewriter ribbons. He needs to find the cost for one of each item. He also needs to figure out the total cost for all the items he wants to order.

The price of one item is called the **unit cost**. **Unit** means one item. **Total cost** is found by multiplying the unit cost by the number of units you want.

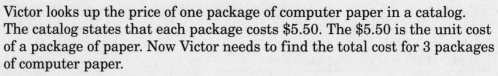
Total Cost = Unit Cost x Number of Units

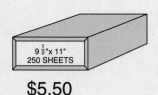

$5.50

Victor looks up the price of one package of computer paper in a catalog. The catalog states that each package costs $5.50. The $5.50 is the unit cost of a package of paper. Now Victor needs to find the total cost for 3 packages of computer paper.

Which is the correct expression to find the total cost of the computer paper?

(1) $5.50 × 0.03
(2) $5.50 × 3
(3) $5.50 × 0.3
(4) $5.50 ÷ 3
(5) 3 ÷ $5.50

Answer 2 is the correct choice. Victor needs to find the total cost of the computer paper. He knows the cost of 1 package of paper ($5.50) and he needs 3 packages. He should multiply the unit ($5.50) by the number of units (3).

$5.50 x 3 = $16.50

The total cost of the 3 packages of computer paper is $16.50.

Next Victor looks up the price of typewriter ribbons. He finds a special sale price on the ribbons. He can buy a box of 10 ribbons for $41.00. The total cost for 10 ribbons is $41.00. But Victor needs to know the cost of one ribbon. He needs to find the unit cost.

Which is the correct expression to find the cost of one typewriter ribbon?

   (1) $41.00 × 10
   (2) $41.00 × 1
   (3) $41.00 ÷ 1
   (4) $41.00 ÷ 10
   (5) 10 ÷ $41.00

Answer 4 is the correct choice. Victor needs to find the cost per ribbon. Victor knows what 10 ribbons cost. He knows the total cost and the number of ribbons. He can find the unit cost by dividing the total cost ($41.00) by the number of ribbons (10).

 Unit Cost = Total Cost ÷ Number of Units

$41.00 ÷ 10 = $4.10

The cost of 1 typewriter ribbon is $4.10.

Practice Circle the best answer for each item.

1. Erica is having a party. She plans to order four large pizzas. The cost of one large pizza is $8.50. Which is the correct expression to find the total cost of her order?

   (1) $8.50 ÷ 4
   (2) $8.50 × 0.4
   (3) 4 ÷ $8.50
   (4) $8.50 × 4
   (5) 1 ÷ $8.50

2. The Music Mart is having a sale. You can buy five cassette tapes for $14.95. Jose wants to buy one tape. Which is the correct expression to find the cost of one cassette tape?

   (1) $14.95 ÷ 1
   (2) $14.95 × 5
   (3) $14.95 ÷ 5
   (4) 5 ÷ $14.95
   (5) $14.95 × 0.5

3. Rita sees an ad in a store window for men's sport socks. The store is selling 6 pairs for $9.00. She wants 1 pair. Which is the correct expression to find the cost of 1 pair of socks?

   (1) $9.00 ÷ 6
   (2) 6 × $9.00
   (3) 6 ÷ $9.00
   (4) $9.00 × 0.6
   (5) $9.00 ÷ 0.6

4. While shopping for school supplies for his children, Kelvin buys 25 pencils. The pencils cost $0.05 each. Which is the correct expression to find the total cost of the pencils?

   (1) $0.05 × 0.25
   (2) $0.05 ÷ 25
   (3) $0.05 × 2.5
   (4) 25 ÷ $0.05
   (5) $0.05 × 25

Items 5–10 refer to the following information.

Tom's Market Food Specials

Scrub Paper Towels	$0.69 each roll	Velez Tomato Sauce	6 cans for $0.90
Lean Ground Beef	$2.19 per pound	Vita Fruit Drink	3 bottles for $5.40
Bananas	$0.89 per pound	Tasty Brand Cat Food	5 cans for $2.00

5. Gina wants to buy 3 pounds of lean ground beef. Which is the correct expression to find the total cost of the ground beef?

   (1) $2.19 ÷ 3
   (2) $2.19 × 3
   (3) $2.79 ÷ 3
   (4) 0.3 × $2.19
   (5) Not enough information is given.

6. Sonny plans to buy the Tasty Brand cat food that is on sale. He buys 5 cans at the sale price of $2.00. The usual price is $0.50 per can. Which is the correct expression to find the amount he paid for each can of cat food?

   (1) 5 ÷ $2.00
   (2) $2.00 × 5
   (3) $2.00 ÷ 5
   (4) 5 × $0.50
   (5) $2.00 ÷ $5.00

7. Sibyl buys 3 bottles of Vita Fruit Drink at the sale price. Last week she paid $1.95 for one bottle. Which is the correct expression to find the amount she is paying per bottle at the sale price?

   (1) $5.40 ÷ 3
   (2) $1.95 × 3
   (3) $1.95 ÷ 3
   (4) $5.40 × 3
   (5) Not enough information is given.

8. Andres bought 5 bananas. Which is the correct expression to find the total cost of the bananas?

   (1) $0.89 × 5
   (2) $0.89 ÷ 5
   (3) $8.90 × 5
   (4) $0.89 ÷ 0.5
   (5) Not enough information is given.

9. Esther decides to stock up on paper towels for her day-care business. She wants to buy 25 rolls of paper towels. Which is the correct expression to find the total cost of the paper towels?

   (1) $0.69 × 0.25
   (2) $0.69 × 25
   (3) 25 ÷ 69
   (4) $0.69 ÷ 25
   (5) $2.50 ÷ 0.69

10. Last week the unit cost of a can of tomato sauce was $0.18. Which is the correct expression to find the current unit cost of a can of Velez tomato sauce?

   (1) $0.18 × 6
   (2) $0.18 ÷ 6
   (3) $0.90 × 6
   (4) $0.90 ÷ 6
   (5) Not enough information is given.

Check your answers on pages 283–284.

Multiplying Decimals

Multiplying decimals is almost the same as multiplying whole numbers. There is only one difference. You have to put the decimal point in the answer.

Example

Multiply 6.03 by 0.5.

Step 1. Write the problem. In multiplication, you don't have to line up the decimal points.

$$\begin{array}{r} 6.03 \\ \times\ 0.5 \end{array}$$

Step 2. Multiply as you would with whole numbers.

$$\begin{array}{r} 6.03 \\ \times\ 0.5 \\ \hline 3015 \end{array}$$

Step 3. Count the total number of decimal places in the problem. The number of decimal places are the number of digits to the right of the decimal point.

$$\begin{array}{rl} 6.03 & \text{2 places} \\ \times\ 0.5 & \text{1 place} \\ \hline 3.015 & \text{3 places} \end{array}$$

Step 4. Finally, place the decimal point in the answer. Start at the right and count the same number of decimal places to the left. Then write the decimal point. The answer is 3.015.

$$\begin{array}{rl} 6.03 & \text{Count three} \\ \times\ 0.5 & \text{places to} \\ \hline 3.015 & \text{the left.} \end{array}$$

Sometimes there are not enough digits in the answer. Then you need to use zeros as place holders.

Example

Multiply 0.014 by 0.6.

Step 1. Multiply. Then count the total number of decimal places in the problem. There are 4 decimal places, but the answer has only 2 digits.

$$\begin{array}{rl} .014 & \text{3 places} \\ \times\ 0.6 & \text{1 place} \\ \hline 84 & \text{4 places} \end{array}$$

Step 2. From the right, count the number of decimal places you need. Write extra zeros as place holders. The answer is 0.0084.

$$\begin{array}{rl} .014 & \text{Count 4} \\ \times\ 0.6 & \text{places to} \\ \hline 0.0084 & \text{the left.} \end{array}$$

Practice ■ Multiply.

1. $\begin{array}{r} \overset{1}{1}3 \\ \times\ 0.4 \\ \hline 5.2 \end{array}$

2. $\begin{array}{r} 9.1 \\ \times\ 8 \\ \hline \end{array}$

3. $\begin{array}{r} 12.3 \\ \times\ 0.5 \\ \hline \end{array}$

4. $\begin{array}{r} 1.04 \\ \times\ 0.07 \\ \hline \end{array}$

5. $\begin{array}{r} 0.75 \\ \times\ 11 \\ \hline \end{array}$

6. $\begin{array}{r} 136 \\ \times\ 0.006 \\ \hline \end{array}$

7. $\begin{array}{r} 128 \\ \times\ 0.2 \\ \hline \end{array}$

8. $\begin{array}{r} 17.3 \\ \times\ 1.6 \\ \hline \end{array}$

9. $\begin{array}{r} 0.42 \\ \times\ 0.03 \\ \hline \end{array}$

10. $\begin{array}{r} 2.05 \\ \times\ 0.9 \\ \hline \end{array}$

Check your answers on page 284.

Dividing Decimals

Dividing a decimal by a whole number is the same as dividing whole numbers. You just need to put the decimal point in the answer.

Example

Divide 8.6 by 2.

Step 1. Write the problem. Put the decimal point in the answer space. It goes above the decimal point in the problem.

$$2\overline{)8.6} \qquad \begin{array}{r} 4.3 \\ 2\overline{)8.6} \\ -8 \\ \hline 0\,6 \\ -6 \\ \hline 0 \end{array}$$

Step 2. Now solve the problem. Divide as you would with whole numbers. The answer is 4.3. Check by multiplying.

$$\begin{array}{r} 4.3 \\ \times\ 2 \\ \hline 8.6 \end{array}$$

Example

Divide 0.028 by 4.

Step 1. Put the decimal point in the answer space. Since you can't divide 0 or 2 by 4, put zeros in the answer as place holders.

$$4\overline{)0.028}^{\,0.00} \qquad \begin{array}{r} 0.007 \\ 4\overline{)0.028} \\ -28 \\ \hline 0 \end{array}$$

Step 2. Then divide 28 by 4. You get 7. The answer is 0.007. Check.

$$\begin{array}{r} 0.007 \\ \times\ 4 \\ \hline 0.028 \end{array}$$

Sometimes you will need to put zeros at the end of a decimal to solve the problem. Putting zeros after the last decimal place doesn't change the value of the number.

Example

Divide 1.2 by 5.

Step 1. Put the decimal point in the answer space and divide.

Step 2. Write zeros until the problem comes out evenly. The answer is 0.24.

$$\begin{array}{r} 0.2 \\ 5\overline{)1.2} \\ -1\,0 \\ \hline 2 \end{array} \qquad \begin{array}{r} 0.24 \\ 5\overline{)1.20} \\ -1\,0 \\ \hline 20 \\ -20 \\ \hline 0 \end{array}$$

Some division problems won't work out evenly no matter how many zeros you add. Figure out how many decimal places you will need in your answer. Then round your answer. For instance, if the problem is about dollars and cents, you would round the answer to the hundredths place.

To divide by a decimal, you need to change that decimal to a whole number by moving the decimal point as far to the right as you can. Then move the decimal point in the number you are dividing the same number of places to the right.

Example

Divide 2.032 by 0.8.

Step 1. Move the decimal point in 0.8 to the right. You have to move it one place.

Step 2. Move the decimal point in 2.032 one place to the right.

Step 3. Place the decimal point in the answer space and divide.

$$0.8\overline{)2.032}$$

$$\begin{array}{r} 2.54 \\ 8\overline{)20.32} \\ -16 \\ \hline 4\,3 \\ -4\,0 \\ \hline 32 \\ -32 \\ \hline 0 \end{array}$$

You might need to use zeros as place holders when you move the decimal point.

Example

Divide 7 by 0.05.

Step 1. Move the decimal point in 0.05 all the way to the right (two places).

Step 2. You need to write two zeros as place holders. Now you can move the decimal point in 7 two places to the right.

Step 3. Divide. The answer is 140.

$$0.05\overline{)7.00}$$

$$\begin{array}{r} 140 \\ 5\overline{)700} \\ -5 \\ \hline 20 \\ -20 \\ \hline 0 \end{array}$$

Practice Divide.

1.
$$\begin{array}{r} .47 \\ 6\overline{)2.82} \\ -2\,4 \\ \hline 42 \\ -42 \\ \hline 0 \end{array}$$

2. $9\overline{)5.67}$

3. $7\overline{)41.3}$

4. $12\overline{)33.6}$

5. $13\overline{)110.5}$

6. $4\overline{)1.224}$

7. $21\overline{)0.882}$

8. $0.5\overline{)0.001}$

9. $0.08\overline{)0.0248}$

10. $0.12\overline{)1.0236}$

11. $0.105 \div 0.06 =$

12. $0.51 \div 0.012 =$

Check your answers on pages 284–285.

Using the Metric System

Problem-Solving Strategy: Mental Math—Powers of Ten

Jane works in a factory that makes hair-care products. One of the products contains a fruit extract. The extract is weighed in **kilograms**. Using a machine, Jane fills plastic tubes with small amounts of the extract. These amounts are so small that they are weighed in grams.

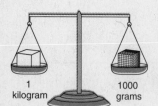

1
kilogram

1000
grams

Kilograms and grams are units of weight in the metric system. A kilogram is a little more than 2 pounds. A gram is much smaller. To do her work, Jane needs to know the relationship between kilograms and grams.

 1 kilogram (kg) = 1,000 grams (g)

This morning Jane received a shipment weighing 25.6 kilograms. She needs to figure out how many grams the shipment weighs. She needs to convert the kilograms to grams.

Because there are 1,000 grams in 1 kilogram, Jane should multiply the number of kilograms by 1,000. But she doesn't need to work out the problem on paper. She can do the work using a shortcut.

The numbers 10, 100, and 1,000 are called the **powers of ten.** Look what happens when a number is multiplied by a power of ten.

$$3.25 \times 10 = 32.5 \qquad 3.25 \times 100 = 325 \qquad 3.25 \times 1,000 = 3,250$$

The decimal point moves to the right. It moves one place for each zero in the power of ten.

To multiply by a power of ten, count the number of zeros in the number. Then move the decimal point the same number of places to the right. Write zeros as place holders, if needed.

Jane needs to set her machine for the number of grams of fruit extract she puts in the tubes. To find out how many grams are in 25.6 kilograms, Jane needs to multiply 25.6 by 1,000. Since there are 3 zeros in 1,000, she moves the decimal point 3 places to the right. She writes zeros as place holders.

25.6 x 1,000 = 25,600   **25.6 kilograms = 25,600 grams**

Jane prepares the machine to fill the tubes with 25,600 grams of fruit extract.

1 milliliter

1 liter

Jane's coworker, Leon, prepares the liquid base for the hair-care product. The ingredients are measured in milliliters. A **milliliter** is a very small unit of liquid volume. For example, a teaspoon holds about 5 milliliters.

Today Leon prepares 45,000 milliliters of the liquid. After he finishes the job, he needs to record the amount in liters on a report form. A **liter** is a larger metric unit than a milliliter. Leon needs to know the relationship between milliliters and liters to do his job.

1 liter (L) = 1,000 milliliters (ml)

To convert 45,000 milliliters to liters, Leon needs to divide by 1,000. The same shortcut will help him do the work. To divide by a power of ten, count the number of zeros. Then move the decimal point the same number of places to the left.

Since there are three zeros in 1,000, Leon moves the decimal point in 45,000 three places to the left.

45,000 ÷ 1,000 = 45.000   **45,000 milliliters = 45 liters**

Leon has made 45 liters of the liquid base. He writes the amount on the report form.

LIQUID BASE PRODUCTION REPORT		
Date	Prepared By	Number of Liters
5-23	*Leon*	45

The most common metric units are shown on the chart below.

Length	10 millimeters (mm)	= 1 centimeter (cm)
	100 centimeters (cm)	= 1 meter (m)
	1,000 meters (m)	= 1 kilometer (km)
Mass (Weight)	1,000 milligrams (mg)	= 1 gram (g)
	1,000 grams (g)	= 1 kilogram (kg)
Volume	1,000 milliliters (ml)	= 1 liter (L)

Practice ▪ Write your answer in the blanks. Show your work. Refer to the chart on page 131 if necessary.

1. Ramona weighs 50 kilograms. How many grams does she weigh?

   _____

2. A large can of tomato sauce holds 600 milliliters. How many liters does it hold?

   _____

3. A race is 40 kilometers long. How many meters long is the race?

   _____

4. A wall is 2.4 meters high. How many centimeters high is the wall?

   _____

5. A portable TV screen is 320 millimeters wide. How many centimeters wide is the screen?

   _____

6. A bag of sugar weighs 4.5 kilograms. How many grams does the bag weigh?

   _____

▪ Circle the best answer for each item.

7. Ana's personal best in the long jump is 17.5 meters. How many centimeters did she jump?

   (1)   0.0175 cm
   (2)   0.175 cm
   (3)   1.75 cm
   (4)   175 cm
   (5)   1,750 cm

8. Rick ate a bowl of chili that had 5.5 grams of fat. How many milligrams of fat were in the chili?

   (1)   0.0055 mg
   (2)   0.55 mg
   (3)   550 mg
   (4)   5,500 mg
   (5)   55,000 mg

9. A square measures 0.4 meters on each side. What is the perimeter of the square in centimeters?

   (1)   1.6 cm
   (2)   160 cm
   (3)   1,600 cm
   (4)   16,000 cm
   (5)   160,000 cm

10. A tube contains 100 milliliters of lotion. How many liters of lotion does the tube contain?

    (1)   0.001 L
    (2)   0.01 L
    (3)   0.1 L
    (4)   1 L
    (5)   10 L

Check your answers on page 285.

Finding the Mean and Median

Problem-Solving Strategy: Multistep Problems

Numbers that people group and study to make decisions are called **data**. Here are some examples of data.

- the ages of the baseball players in the major leagues

- the number of points a basketball player scores each game during the season

Stan works at a department store that closes at 6 P.M. His boss wants to find out how many customers usually shop between 4 P.M. and 6 P.M. What would be the best way for Stan to get this information?

On Monday Stan decides to count the people who go through the checkout lines within the two-hour period. He counts 106 shoppers. Joya, a clerk, tells Stan the store had more customers than usual that afternoon. Stan's boss wants to know the <u>usual</u> number of shoppers per day. How can Stan figure out what happens on a usual day?

Stan decides to count the shoppers every day for one week. Then he will study the data and figure out the usual or <u>average</u> number of shoppers.

> **Finding the *average* is one way to figure out the usual value of a set of data. For a set of data, the average will be less than the greatest number in the set and greater than the least number in the set. The average is also called the *mean*.**

Stan collects the following data during the week. The store is open only six days, so he has six numbers in the set of data.

Monday, 106; Tuesday, 94; Wednesday, 75; Thursday, 82; Friday, 100; Saturday, 104

First Stan finds the **range** of the set of data. The least number is 75 and the greatest number is 106. The range of the set is 75 to 106. He knows the average or mean will fall between the numbers 75 and 106. Stan follows these steps to find the mean.

Step 1. Find the total of the numbers in the set of data.

$106 + 94 + 75 + 82 + 100 + 104 = 561$

Step 2. Divide the total by how many are in the set. There are six numbers in the set. He divides 561 by 6.

$$
\begin{array}{r}
93.5 \\
6)\overline{561.0} \\
-54 \\
\hline
21 \\
-18 \\
\hline
30 \\
-30 \\
\hline
0
\end{array}
$$

The answer, 93.5, falls between 75 and 106. Stan is pretty sure his answer is reasonable.

Stan reports to his boss that the usual number of shoppers between 4 P.M. and 6 P.M. is 93.5. Of course, you can't really have a decimal part of a shopper. The 93.5 represents the usual value of the set of data. It isn't an exact number of shoppers. Averages often have a decimal part. In some situations, you may need to round your answer. Stan rounds 93.5 to 94 shoppers.

Next Mr. Diaz wants Stan to study some data about overtime work. Mr. Diaz wants to know how many hours of overtime a typical employee usually works in a month. He gives Stan this chart.

Overtime Hours for March	
Ray	6
Lana	8.5
Luis	11
Tony	14
Linda	11
Debra	38
Ky	13
Ryan	15.5
Karen	9.5

Stan could find the mean of the numbers, but he notices that Debra has worked many more overtime hours than the others. The mean is not the best way to find the usual value when one number is much greater or less than the others because the unusual throws off the mean. Stan needs to find the **median** of the data.

> The *median* is another kind of usual value. The median is the middle number of a set of data.

To find the median, first Stan arranges the numbers in order from least to greatest. Then he finds the middle number by counting how many numbers are on each side. The number 11 is the median of the set of data.

$$6, 8.5, 9.5, 11, \underset{\uparrow}{11}, 13, 14, 15.5, 38$$
$$\text{middle} = \text{median}$$

Stan tells Mr. Diaz that the median number of overtime hours is 11. The median (11) shows a value that is typical of the set of data. The average or mean of this set of data (14) is too high to be typical.

When there is an even amount of numbers in the set of data, there will be two middle numbers. Find the average of the two middle numbers to find the median.

Example

Mr. Diaz forgot to give Stan the overtime hours worked by one employee. Dana had worked 13 overtime hours in March. Stan must add this number to the set of data and find the median.

Step 1. Arrange the numbers in order.

$$6, 8.5, 9.5, 11, \underbrace{11, 13}, 13, 14, 15.5, 38$$
$$\text{middle}$$

Step 2. Find the mean of the two middle numbers.

The median number of overtime hours is 12.

$$\begin{array}{r} 11 \\ +13 \\ \hline 24 \end{array} \qquad \begin{array}{r} 12 \\ 2\overline{)24} \\ -2 \\ \hline 04 \\ -4 \\ \hline 0 \end{array}$$

Practice ◼ Find the mean and median for each set of numbers. Then circle the answer that is more typical for the set of data.

1. Number of hot dogs sold for 5 days: 672, 256, 410, 350, 367

   Mean _____ Median _____

2. Bowling scores for 4 games: 260, 254, 102, 280

   Mean _____ Median _____

3. Hours worked Monday by a group of employees: 8, 8.5, 8.7, 9, 8, 10

   Mean _____ Median _____

4. Calories eaten each day for a week: 2,450; 2,100; 1,970; 2,430; 2,840; 1,800; 2,860

   Mean _____ Median _____

◼ Circle the best answer for each item.

5. The Ortez family is planning to rent an apartment. The monthly rents of 3 apartments are $450, $395, and $430. What is the average rent of the apartments?

   (1) $395
   (2) $400
   (3) $420
   (4) $425
   (5) $430

6. On Friday Doris kept a record of the number of customers she had each hour during the 9 hours her fruit stand was open: 25, 42, 45, 37, 102, 86, 46, 38, 27. What is the median number of customers per hour?

   (1) 26
   (2) 36
   (3) 42
   (4) 46
   (5) 48

Items 7 and 8 refer to the following information.

Movie Attendance on Saturday Evening, Nov. 1

Cinema 1 502	Cinema 2 147
Cinema 3 425	Cinema 4 454
Cinema 5 518	Cinema 6 504

7. What is the median of the data?

   (1) 264
   (2) 339.5
   (3) 367
   (4) 425
   (5) 478

8. What is the mean attendance?

   (1) 264
   (2) 339.5
   (3) 425
   (4) 476
   (5) 1,101

Check your answers on pages 285–286. *Section 9: Multiplying and Dividing Decimals* 135

Using Your Math Skills

Multiply or divide.

1. 3.2
    × 6

2. 2.06
    × 0.04

3. 4.17
    × 0.3

4. 12.4
    × 2.7

5. 0.752
    × 0.18

6. 6)4.56

7. 4)3.3

8. 0.5)1.935

9. 0.08)5.42

10. 1.5)13.95

11. 0.56 × 0.009 =

12. 37.6 ÷ 0.16 =

Write your answers in the blanks. Show your work.

13. A can of tuna contains 12.5 grams of protein. How many milligrams of protein are in the tuna?

_____

14. Miguel works 5 days each week. He takes the same route to and from work each day. If he drives a total of 74.5 miles to and from work each week, how far does he drive to and from work each day?

_____

15. Risa bought 1.6 pounds of ground beef on sale for $1.85 a pound. How much did she pay for the ground beef?

_____

16. During the first hour the store was open, Tony made sales of $24.50, $31.75, $18.41, and $20.38. What was the average sale Tony made?

_____

Check your answers on pages 286–287.

17. Anna bought a set of 4 tires for $197.00. Which is the correct expression to find the cost of one tire?

(1) 4 × $197.00
(2) $197.00 ÷ 4
(3) $197.00 × 0.4
(4) 4 ÷ $197.00
(5) Not enough information is given.

18. Savemore Foods has bananas for $0.28 per pound. Kai bought 4 pounds of bananas. How much did he pay for bananas?

(1) $0.07
(2) $0.70
(3) $1.12
(4) $8.32
(5) $11.20

19. The heights of the starting players on a basketball team are 80 inches, 76 inches, 75 inches, 80 inches, and 79 inches. What is the mean height of the players?

(1) 75 inches
(2) 77.5 inches
(3) 78 inches
(4) 79 inches
(5) 80 inches

20. Mrs. Quan is buying notebooks for her children. Each notebook costs $1.29. Which is the correct expression to find the cost of 3 notebooks?

(1) $1.29 ÷ 3
(2) $1.29 ÷ 1
(3) $1.29 × 0.3
(4) $1.29 × 3
(5) $3 ÷ 1.29

21. Raphael is building shelves. He needs to cut pieces of wood 1.2 meters long. Which is the correct expression to find how many pieces he can cut from a board 5 meters long?

(1) 5 ÷ 1.2
(2) 5 × 1.2
(3) 1.2 ÷ 5
(4) 5 ÷ 1.02
(5) Not enough information is given.

22. Each dose of cold medicine contains 0.013 gram of decongestant. Which is the correct expression to find how many grams of decongestant are needed for each bottle of cold medicine?

(1) 100 × 0.013
(2) 0.013 ÷ 100
(3) 0.013 × 12
(4) 0.013 ÷ 12
(5) Not enough information is given.

23. A kitchen is 398 centimeters wide. How many meters wide is the kitchen?

(1) 0.398 meters
(2) 3.98 meters
(3) 39.8 meters
(4) 3,980 meters
(5) 39,800 meters

24. George drove 291.6 miles on 12 gallons of gas. How many miles per gallon does his car get?

(1) 1.2 miles per gallon
(2) 2.43 miles per gallon
(3) 12 miles per gallon
(4) 24.3 miles per gallon
(5) 29.16 miles per gallon

Unit 3 Review:
Decimals

Write the value of the underlined digit in words.

1. 5.394<u>6</u> _____   2. 7.2<u>8</u>13 _____

Compare each pair of numbers. Write >, <, or = between the two numbers.

3. 0.25 _____ 0.025   4. 0.97 _____ 0.970

Write your answers in the blanks.

5. Round 5.362 to the nearest hundredth.   6. Round 7.351 to the nearest tenth.

_____   _____

Solve. Show your work.

7.   3.925   8.   25.36   9.   8.4   10. 4)‾37.6‾
        4.6   − 17.5   − 3.257
      + 3.26

11. 6.3   12.   2.54   13. 0.06)‾2.7‾   14. 0.016)‾7.488‾
     × 8   × 0.9

15. 3.54 + 6.83 + 5.19 =   16. 0.0357 ÷ 0.07 =

17. 45.4 − 2.92 =   18. 0.57 × 0.05 =

19. 4.38 + 2.7 + 1.916 =   20. 16.4 × 2.7 =

Check your answers on pages 287–288.

Write your answers in the blanks. Show your work.

21. Bryant bought a pair of athletic shoes for $64.95 and a package of socks for $5.99. Sales tax on his purchases was $3.55. Bryant gave the clerk $80.00 in cash. How much change should the clerk have given Bryant?

_____

22. Juanita's record in the high jump is 1.9 meters. What is her record in centimeters?

_____

Items 23–25 refer to the following information.

Freddie drives a van for a delivery service. The number of miles he drove on each of the 5 days he worked last week are 62, 28, 57, 66, and 63.

Circle the best answer for each item.

26. Lauren is fencing a rectangular garden that is 6.8 meters long and 2.4 meters wide. Which is the correct expression to find the perimeter of the garden?

(1) 6.8 + 2.4
(2) 6.8 − 2.4
(3) 6.8 × 2.4
(4) 6.8 + 6.8 + 2.4
(5) 6.8 + 6.8 + 2.4 + 2.4

27. Auto Buys has tires on sale this week for $42.50 each. Lin needs to buy 4 tires. Which is the correct expression to find the total cost of the tires?

(1) 4 ÷ $42.50
(2) $42.50 × 0.4
(3) $42.50 × 1
(4) $42.50 × 4
(5) $42.50 ÷ 4

23. What is the mean number of miles Freddie drove last week?

_____

24. What is the median number of miles Freddie drove last week?

_____

25. Which is more typical of the set of data, the mean or the median?

_____

Item 28 refers to the following graph.

PARTS PRODUCED, JULY–DEC. 1991

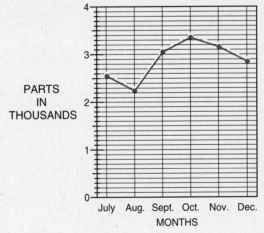

28. How many parts were produced during the last two months of 1991?

(1) 0.3 thousand
(2) 4.9 thousand
(3) 5.1 thousand
(4) 5.11 thousand
(5) 6.1 thousand

Check your answers on page 288.

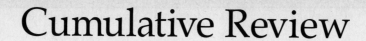

Cumulative Review

Write the value of the underlined digit in words.

1. 5<u>2</u>6,438 _____

2. <u>7</u>,028,651 _____

3. 8.<u>3</u>296 _____

4. 9.01<u>4</u>8 _____

Solve. Show your work.

5. $\begin{array}{r} 700 \\ -\ 352 \\ \hline \end{array}$

6. $\begin{array}{r} 973 \\ \times\ 206 \\ \hline \end{array}$

7. $42\overline{)8,760}$

8. $2.4\overline{)36}$

9. $\begin{array}{r} 2\frac{3}{4} \\ +\ 3\frac{5}{8} \\ \hline \end{array}$

10. $\begin{array}{r} 8\frac{2}{5} \\ -\ 3\frac{2}{3} \\ \hline \end{array}$

11. $28 + 376 + 49 =$

12. $\$9.05 - \$3.59 =$

13. $3\frac{5}{8} \div 1\frac{1}{2} =$

14. $25.6 - 3.842 =$

15. $9^3 =$

16. $1.7 \div 0.04 =$

17. $5\frac{1}{3} \times 2\frac{7}{10} =$

18. $3.27 + 54.8 + 9.071 =$

19. $0.063 \times 0.7 =$

20. $\sqrt{36}$

Check your answers on pages 288–289.

Write your answers in the blanks. Show your work.

Items 21 and 22 refer to the following map.

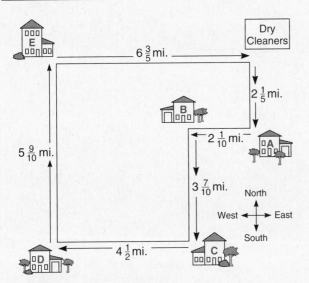

21. Monica makes pickups and deliveries for a dry cleaner. She takes a lunch break after stopping at point C. Estimate how many miles she drives before lunch.

_____

22. Monica's entire route is 25 miles long. How far has she driven when she stops at point E?

_____

Circle the best answer for each item.

23. Penny is buying new carpet for her living room. The living room is 24 feet long and 20 feet wide. What is the area of Penny's living room in square feet?

24 ft.

20 ft.

   (1)   44
   (2)   88
   (3)   160
   (4)   480
   (5)   960

24. Rosa is making lasagna for a block party. Her recipe calls for $\frac{2}{3}$ pound of ricotta cheese. Rosa plans to triple the recipe. Which is the correct expression to find the number of pounds of ricotta cheese she should use?

   (1) $\frac{1}{3} \div \frac{2}{3}$

   (2) $\frac{2}{3} \times \frac{1}{3}$

   (3) $\frac{2}{3} \times 3$

   (4) $\frac{2}{3} \div 3$

   (5) $3 + \frac{2}{3}$

25. Mike worked from 8:28 A.M. to 12:21 P.M. on Monday. He returned from lunch at 1:06 P.M. and worked until 5:36 P.M. How many hours to the nearest quarter hour did Mike work on Monday?

   (1) $3\frac{3}{4}$

   (2) $4\frac{1}{2}$

   (3) $7\frac{1}{4}$

   (4) 8

   (5) $8\frac{1}{4}$

26. Of the 21 days Mario worked last month, he worked overtime 12 days. What fraction of the days did he work overtime?

   (1) $\frac{1}{12}$

   (2) $\frac{1}{21}$

   (3) $\frac{4}{7}$

   (4) $\frac{2}{3}$

   (5) $1\frac{3}{4}$

Check your answers on page 289.

RATIO, PROPORTION, AND PERCENT

Percents have many applications in everyday life. Here a store is advertising a savings of 75% off the regular price.

Imagine you are working at a clothing store. There are 2 employees working on the floor for every 1 employee who is working at a cash register. You are working at a register. A sign above a rack of coats says *20% off.* Your first customer puts a coat on layaway by paying 25% of the cost of the coat. A sign above a display of socks says *3 pairs for $10.* Your second customer buys 6 pairs of socks for $20. You add 6% sales tax to the cost of the socks to find the total amount the customer owes.

Ratio and proportion are used often in business. A **ratio** is a way to compare two numbers. In this example, you can compare the number of employees working on the floor to the number of employees working at a register. The ratio is 2 to 1, which can be written 2:1 or $\frac{2}{1}$.

In a **proportion**, two ratios are equal. The sign above the display of socks advertises 3 pairs for $10. The customer buys 6 pairs for $20. The customer buys the socks at the same rate shown on the sign. In other words, three pairs at $10 is equal to six pairs at $20.

You can write a proportion to show that the ratios are equal.

$$\frac{3 \text{ pairs}}{\$10} = \frac{6 \text{ pairs}}{\$20}$$

In Unit 4 you will learn how to write ratios and solve proportion problems. You will also learn to solve percent problems using your knowledge of ratio and proportion.

Percent is another way to show part of a whole amount. When you work with percents, the whole amount is always said to be 100%. The part of the whole is expressed as a number "out of 100."

To understand percent, think about what you know about dollars and cents. You know that 1 dollar equals 100 cents. Now imagine that the dollar is the whole amount, or 100%.

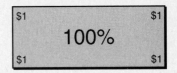

The other coins in our money system represent a part of the dollar.

- A half dollar ($\frac{1}{2}$) is 50 cents ($0.50) or 50% of the dollar.

- A quarter ($\frac{1}{4}$) is 25 cents ($0.25) or 25% of the dollar.

- A dime ($\frac{1}{10}$) is 10 cents ($0.10) or 10% of the dollar.

- A nickel ($\frac{1}{20}$) is 5 cents ($0.05) or 5% of the dollar.

- A penny ($\frac{1}{100}$) is 1 cent ($0.01) or 1% of the dollar.

From these money examples, you can see that fractions, decimals, and percents can all be used to represent part of a whole. You will learn how to convert fractions, decimals, and percents in Unit 4.

Percent problems always have three elements: the base, the part, and the rate. The rate is always followed by the percent sign, %. In the clothing store example, three rates are given: 20%, 25%, and 6%.

- The coats on the rack are 20% off.

- The first customer pays 25% of the cost of a coat to put it on layaway.

- You add 6% sales tax to the second customer's purchase.

In a percent problem, you will be given two of the three elements in order to solve for the missing element. You will learn how to solve for the missing element in Unit 4.

Here are a few of the problem-solving situations presented in Unit 4:

- calculating gasoline mileage

- working with sale prices

- using a map scale to estimate distances

- using a pictograph to make comparisons

- solving simple interest problems

- using a circle graph to make decisions about a family's budget

- figuring out what percent of a paycheck is deducted to pay taxes

- finding the percent of change in an employee's wages

Section 10

Ratio and Proportion

Understanding Ratio and Proportion

A **ratio** is a way to compare two numbers. To compare 3 and 8, you could write 3:8 or $\frac{3}{8}$. Both are read "the ratio of 3 to 8."

Ratios compare quantities or amounts. When you compare inches to inches or dollars to dollars, you are comparing **like** quantities. In the following example, Tanya is comparing hours to hours.

Tanya works for a photo lab. During an 8-hour day, Tanya works 2 hours at the counter helping customers and 6 hours in the lab. What is the ratio of the time Tanya works at the counter to the time she works in the lab?

The ratio of hours working at the counter to hours working in the lab is 2:6 or $\frac{2}{6}$. Since a ratio is a fraction, it can be reduced to lowest terms.

$$\frac{2}{6} = \frac{2 \div 2}{6 \div 2} = \frac{1}{3} \text{ or } 1:3$$

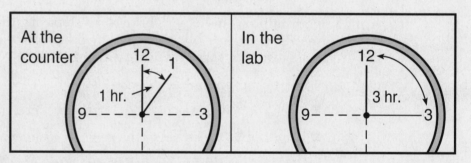

The ratio shows that for every 1 hour Tanya works at the counter, she works 3 hours in the lab.

You can also compare **unlike** quantities or amounts. A ratio comparing unlike quantities is called a **rate.** In the following example, Dean is comparing miles to gallons.

Dean does a lot of driving in the city. He wants to know how many miles he can drive on a gallon of gas. When Dean fills the tank with gas, he records how many miles he has driven. After he has driven 90 miles, he fills the tank. Dean finds that he used 6 gallons of gas to drive 90 miles. He wants to figure out the rate of miles to gallons.

The rate of miles to gallons is 90:6 or $\frac{90}{6}$. Dean reduces the fraction and finds he can drive 15 miles for every one gallon of gas.

$$\frac{90 \text{ miles}}{6 \text{ gallons}} = \frac{90 \div 6}{6 \div 6} = \frac{15 \text{ miles}}{1 \text{ gallon}}$$

Since a ratio is like a fraction, you can find equal ratios the same way you find equal fractions. When you reduce a ratio to lowest terms or raise a ratio to higher terms, you can find equal ratios.

Dean reduces $\frac{90}{6}$ to lowest terms and finds an equal ratio. He writes the ratio as follows:

$$\frac{90 \text{ miles}}{6 \text{ gallons}} = \frac{15 \text{ miles}}{1 \text{ gallon}}$$

When two ratios are written as equal ratios, the equation is called a **proportion.**

Dean checks to make sure the ratios in his proportion are equal by **cross-multiplying.** He multiplies the top number of the first ratio by the bottom number of the second ratio. Then he multiplies the top number of the second ratio by the bottom number of the first ratio. If the two answers are equal, the ratios are equal.

$\frac{90}{6} \diagdown\diagup \frac{15}{1}$ $90 \times 1 = 90$ Both answers are the same,
$$$6 \times 15 = 90$ 90, so the ratios are equal.

In the following example, an equal ratio is found by raising a ratio to higher terms.

Ned is making bread. The recipe calls for 1 cup of sugar and 6 cups of flour. The ratio of sugar to flour can be written 1:6 or $\frac{1}{6}$. Ned wants to double the recipe. He is going to make a larger amount of bread dough, but he needs the amount of sugar and flour to have the same ratio as before. So he multiplies both ingredients by 2. As long as he multiplies each amount by the same number, the ratios will be equal.

$$\frac{1}{6} = \frac{1 \times 2}{6 \times 2} = \frac{2}{12}$$

When he doubles the recipe, he needs 2 cups of sugar for every 12 cups of flour.

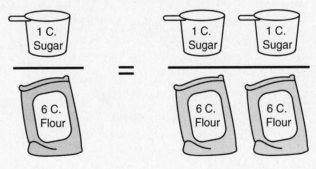

$\frac{1}{6} = \frac{2}{12}$ is a proportion.

Ned checks to make sure the ratios are equal by cross-multiplying.

$\frac{1}{6} \diagdown\diagup \frac{2}{12}$ $1 \times 12 = 12$ The ratios are equal.
$$$6 \times 2 = 12$

Sale Prices

Matt works in a hardware store. One morning, Jack Prow, Matt's boss, gives Matt a list of a few items to put on sale.

*** PROW'S PAINT AND HARDWARE ***

Sale Prices

2-inch brushes   4 for $12.00

masking tape   2 rolls for $4.98

latex paint   3 quarts for $14.40

A few hours later Ms. Okano, an art teacher, calls the store. She wants to buy supplies for her students. Ms. Okano tells Matt she needs ten 2-inch brushes. Matt knows that the sale price of 4 brushes is $12. He needs to figure out how much 10 brushes would cost at the same rate.

First, Matt writes a ratio to compare the number of brushes, 4, to the sale price, $12. Which is the correct ratio to compare the number of brushes to the sale price?

(1) $\frac{4}{\$12}$

(2) $\frac{2}{\$12}$

(3) $\frac{\$12}{4}$

(4) $\frac{\$12}{2}$

(5) $\frac{4}{2}$

Answer 1 is the correct choice. Matt wants to compare 4 brushes to $12. The first amount, 4, is written on top. The second amount, $12, is written on the bottom. The ratio means that every group of 4 brushes costs $12.

Next, Matt writes a second ratio to compare the number of brushes Ms. Okano is buying to the price of those brushes. He knows Ms. Okano wants to buy 10 brushes. He needs to find the price of 10 brushes. He writes a question mark in the ratio to represent the price of 10 brushes.

Which is the correct ratio to compare 10 brushes to the unknown price?

(1) $\frac{?}{10}$

(2) $\frac{10}{?}$

(3) $\frac{4}{?}$

(4) $\frac{?}{4}$

(5) $\frac{?}{\$12}$

Answer 2 is the correct choice. He wants to compare the number of brushes, 10, to their price, which is not known. As in the first ratio, the number of brushes is the top number and the price is the bottom number.

To solve for the unknown amount, Matt sets up a proportion. Which is the correct proportion to find the price of the 10 brushes?

(1) $\frac{4}{\$10} = \frac{12}{?}$

(2) $\frac{10}{\$12} = \frac{?}{4}$

(3) $\frac{\$12}{4} = \frac{10}{?}$

(4) $\frac{4}{\$12} = \frac{10}{?}$

(5) $\frac{\$12}{10} = \frac{4}{?}$

Answer 4 is the correct choice. The first ratio, $\frac{4}{\$12}$, means that 4 brushes cost \$12. The second ratio, $\frac{10}{?}$, is in the same order as the first ratio. In both ratios, the number of brushes is the top number and the price is the bottom number. The equal ratios make a proportion.

$$\frac{4 \text{ brushes}}{\$12 \text{ price}} = \frac{10 \text{ brushes}}{? \text{ price}}$$

Matt is ready to solve the problem. He cross-multiplies \$12 and 10. Then he divides \$120 by 4 to find the price of 10 brushes.

Set up proportion. Cross-multiply. Divide.

$$\frac{4}{\$12} \diagdown\!\!\!\!\diagup \frac{10}{?} \qquad \$12 \times 10 = \$120 \qquad \begin{array}{r} \$\ 30 \\ 4\overline{)\$120} \\ -12 \\ \hline 00 \end{array}$$

Based on the sale price of 4 brushes for \$12, 10 brushes will cost \$30.

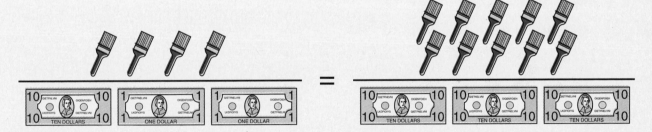

Matt checks his work by cross-multiplying.

$$\frac{4}{\$12} \diagdown\!\!\!\!\diagup \frac{10}{\$30} \qquad \begin{array}{l} 4 \times \$30 = \$120 \\ \$12 \times\ \ 10 = \$120 \end{array}$$

Since the results are the same, Matt knows his answer is correct.

Practice ◼ Circle the best answer for each item.

Items 1–3 refer to the following ad.

OFFICE SUPPLY WAREHOUSE		
Bond Paper	10 reams for	$22.50
Steno Pads	12 for	$3.96
Correction Fluid (0.75 oz.)	3 bottles for	$2.49

1. Cindy bought 6 reams of paper. Which is the correct expression to find the price of 6 reams of paper?

   (1) $\frac{6}{10} = \frac{\$22.50}{?}$

   (2) $\frac{6}{\$22.50} = \frac{10}{?}$

   (3) $\frac{10}{\$22.50} = \frac{6}{?}$

   (4) $\frac{10}{\$22.50} = \frac{?}{6}$

   (5) $\frac{\$22.50}{10} = \frac{6}{?}$

2. Cindy also bought 18 steno pads. Which is the correct expression to find the price of 18 steno pads?

   (1) $\frac{12}{2} = \frac{\$3.96}{?}$

   (2) $\frac{12}{18} = \frac{?}{\$3.96}$

   (3) $\frac{12}{\$3.96} = \frac{2}{?}$

   (4) $\frac{12}{\$3.96} = \frac{18}{?}$

   (5) $\frac{18}{\$3.96} = \frac{12}{?}$

3. Cindy also bought 4 bottles of correction fluid. Which is the correct expression to find the price of 4 bottles of correction fluid?

   (1) $\frac{0.75}{3} = \frac{?}{\$2.49}$

   (2) $\frac{0.75}{4} = \frac{\$2.49}{?}$

   (3) $\frac{0.75}{\$2.49} = \frac{4}{?}$

   (4) $\frac{3}{4} = \frac{?}{\$2.49}$

   (5) $\frac{3}{\$2.49} = \frac{4}{?}$

Items 4–6 refer to the following ad.

GREEN'S PRODUCE		
Lettuce	2 heads for	$1.28
Potatoes	5 pounds for	$3.15
Carrots	3 bags for	$1.22

4. Marvin needs 5 heads of lettuce to make a salad. Which is the correct expression to find the price of 5 heads of lettuce?

   (1) $\frac{2}{5} = \frac{?}{\$1.28}$

   (2) $\frac{2}{\$1.28} = \frac{5}{?}$

   (3) $\frac{2}{\$1.28} = \frac{?}{5}$

   (4) $\frac{5}{2} = \frac{\$1.28}{?}$

   (5) $\frac{5}{\$1.28} = \frac{2}{?}$

5. Marshall needs 2 bags of carrots for a stew. Which is the correct expression to find the price of 2 bags of carrots?

   (1) $\frac{2}{3} = \frac{\$1.22}{?}$

   (2) $\frac{2}{\$1.22} = \frac{3}{?}$

   (3) $\frac{3}{2} = \frac{?}{\$1.22}$

   (4) $\frac{3}{\$1.22} = \frac{2}{?}$

   (5) $\frac{3}{\$1.22} = \frac{?}{2}$

6. Vernon spent $4.41 on potatoes. Which is the correct expression to find the number of pounds of potatoes Vernon bought?

   (1) $\frac{\$3.15}{\$4.41} = \frac{?}{5}$

   (2) $\frac{5}{\$3.15} = \frac{?}{\$4.41}$

   (3) $\frac{5}{\$3.15} = \frac{\$4.41}{?}$

   (4) $\frac{5}{\$4.41} = \frac{?}{\$3.15}$

   (5) $\frac{5}{\$4.41} = \frac{\$3.15}{?}$

Check your answers on page 290.

Working with Ratios

Follow these guidelines when working with ratios:

■ Always write the quantities in a ratio in the same order they appear in the problem. Label unlike quantities (amounts with different units of measurement).

Example

the ratio of 4 inches to 3 inches $\frac{4}{3}$

the ratio of 2 gallons of paint to 400 square feet $\frac{2 \text{ gal.}}{400 \text{ sq. ft.}}$

the ratio of 2 pounds of apples to $1.50 $\frac{2 \text{ lb.}}{\$1.50}$

■ Reduce ratios to lowest terms the same way you reduce fractions. Divide the top number and the bottom number by the same number. The ratio is in lowest terms when no number except 1 will divide both numbers evenly.

Example

Clyde worked 8 hours on Thursday and 10 hours on Friday. What is the ratio of hours worked on Thursday to hours worked on Friday?

$$\frac{8}{10} = \frac{8 \div 2}{10 \div 2} = \frac{4}{5}$$

■ When a ratio is an improper fraction, do *not* change it to a mixed number or a whole number.

Example

Nancy earned $100 for 10 hours of work. What is the ratio of her earnings to the hours she worked?

$$\frac{\$100}{10 \text{ hr.}} = \frac{\$100 \div 10}{10 \div 10} = \frac{\$10}{1 \text{ hour}}$$

The fraction $\frac{10}{1}$ equals the whole number 10, but do not change the ratio $\frac{\$10}{1 \text{ hr.}}$ to a whole number.

Practice ■ Write each ratio in lowest terms.

1. It rained 9 days out of 31 days last month. What is the ratio of rainy days to total days in the month?

$$\frac{9 \text{ rainy days}}{31 \text{ days in the month}}$$

$$\frac{9}{31}$$

2. Mary's softball team won 12 games out of 18 games played. What is the ratio of games won to games played?

3. Midtown Motors sold 35 cars and 14 vans last week. What is the ratio of cars sold to vans sold?

5. Today 15 of Ramona's customers paid with cash and 25 customers used a credit card. What is the ratio of cash customers to charge customers?

_____

4. Anwar drove 230 miles on 10 gallons of gas. What is the ratio of miles to gallons?

_____

6. Kara earned $42 for 7 hours of work. What is the ratio of her earnings to the hours she worked?

_____

_____

Computation | **Solving Proportions**

A **proportion** is an equation containing two equal ratios. The numbers in the proportion are called **terms**. A proportion has four terms. Sometimes one of the terms is not known. If you know three of the four terms, you can solve for the unknown term.

Example

Find the value of the unknown term: $\frac{10}{2} = \frac{?}{5}$

Follow these steps to solve the proportion.

Step 1. Cross-multiply the two numbers you know.

$\frac{10}{2} \searrow \frac{?}{5}$ $10 \times 5 = 50$

Step 2. Divide the result by the remaining number. The answer, 25, is the unknown number.

$50 \div 2 = 25$

Step 3. Check your answer by cross-multiplying. If the results are the same, you know your answer is correct.

$\frac{10}{2} \times \frac{25}{5}$ $10 \times 5 = 50$
$2 \times 25 = 50$

When you divide, if the numbers do not divide evenly, write the remainder as a fraction.

Example

Find the value of the unknown term: $\frac{3}{4} = \frac{?}{6}$

Cross-multiply the two numbers you know. Divide the result by the remaining number. Write the remainder as the numerator of the fraction. Reduce to lowest terms. Check by cross-multiplying.

$3 \times 6 = 18$

$$4\overline{)18} \quad \begin{array}{c} 4\frac{2}{4} = 4\frac{1}{2} \\ \end{array}$$
$$\underline{-16}$$
$$2$$

$$\frac{3}{4} \diagtimes \frac{4\frac{1}{2}}{6}$$

$3 \times 6 = 18$

$4 \times 4\frac{1}{2} = \frac{\overset{2}{\cancel{4}}}{1} \times \frac{9}{\underset{1}{\cancel{2}}} = \frac{18}{1} = 18$

Practice ◤ Solve each proportion. Show your work.

1. $\frac{3}{4} = \frac{?}{12}$ $\frac{3}{4} = \frac{9}{12}$

$3 \times 12 = 36$
$36 \div 4 = 9$

2. $\frac{4}{?} = \frac{12}{18}$

3. $\frac{30}{18} = \frac{10}{?}$

4. $\frac{7}{14} = \frac{?}{4}$

5. $\frac{20}{?} = \frac{4}{11}$

6. $\frac{?}{30} = \frac{10}{12}$

7. $\frac{?}{42} = \frac{10}{12}$

8. $\frac{5}{24} = \frac{4}{?}$

9. $\frac{5}{8} = \frac{?}{40}$

10. $\frac{15}{?} = \frac{9}{10}$

Section 10: Ratio and Proportion   151

Data Analysis

Problem-Solving Strategy: Using a Pictograph

Brad works at an airport. He is in charge of the airport parking lots. His boss, Juanita, is reviewing the number of parking spaces in the different lots at the airport. She is gathering information to decide whether more or fewer spaces are needed.

The airport has four different lots. Lot A has rows of parking meters. Lot B is the short-term parking lot, and Lot C is the long-term lot. Lot D is the economy lot.

Juanita gives Brad a pictograph and asks him to find the answers to these questions:

- How many spaces are available in the largest lot?

- How many more spaces are there in Lot D than in Lot A?

- What is the ratio of spaces in Lot C to spaces in Lot B?

Brad uses the following pictograph to answer the questions.

Airport Parking Spaces

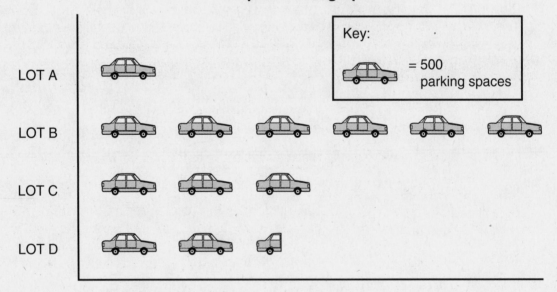

A **pictograph** is like a bar graph. Instead of bars, the amounts on the graph are shown with pictures or **symbols**. A key shows you the value of each symbol. In this pictograph, each car symbol has a value of 500 parking spaces. In the row labeled *Lot D*, there are $2\frac{1}{2}$ symbols. The half symbol has a value of $\frac{1}{2}$ of 500, or 250.

$$\frac{1}{\overset{1}{\cancel{2}}} \times \frac{\overset{250}{\cancel{500}}}{2} = \frac{250}{1} = 250$$

A long row of symbols has a greater value than a short row. To find the value of a row of symbols, multiply the number of symbols in the row by the value of one symbol.

Brad uses the pictograph to find the answers to the questions for his boss.

■ How many spaces are available in the largest lot? The longest row on the graph is labeled *Lot B,* so it is the largest lot. There are 6 car symbols in the row. Multiply 500 by 6 to find the number of parking spaces in Lot B. There are 3,000 parking spaces in Lot B, the largest lot.

$$\begin{array}{r} 500 \\ \times\ 6 \\ \hline 3{,}000 \end{array} \text{ spaces}$$

■ How many more spaces are there in Lot D than in Lot A? There are two ways to find the answer to this question. Brad could figure out the number of spaces in each lot and then find the difference between the amounts. If he uses this method, he will have to multiply twice and then subtract.

Lot A:
$$\begin{array}{r} 500 \\ \times\ 1 \\ \hline 500 \end{array}$$

Lot D: $500 \times 2\frac{1}{2} =$

$$\frac{\overset{250}{\cancel{500}}}{1} \times \frac{5}{\underset{1}{\cancel{2}}} = \frac{1250}{1} = 1{,}250$$

Subtract:
$$\begin{array}{r} 1{,}250 \\ -\ 500 \\ \hline 750 \end{array}$$

An easier way to find the difference is to compare the two rows on the pictograph. The row labeled *Lot D* has $2\frac{1}{2}$ car symbols. The row labeled *Lot A* has only 1 symbol. Since $2\frac{1}{2} - 1 = 1\frac{1}{2}$, the difference between the two lots is represented by $1\frac{1}{2}$ symbols. Brad multiplies 500 by $1\frac{1}{2}$ to find the difference.

$$500 \times 1\frac{1}{2} = \frac{\overset{250}{\cancel{500}}}{1} \times \frac{3}{\underset{1}{\cancel{2}}} = \frac{750}{1} = 750$$

There are 750 more parking spaces in Lot D than in Lot A.

■ What is the ratio of the spaces in Lot C to the spaces in Lot B?

To write the ratio, Brad looks at the rows labeled *Lot C* and *Lot B*. He doesn't need to find the values of the rows. The easiest way to find the ratio is to put the number of Lot C symbols, 3, over the number of Lot B symbols, 6.

He writes the ratio and reduces it to lowest terms. The ratio of the spaces in Lot C to the spaces in Lot B is 1:2. In other words, for every 1 space in Lot C there are 2 spaces in Lot B.

$$\frac{3}{6} = \frac{3 \div 3}{6 \div 3} = \frac{1}{2}$$

Practice ◢ Circle the best answer for each item.

Items 1–6 refer to the following graph.

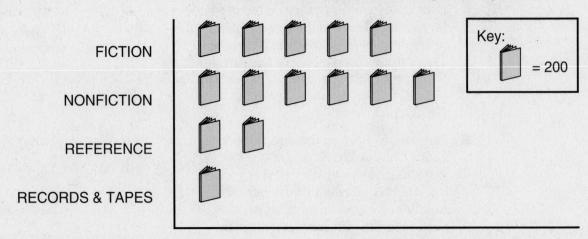

Materials Checked Out of City Library, 9/12

FICTION

NONFICTION

REFERENCE

RECORDS & TAPES

Key: = 200

1. How many nonfiction books were checked out of the library?

   (1)   200
   (2)   600
   (3)   800
   (4)   1,000
   (5)   1,200

2. How many items from the smallest category were checked out of the library?

   (1)   100
   (2)   200
   (3)   400
   (4)   1,200
   (5)   2,000

3. How many more fiction books than reference materials were checked out of the library?

   (1)   3
   (2)   7
   (3)   300
   (4)   600
   (5)   700

4. What is the total number of nonfiction and reference materials checked out of the library?

   (1)   8
   (2)   16
   (3)   400
   (4)   800
   (5)   1,600

5. In lowest terms, what is the ratio of nonfiction books to fiction books checked out of the library?

   (1) $\frac{1}{2}$

   (2) $\frac{5}{6}$

   (3) $1\frac{1}{5}$

   (4) $\frac{6}{5}$

   (5) $\frac{1,200}{1,000}$

6. In lowest terms, what is the ratio of records and tapes to all materials checked out of the library?

   (1) $\frac{1}{13}$

   (2) $\frac{1}{14}$

   (3) $\frac{13}{1}$

   (4) $\frac{13}{14}$

   (5) $\frac{14}{1}$

■ Write your answers in the blanks. Show your work.

Items 7–12 refer to the following graph.

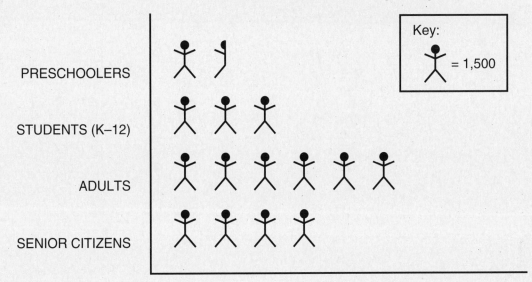

State Fair Attendance, Opening Day

PRESCHOOLERS

STUDENTS (K–12)

ADULTS

SENIOR CITIZENS

Key:

= 1,500

7. How many students in grades K–12 attended the fair on opening day?

_____

8. How many people from the largest category attended the fair?

_____

9. How many more senior citizens than preschoolers attended the fair on opening day?

_____

10. What was the total attendance on opening day?

_____

11. In lowest terms, what is the ratio of adults to students?

_____

12. In lowest terms, what is the ratio of senior citizens to all people attending on opening day?

_____

Check your answers on pages 290–291.

Using a Map Scale

Problem-Solving Strategy: Reading a Scale

Nicole is planning a trip. She plans to drive east from Lake City to Mt. Vernon. Then she will drive south from Mt. Vernon to Hartford. She wants to figure out the total number of miles she will travel.

She has the following map showing the cities and main roads in the area.

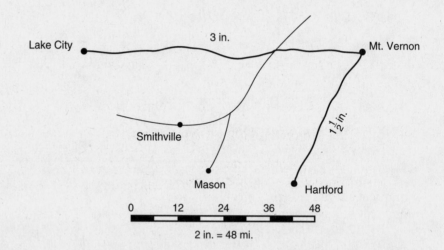

The map has a **scale** that shows you how to figure out distances. The scale shows the ratio of inches on the map to miles of actual distance. On Nicole's map, 2 inches equal 48 miles of actual distance.

First, Nicole figures out the distance from Lake City to Mt. Vernon. She uses a ruler to measure the distance on the map. Although the road does not exactly follow a straight line, she can see that the road on the map measures about 3 inches. She needs to find how many miles 3 inches represents.

Nicole can use a proportion to solve the problem. First she writes a ratio using the information from the map scale. She needs to compare the distance on the map to the actual distance. She writes $\frac{2 \text{ in.}}{48 \text{ mi.}}$.

Then she writes a second ratio to solve for the unknown number. She knows that the distance on the map between the cities is 3 inches. She does not know the actual distance. She writes the ratio $\frac{3 \text{ in.}}{? \text{ mi.}}$.

Using the two ratios, Nicole writes a proportion.

$$\frac{2 \text{ in.}}{48 \text{ mi.}} = \frac{3 \text{ in.}}{? \text{ mi.}}$$

What is the actual distance in miles from Lake City to Mt. Vernon?

(1) 56
(2) 68
(3) 72
(4) 78
(5) 94

Answer 3 is the correct choice. Nicole uses the proportion to solve for the unknown. She cross-multiplies 48 by 3. Then she divides by 2, the remaining number.

Set up proportion.	Cross-multiply.	Divide.
$\dfrac{2 \text{ in.}}{48 \text{ mi.}} = \dfrac{3 \text{ in.}}{? \text{ mi.}}$	$48 \times 3 = 144$	$144 \div 2 = 72 \text{ miles}$

Nicole cross-multiplies to check her work.

$$\frac{2 \text{ in.}}{48 \text{ mi.}} \diagdown\!\!\!\!\diagup \frac{3 \text{ in.}}{72 \text{ mi.}} \qquad \begin{array}{l} 2 \times 72 = 144 \\ 48 \times 3 = 144 \end{array} \qquad \begin{array}{l} \text{The distance from Lake City} \\ \text{to Mt. Vernon is 72 miles.} \end{array}$$

Now she needs to find the distance from Mt. Vernon to Hartford. She uses a ruler and finds that the cities are $1\frac{1}{2}$ inches apart on the map. Nicole has all the information she needs to set up a proportion and solve for the unknown. What is the actual distance in miles from Mt. Vernon to Hartford?

(1) 12
(2) 24
(3) 25
(4) 36
(5) 48

Answer 4 is the correct choice. Nicole sets up the proportion:

$$\frac{2 \text{ in.}}{48 \text{ mi.}} = \frac{1\frac{1}{2} \text{ in.}}{? \text{ mi.}}$$

To solve the proportion, she cross-multiplies and divides.

Set up proportion.	Cross-multiply.	Divide.
$\dfrac{2 \text{ in.}}{48 \text{ mi.}} = \dfrac{1\frac{1}{2} \text{ in.}}{? \text{ mi.}}$	$48 \times 1\frac{1}{2} = \dfrac{48}{1} \times \dfrac{3}{2} = \dfrac{\overset{24}{\cancel{48}}}{1} \times \dfrac{3}{\underset{1}{\cancel{2}}} = \dfrac{72}{1} = 72$	$72 \div 2 = 36 \text{ miles}$

Nicole cross-multiplies to check her work.

$$\frac{2 \text{ in.}}{48 \text{ mi.}} \diagdown\!\!\!\!\diagup \frac{1\frac{1}{2} \text{ in.}}{? \text{ mi.}} \qquad \begin{array}{l} 2 \times 36 = 72 \\ 48 \times 1\frac{1}{2} = 72 \end{array} \qquad \begin{array}{l} \text{The correct distance is} \\ \text{36 miles.} \end{array}$$

Finally, she adds the two distances to find the total miles from Lake City to Hartford. Her entire trip will cover 108 miles.

$$\begin{array}{r} 72 \\ + 36 \\ \hline 108 \text{ miles} \end{array}$$

Practice ■ Circle the best answer for each item.

<u>Items 1– 3</u> refer to the following map.

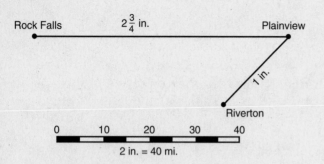

1. What is the actual distance from Riverton to Plainview in miles?

   (1)   1
   (2)   10
   (3)   20
   (4)   40
   (5)   80

2. What is the actual distance from Plainview to Rock Falls in miles?

   (1)   50
   (2)   55
   (3)   60
   (4) 110
   (5) 220

3. Hillsdale is 60 miles north of Plainview. If Hillsdale were shown on this map, how many inches north of Plainview would it be?

   (1) $1\frac{1}{3}$
   (2) $1\frac{1}{2}$
   (3)   3
   (4)   6
   (5) 60

■ Write your answers in the blanks. Show your work.

<u>Items 4 – 6</u> refer to the following map.

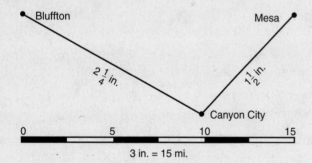

4. What is the actual distance from Mesa to Canyon City in miles?

_____

5. What is the actual distance from Bluffton to Canyon City in miles?

_____

6. Eagle Rock is 35 miles south of Mesa. If Eagle Rock were shown on this map, how many inches south of Mesa would it be?

_____

Using Your Math Skills

Write each ratio in lowest terms.

1. At Quality Products, 20 employees work in the office and 28 work in the warehouse. What is the ratio of employees who work in the office to employees who work in the warehouse?

_____

2. During a football game, the Bears scored 36 points. Of the total points, 15 were scored by kicking field goals. What is the ratio of points scored with field goals to total points scored?

_____

Solve each proportion. Show your work.

3. $\frac{6}{7} = \frac{?}{42}$

4. $\frac{12}{8} = \frac{30}{?}$

5. $\frac{?}{77} = \frac{5}{11}$

6. $\frac{10}{?} = \frac{16}{40}$

Circle the best answer for each item.

<u>Item 7</u> refers to the following ad.

CRAFTER'S WORLD		
Fabric paints	5 bottles for	$2.25
Plastic canvas	3 sheets for	$0.99
Yarn, 4 oz.	2 skeins for	$2.86

7. Eva needs 5 sheets of plastic canvas to make holiday decorations. What is the price of the plastic canvas she needs?

(1) $0.33
(2) $0.60
(3) $0.99
(4) $1.65
(5) $4.95

Check your answers on page 291.

Use proportions to solve the problems. Write your answers in the blanks. Show your work.

8. Andre drove 106 miles in 2 hours. If he can continue this speed, how far can he drive in 5 hours?

   _____

9. Michela is planning to paint her house. The color she wants requires 3 parts blue to 4 parts gray paint. How many gallons of blue paint does she need to mix with 10 gallons of gray paint?

   _____

10. Of every 400 parts Tri-State Assembly makes, an average of 3 parts are defective. On Monday, Tri-State Assembly made 1,600 parts. How many of these parts are likely to be defective?

    _____

11. At Pioneer Insurance, 5 out of 9 employees are female. Pioneer Insurance employs 432 people. How many females work at Pioneer Insurance?

    _____

12. It takes Manuel 2 hours to mat and frame 5 pictures. How long will it take him to mat and frame 16 pictures?

    _____

13. Darius drove 300 miles on 12 gallons of gas. His tank holds 16 gallons. How far could Darius drive on a full tank of gas?

    _____

14. Elena is a caterer. She uses 3 cups of ground coffee to serve 16 people. How many cups of ground coffee should she use to serve 80 people?

    _____

15. During a 40-hour week, Toya earns $240 in her job as a receptionist. This week she worked only 35 hours. How much did she earn?

    _____

Check your answers on page 291.

Items 16–18 refer to the following map.

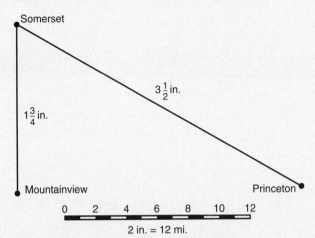

Somerset

$3\frac{1}{2}$ in.

$1\frac{3}{4}$ in.

Mountainview   Princeton

0   2   4   6   8   10   12

2 in. = 12 mi.

16. What is the actual distance from Mountainview to Somerset in miles?

_____

17. What is the actual distance from Somerset to Princeton in miles?

_____

18. Pine Ridge is 30 miles north of Somerset. If Pine Ridge were shown on this map, how many inches north of Somerset would it be?

_____

Circle the best answer for each item.

Items 19 – 21 refer to the following graph.

Record Mart Sales, 11/21
Tapes and Compact Discs

COUNTRY   ⊙ ⊙ ⊙ ⊙ ⊙

JAZZ   ⊙ ⊙ ⊙

ROCK   ⊙ ⊙ ⊙ ⊙ ⊙ ⊙

OTHER   ⊙ ⊙

Key:
⊙ = 20

19. How many tapes and compact discs were sold in the largest category?

(1)   6
(2)   20
(3)   60
(4)   80
(5)   120

20. How many more country than jazz tapes and compact discs were sold?

(1)   2
(2)   8
(3)   40
(4)   100
(5)   160

21. How many tapes and compact discs were sold in all?

(1)   16
(2)   20
(3)   160
(4)   300
(5)   310

Check your answers on pages 291–292.

Section 11

Percent Theory

The Meaning of Percent

Lana, a clerk in a store, is selling a car stereo for $100. The customer wants to make a down payment and pay the rest of the money later. Lana tells the customer that he must make a 25% down payment. She figures out that 25% of $100 is $25.

Percent is another way to show part of a whole. The sign for percent is %. *Percent* means "for every 100" or "out of 100."

In the example above, the whole cost of the stereo can be thought of as 100%. The part the customer will pay as a down payment is 25% of the whole amount. Since 25% means "25 for every 100," the customer needs to pay $25 down for every $100 of cost.

The figure below is divided into 100 equal parts. Twenty-five of the parts are shaded. Since 25 out of 100 parts are shaded, the shaded portion is 25% of the whole figure.

You can also describe the shaded portion with a fraction or a decimal. To write the fraction, write the number of shaded parts over the total number of parts. Then reduce the fraction to lowest terms. The fraction $\frac{25}{100}$ reduces to $\frac{1}{4}$.

$$\frac{\text{the number of shaded parts}}{\text{the total number of parts}} = \frac{25}{100} = \frac{25 \div 25}{100 \div 25} = \frac{1}{4}$$

You can also write the fraction $\frac{25}{100}$ as the decimal 0.25. Both are read "twenty-five hundredths."

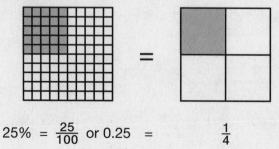

$$25\% = \frac{25}{100} \text{ or } 0.25 = \frac{1}{4}$$

You can write any percent as a decimal or fraction. Percents, fractions, and decimals are different ways to show part of a whole. When the customer gave Lana the $25 down payment, he was paying 25%, 0.25, or $\frac{1}{4}$ of $100, the total cost of the stereo.

Practice ◆ Write a fraction, a decimal, and a percent to describe the shaded portion of each figure.

1. Fraction $\frac{1}{2}$

   Decimal   0.50

   Percent   50%

4. Fraction   _____

   Decimal   _____

   Percent   _____

2. Fraction   _____

   Decimal   _____

   Percent   _____

5. Fraction   _____

   Decimal   _____

   Percent   _____

3. Fraction   _____

   Decimal   _____

   Percent   _____

6. Fraction   _____

   Decimal   _____

   Percent   _____

Percents, Fractions, and Decimals

Percents, fractions, and decimals are used in different situations.

■ Fractions are used mostly when you are making measurements.

■ Decimals are used when you are working with money or the metric system.

■ Percents are used in many business and everyday situations. Taxes, sale prices, and interest on loans are common uses of percents.

To solve a percent problem, you have to change the percent to a fraction or a decimal before you can do the work. At other times, you need to change a fraction or a decimal to a percent.

Check your answers on page 292.

Changing Percents to Decimals

To change a percent to a decimal, follow these steps.

Step 1. Drop the percent sign (%).

Step 2. Move the decimal point two places to the left. Add a zero as a place holder if necessary. If a percent does not have a decimal point, it is understood to have one to the right of the ones place.

Example

		Drop the %.		Move the decimal point.		
15%	=	15	=	.15.	=	0.15
8%	=	8	=	.08.	=	0.08
150%	=	150	=	1.50.	=	1.5

Example

Some percents contain a fractional part.

Change $5\frac{3}{4}\%$ to a decimal.

To change a fractional percent to a decimal, first change the fraction to a decimal. Divide the top number (numerator) by the bottom number (denominator).

```
  0.75
4) 3.00
 - 2 8
    20
  - 20
     0
```

	Change the fraction to a decimal.		Drop the %.		Move the decimal point.	
$5\frac{3}{4}\%$ =	5.75%	=	5.75	=	0.05.75	= 0.0575

Changing Decimals to Percents

To change a decimal to a percent, follow these steps.

Step 1. Move the decimal point two places to the right.

Step 2. Write the percent sign after the number.

You don't need to show the decimal point as part of a percent unless the percent has a decimal part. Once you move the decimal point, drop any zeros you no longer need.

Example

		Move the decimal point.		Write the percent sign.	
1.40	=	1.40.	=	140%	← Don't show the decimal point.
0.03	=	0.03.	=	3%	← Drop the place holder zeros.
0.875	=	0.87.5	=	87.5%	← Keep the decimal point.

Changing Percents to Fractions

Follow these steps to change a percent to a fraction.

Step 1. Drop the percent sign and write the number as a fraction with a denominator of 100.

Step 2. Reduce the fraction to lowest terms.

Example

		Drop the %.		Write a fraction.		Reduce the fraction.		
75%	=	75	=	$\frac{75}{100}$	=	$\frac{75 \div 25}{100 \div 25}$	=	$\frac{3}{4}$
60%	=	60	=	$\frac{60}{100}$	=	$\frac{60 \div 20}{100 \div 20}$	=	$\frac{3}{5}$
70%	=	70	=	$\frac{70}{100}$	=	$\frac{70 \div 10}{100 \div 10}$	=	$\frac{7}{10}$

Changing Fractions to Percents

Follow these steps to change a fraction to a percent.

Step 1. Change the fraction to a decimal.

Step 2. Change the decimal to a percent.

To change a fraction to a decimal, divide the numerator by the denominator. Think of the line between the top and bottom numbers in a fraction as a division symbol. The fraction $\frac{1}{2}$ means "1 divided by 2."

Example

Change $\frac{1}{8}$ to a percent.

First change $\frac{1}{8}$ to a decimal using division.

Divide: $1 \div 8 = 0.125$.

Now change 0.125 to a percent. Move the decimal point two places to the right, and write the % sign.

$$\begin{array}{r} 0.125 \\ 8\overline{)1.000} \\ -8 \\ \hline 20 \\ -16 \\ \hline 40 \\ -40 \\ \hline 0 \end{array}$$

Fraction		Decimal				Percent
$\frac{1}{8}$	=	0.125	=	0.12.5	=	12.5%

The fractions $\frac{1}{3}$ and $\frac{2}{3}$ appear often in problems. When you divide to convert these fractions to decimals, the division will not work out evenly. You will always have a remainder. It is a good idea to memorize the decimal and percent conversions of these common fractions.

Fraction		Decimal		Percent
$\frac{1}{3}$	=	$0.33\frac{1}{3}$	=	$33\frac{1}{3}\%$
$\frac{2}{3}$	=	$0.66\frac{2}{3}$	=	$66\frac{2}{3}\%$

Using Your Math Skills

Change each percent to a decimal.

1. 37%

   _____

2. 4%

   _____

3. 225%

   _____

4. $6\frac{1}{2}\%$

   _____

Change each decimal to a percent.

5. 0.46

   _____

6. 0.08

   _____

7. 2.5

   _____

8. 0.375

   _____

Change each percent to a fraction.

9. 50%

   _____

10. 40%

    _____

11. 25%

    _____

12. 90%

    _____

Change each fraction to a percent.

13. $\frac{7}{10}$

    _____

14. $\frac{3}{4}$

    _____

15. $\frac{4}{5}$

    _____

16. $\frac{7}{8}$

    _____

Check your answers on page 292.

Section 12

Solving for the Part (p)

The Percent Formula

Every percent problem has three elements: the base, the rate, and the part.

Example

Chris earns $240 a week as a receptionist. Each week he puts $9.60 or 4% of his earnings into a savings account.

- The **base,** $240, is the whole amount. The base represents 100%.

- The **rate,** 4%, is easy to find because it is always followed by the percent sign, %, or the word *percent.*

- The **part,** $9.60, is part of the whole amount.

You can see the relationship of the three elements in the following formula.

▌ *base* x *rate* = *part*

$240.00 × 4% = $9.60

In percent problems, you will be given two of the elements. The third element will be unknown. To solve a percent problem, first identify the elements that you know. Then solve for the unknown element.

Example

What is 20% of $500?

The base is $500, and the rate is 20%. The part is the unknown element.

What percent of 200 miles is 50 miles?

The base is 200 miles, and the part is 50 miles. The rate is the unknown element.

How much does Sheila earn each week if 10% of her weekly earnings is $30?

The rate is 10%, and the part is $30. The base is the unknown element.

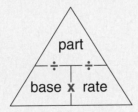

This triangle will help you remember how the three elements of the formula are related. Use the triangle to help you solve percent problems.

Time

Karl makes repairs for a large apartment building. Karl's supervisor, Velma, makes a list of jobs for Karl to do each day. Next to each job, Velma writes a percent showing what part of his total day Karl should spend on that job. In the last column of the list, Karl writes how many hours each job should take based on the percent.

Here is the list of Karl's jobs for today.

Apartment	Job	% of Time	Time in Hours
3B	1. Fix garbage disposal.	20%	
9A	2. Check furnace.	5%	
16B	3. Replace tiles in bathroom.	25%	
4B	4. Unclog bathtub drain.	20%	
18A	5. Install new bathroom sink.	30%	

The percents in the list add up to 100%, or Karl's whole day. You know the percents are rates because they are followed by the percent sign, %.

Karl is scheduled to work 10 hours today. Since 10 hours is the whole amount of time Karl works, 10 hours is the base.

```
  20%
   5%
  25%
  20%
+ 30%
 100%
```

Karl knows the base and rate. To find how many hours Velma wants him to spend on each job, he needs to solve for the part. Karl uses the percent formula to find the time in hours for each job.

 base x rate = part

Karl starts with the first job. Velma expects him to spend 20% of his 10-hour day fixing the garbage disposal in Apartment 3B. He knows the base and the rate. He needs to find the part. Which is the correct expression to find how many hours the job should take?

(1) 20 × 10%
(2) 20 ÷ 10%
(3) 20% ÷ 10
(4) 10 ÷ 20%
(5) 10 × 20%

Answer 5 is the correct choice. Karl multiplies
the base, 10, and the rate, 20%, to find the part.
He changes the rate to a decimal and multiplies.
He should spend 2 hours fixing the garbage disposal.

$$20\% = .20. = 0.2$$

$$\begin{array}{r} 10 \\ \times\ 0.2 \\ \hline 2.0 = 2 \text{ hours} \end{array}$$

Now Karl goes on to the second job on the list. He plans to spend 5% of his
10-hour day checking the furnace in Apartment 9A. Which is the correct
expression to find how many hours the job should take?

(1) $10 \times 5\%$
(2) $10 \div 5\%$
(3) $5\% \div 10$
(4) $5 \times 10\%$
(5) $5 \div 10\%$

Answer 1 is the correct choice.
Karl multiplies the base, 10, and
the rate, 5%, to find the part. He
changes the rate to a decimal and
multiplies. He changes the answer,
0.5, to a fraction. Karl should spend
$\frac{1}{2}$ hour checking the furnace.

$$5\% = .05. = 0.05$$

$$\begin{array}{r} 10 \\ \times\ 0.05 \\ \hline 0.50 = 0.5 \text{ hours} \end{array}$$

$$0.5 = \frac{5}{10} = \frac{5 \div 5}{10 \div 5} = \frac{1}{2} \text{ hour}$$

Karl can solve other problems using the information on the list. For
example, jobs 1, 4, and 5 require plumbing work in the apartments.
Karl wants to figure out how many hours he should spend doing
plumbing work today.

First, he figures out the total percent of his time he should spend on jobs
1, 4, and 5. Which is the correct expression to find the total rate for these
three jobs?

(1) $20\% \times 10$
(2) $20\% \times 20\% \times 30\%$
(3) $20\% + 20\% + 30\%$
(4) $30\% \times 10$
(5) $20\% + 30\% + 10$

Answer 3 is the correct choice. The rate for job 1 is 20%.
The rate for job 4 is also 20%, and the rate for job 5 is 30%.
To find the total rate, Karl adds the three rates. He should
spend 70% of his time doing plumbing work.

$$\begin{array}{r} 20\% \\ 20\% \\ +\ 30\% \\ \hline 70\% \end{array}$$

Now Karl uses the percent formula to figure out
how many hours he should spend on plumbing.
He multiplies the base, 10, by the rate, 70%.
He should spend 7 hours doing plumbing work.

$$70\% = .70. = 0.7$$

$$\begin{array}{r} 10 \\ \times\ 0.7 \\ \hline 7.0 = 7 \text{ hours} \end{array}$$

Practice ■ Circle the best answer for each item.

Items 1–3 refer to the following information.

Joyce works 6 hours a day at a school cafeteria. The list shows what part of her total day she spends at each job.

Job	% of Time
Food preparation	40%
Cashier	25%
Dishwashing	20%
Stockroom	15%

1. Which is the correct expression to find how many hours Joyce spends washing dishes each day?

   (1) $6 \div 20\%$
   (2) $6 \times 20\%$
   (3) $20 \div 6\%$
   (4) $20\% \div 6$
   (5) $20 \times 6\%$

2. Which is the correct expression to find the total rate of time Joyce spends at jobs other than food preparation?

   (1) $6 + 25\% + 20\% + 15\%$
   (2) $6 \times (25\% + 20\% + 15\%)$
   (3) $6 \times 40\%$
   (4) $25\% + 20\% + 15\%$
   (5) $25\% \times 20\% \times 15\%$

3. Which is the correct expression to find how many hours Joyce spends on food preparation and stockroom duties?

   (1) $6 \times (40\% + 15\%)$
   (2) $6 + 40\% + 15\%$
   (3) $6 \times 40\% \times 15\%$
   (4) $6\% \times 40\% \times 15\%$
   (5) $40\% + 15\%$

Items 4–6 refer to the following information.

Manuel works 8 hours a day in an office. The list shows what part of his total day he spends at each job.

Job	% of Time
Data entry	60%
Mail distribution	15%
Filing	5%
Copying and collating	20%

4. Which is the correct expression to find how many hours Manuel spends filing each day?

   (1) $5 \times 8\%$
   (2) $5\% \div 8$
   (3) $8 \times 5\%$
   (4) $8 \div 5\%$
   (5) $8 \times 50\%$

5. Which is the correct expression to find how many hours Manuel spends on data entry and on copying and collating?

   (1) $8 + 60\% + 20\%$
   (2) $60\% + 20\%$
   (3) $8\% \times 60\% \times 20\%$
   (4) $8 + 60\% + 20\%$
   (5) $8 \times (60\% + 20\%)$

6. Which is the correct expression to find how many more hours Manuel spends each day doing data entry than distributing mail?

   (1) $8 \times (60\% + 15\%)$
   (2) $8 \times (60\% - 15\%)$
   (3) $8 \times 60\% \times 15\%$
   (4) $60\% + 15\%$
   (5) $60\% - 15\%$

Check your answers on page 292.

Solving for the Part (*p*)

Example

What is 25% of 800?

You know that 25% is the rate because 25 is followed by the percent sign. The number 800 is the base. The word *of* often comes before the base. Since you know the base and the rate, you can solve for the part.

The percent formula tells you to multiply the base and the rate to find the part.

◣ *base* x *rate* = *part*

Use the percent triangle to help you remember the formula. Cover the letter *p* because you need to solve for the part. The other elements, the base and the rate, are connected by the multiplication sign. You can solve the problem by multiplying the base and the rate.

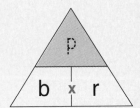

To solve the problem, change the rate to a decimal before you multiply.

Step 1. Drop the percent sign (%).

$$25\% = .25. = 0.25$$

Step 2. Move the decimal point two places to the left.

$$
\begin{array}{r}
800 \longleftarrow \text{base} \\
\times\ 0.25 \longleftarrow \text{rate} \\
\hline
40\ 00 \\
+\ 160\ 0 \\
\end{array}
$$

Step 3. Multiply to solve for the part.

The number 200 is 25% of 800.

$$200.00 \longleftarrow \text{part}$$

Sometimes the rate contains a fraction. Change the fraction to a decimal. Then move the decimal point.

Example

What is $5\frac{1}{2}\%$ of $60?

The rate is $5\frac{1}{2}\%$, and the base is $60. The part is unknown. Multiply the base by the rate to find the part.
Change the fraction to a decimal.
Change the rate to a decimal.

$$5\tfrac{1}{2}\% = 5.5\%$$
$$5.5\% = 0.05.5$$

Multiply.

$$
\begin{array}{r}
\$60 \\
\times\ 0.055 \\
\hline
\$3.300 \\
\end{array}
$$

The amount $3.30 is $5\frac{1}{2}\%$ of $60.

When the rate is greater than 100%, the part will be greater than the base. Change the rate to a decimal as you would with rates less than 100%. For example, 150% becomes 1.5.

Practice ◧ Solve. Show your work.

1. What is 35% of 220? ___77___
   35% = 0.35   220
                 × 0.35
                 ------
                 11 00
               + 66 0

                 77.00

2. What is 40% of $45? _____

3. What is 8% of 16? _____

4. What is 75% of 32? _____

5. What is 300% of $75? _____

6. What is 250% of 48? _____

7. What is $4\frac{1}{2}$% of $50? _____

8. What is $7\frac{1}{4}$% of 144? _____

◧ Write your answers in the blanks. Show your work.

9. Laura bought a pair of jeans that regularly cost $32 for 25% off the regular price. How much did Laura save?

   _____

11. The Jaguars won 80% of the 15 games they played this season. How many games did they win?

    _____

10. Of the 8,000 people at the baseball game, 5% were season ticket holders. How many people at the game were season ticket holders?

    _____

12. Electronic Buys sold 240 items last week. Of the items sold, 45% were kitchen appliances. How many kitchen appliances did Electronic Buys sell last week?

    _____

Simple Interest

Problem-Solving Strategy: Use a Formula

Donna and Gordon Davis want to buy a refrigerator. J & B Appliances has advertised a used refrigerator for $388. They want to pay $100 down on the refrigerator and the rest in monthly payments over two years.

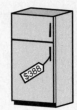

Donna and Gordon want to figure out how much interest they will have to pay on the money they owe. They also want to estimate how much their monthly payments will be. They have budgeted $20 per month for this expense.

Interest is a charge that someone pays to borrow or to use someone else's money. The amount of interest charged is based on the **principal** or amount of money borrowed. An **interest rate** is written as a percent. The interest rate is used to figure out how much interest the borrower has to pay.

Simple interest can be easily found if the original principal does not change.

 The formula for finding the amount of simple interest owed is written $i = p \times r \times t$.

i = the amount of **interest**

p = the **principal**, the amount borrowed

r = the interest **rate**, which is always written as a percent

t = the **time** in years over which the money is borrowed

Donna and Gordon first need to figure out how much they will borrow. The refrigerator costs $388. Donna and Gordon want to pay $100 now. They subtract to figure out how much they will still owe. They will owe $288.

$$\begin{array}{r} \$388 \\ - \ \$100 \\ \hline \$288 \end{array}$$

The amount Donna and Gordon owe, $288, is the principal. They want to pay the money they owe over a 2-year period. The interest rate the store charges is 18%. Donna and Gordon have all the information they need to figure out how much interest they would owe if they were to pay off the loan at the end of 2 years.

Using the simple interest formula, they multiply the principal by the rate and time. To multiply the rate, they first change the percent to a decimal.

$18\% = .18. = 0.18$

$$i = \quad p \quad \times \quad r \quad \times \quad t$$
$$\$288.00 \times 0.18 \times 2$$

$$i = p \times r \times t$$

$288.00 ← principal
×   0.18 ← rate
23 0400
+ 28 800
$51.8400

$51.84
×   2 ← time
$103.68 ← interest

Donna and Gordon will pay $103.68 in interest to borrow the money for two years. Now they need to find the total amount that they will pay back. The **amount paid back** is the total of the principal and the interest.

Donna and Gordon know the principal is $288, and the interest is $103.68. How much will Donna and Gordon have to pay back?

(1) $184.32
(2) $339.84
(3) $391.68
(4) $443.52
(5) $491.68

Answer 3 is the correct choice.
They add the principal and the interest to find the amount paid back.

$288.00 ← principal
+ 103.68 ← interest
$391.68 ← amount paid back

But Donna and Gordon will make monthly payments on the refrigerator. They can estimate the amount of the monthly payments by dividing the total amount to be paid back by the number of months. They need to figure out how many months are in 2 years. Since there are 12 months in 1 year, they multiply 12 by 2 to find the number of months in 2 years.

12
× 2
24 months

To estimate their monthly payment, Donna and Gordon divide the total amount owed, $391.68, into 24 equal payments. They will owe $16.32 per month. Since they had budgeted $20 per month for the refrigerator, they can afford to buy the refrigerator at J & B Appliances.

```
        $  16.32
24 ) $391.68
     – 24
       151
     – 144
        76
      – 72
        48
      – 48
         0
```

NOTE: As each monthly payment is made, the principal or amount owed is reduced by a part of the amount paid. Most banks and stores figure monthly loan payments using a computer that recalculates interest each month as the borrower reduces the amount of principal owed. Borrowers will owe less interest by making monthly payments than if they had paid the total at the end of the time period.

Practice ◤ Find the interest for each loan. Show your work.

1. A loan of $650 for 1 year at 12% interest

3. A loan of $1,240 for 2 years at $8\frac{1}{2}$% interest

_____

2. A loan of $420 for 1 year at 18% interest

4. A loan of $1,600 for 3 years at 14% interest

_____

_____

_____

◤ Find the amount to be paid back for each loan. Show your work.

5. Morris bought a stove for $560. He paid $150 down. He will pay the rest at the end of 2 years at 16% interest.

6. Tanika bought a sofa for $675. She paid $115 down. She will pay the rest at the end of 1 year at $14\frac{1}{2}$% interest.

_____

_____

◤ Estimate the monthly payment for each loan. Show your work.

7. Freddie got a personal loan of $2,100 from a friend. He will pay the money back over 1 year at 12% interest.

8. Gina bought a used car for $4,000. She paid $400 down. She will pay the rest over 2 years at 15% interest.

_____

_____

Reading and Making a Circle Graph

Sonia Velez wants to make a circle graph of the Velez family budget. First, she gathers information about how the family spends its take-home pay. Sonia figures out what percent of the take-home pay goes to rent, food, personal needs, and transportation. Any other expenses are grouped under the category *Other*. She writes the information in a table.

Rent	30%
Food	25%
Personal needs	20%
Transportation	15%
Other	10%

The percents in the table add up to 100% and represent the whole amount of money the family has for expenses.

A circle graph is a good way to compare percents. The whole circle represents 100%. The sections of the circle show parts of the whole. A large section of a circle graph has a greater value than a small section.

$$
\begin{array}{r}
30\% \\
25\% \\
20\% \\
15\% \\
+\ 10\% \\
\hline
100\%
\end{array}
$$

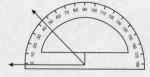

The sections of a circle graph are formed with **central angles.** A central angle is formed when two lines connect at the center point of a circle. Angles are measured in degrees using a protractor. The angle shown has a measure of 45 degrees, 45°.

To make a circle graph, Sonia first draws a circle. The circle represents 100% or the whole amount the family has for expenses. Sonia is ready to put the first section on the graph.

A circle has 360°. The section for rent is 30% of the whole circle. Sonia must find out how many degrees are in the angle representing 30% of the circle.

She uses the percent formula to solve the problem. The base or whole amount is 360°, the number of degrees in a circle. The rate is 30%. Sonia finds the part. She uses the formula *base × rate = part*.

base × rate = part
360° × 30% = ?

Change the percent to a decimal.
30% = .30. = 0.3

Multiply: 360
           × 0.3
           108.0 degrees

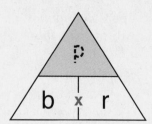

Sonia draws an angle that measures 108°. She draws a line from the center of the circle to the top of the circle. Then she uses a protractor to measure 108°. She completes the angle and writes the label *Rent 30%.*

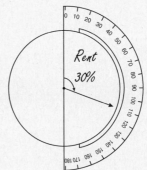

Next Sonia draws the section representing the family's food expenses. The rate shown on the table for food is 25%. The base is still 360°. Sonia multiplies the base and the rate to find the measure of the angle that will represent the family's food expenses.

Change the percent to a decimal.
25% = .25. = 0.25

Using the protractor, Sonia draws a 90° angle and writes the label *Food 25%.*

Multiply:
```
    360
  × 0.25
   18 00
 + 72 0
  90.00 degrees
```

Using the same process for each expense, Sonia completes the graph.

Personal needs
20% = 0.2
```
    360
  × 0.2
   72.0°
```

Transportation
15% = 0.15
```
    360
  × 0.15
   18.00
 + 36.0
  54.00°
```

Other
10% = 0.1
```
    360
  × 0.1
   36.0°
```

Sonia knows the family's take-home pay for one month is $1,800. From the graph, she can see that 15% of the family's take-home pay is spent on transportation. She wants to find out what dollar amount is spent on transportation.

First, Sonia finds the elements in the percent problem. The base is the whole amount of $1,800. The rate is 15%. The amount of money spent on transportation is the part, but the part is not known. She uses the percent formula to solve for the part.

$$base \times rate = part$$
$$\$1{,}800 \times 15\% = ?$$

Change the percent to a decimal: 15% = .15. = 0.15

Multiply:
```
   1,800
  × 0.15
   9 000
 + 18 00
 $270.00
```
The Velez family spends $270 on transportation each month.

Practice ◣ Read and follow the directions below.

◣ Write your answers in the blanks. Show your work.

Items 1– 3 refer to the following table.

Paycheck Deductions	Percent of Total Deductions
Federal income tax	50%
State income tax	20%
Health insurance	15%
Credit union	10%
Retirement fund	5%

Items 4– 6 refer to the following table.

Use of Electricity for Quan Household

Heating	40%
Refrigerator	20%
Water heater	10%
Cooking	5%
Other	25%

1. Marlo wants to make a circle graph of the deductions from her paycheck. Find the number of degrees in each section of the graph.

   Federal income tax _____

   State income tax _____

   Health insurance _____

   Credit union _____

   Retirement fund _____

4. Mr. Quan wants to make a circle graph of the household use of electricity. Find the number of degrees in each section of the graph.

   Heating _____

   Refrigerator _____

   Water heater _____

   Cooking _____

   Other _____

5. Which item uses the least electricity?

_____

◣ Circle the best answer for each item.

2. For which item is the greatest amount deducted?

   (1) federal income tax
   (2) state income tax
   (3) health insurance
   (4) credit union
   (5) retirement fund

6. Last month the Quans' electric bill was $64. What was the cost of heat?

3. The total deducted from Marlo's check this pay period is $120. What amount went for health insurance?

   (1) $12.00
   (2) $15.00
   (3) $18.00
   (4) $54.00
   (5) $120.15

_____

Check your answers on page 293.

Using Your Math Skills

Solve. Show your work.

1. What is 64% of 300?

2. What is 6% of 72?

3. What is 90% of $96?

4. What is 400% of $56?

5. What is 125% of 36?

6. What is $3\frac{1}{2}$% of 150?

Write your answers in the blanks. Show your work.

7. The Mortons' health insurance covers 80% of the cost of medical care. John Morton had a series of lab tests that cost $145. How much of this cost was covered by his insurance?

9. In a survey, 3,000 adults were asked which newspaper they prefer to read. Fifty-five percent said they prefer a morning paper. How many adults prefer a morning paper?

8. Jill buys a coat that regularly sells for $125 for 33% off. How much does Jill save?

10. Miguel puts 12% of his earnings in a savings account. This week Miguel earns $310. How much will he put in savings?

Check your answers on pages 293–294.

11. Seth borrows $1,500 from his brother for 1 year and agrees to pay him $8\frac{1}{2}\%$ interest. How much interest will Seth owe his brother?

_____

12. Mayeta borrows $2,000 from a friend for 2 years at 14% interest to start her own cleaning service. How much interest will Mayeta pay on this loan?

_____

13. Raghib lends his brother $1,200 for 1 year at $12\frac{1}{2}\%$ interest. How much interest will Raghib be paid on the loan?

_____

14. Aretha is recarpeting her house for $1,750. She pays $250 down. She will pay the rest in monthly payments over 2 years at 18% interest. Estimate how much Aretha will have to pay back.

_____

15. Jackie borrows $1,500 from her father for classes at Technical Institute. She agrees to pay the money back at the end of 2 years at 15% interest. What is the amount Jackie will pay back?

_____

16. Jesse buys furniture for $990. He will pay for it in monthly payments over 2 years at 18% interest. Estimate Jesse's monthly payment for the furniture.

_____

17. Juan borrowed $9,350 at 12% interest to start a business. He will pay back the loan at the end of 5 years. How much will Juan pay back at the end of 5 years?

_____

18. The Tallchiefs bought a refrigerator for $475 and a stove for $680. They paid $150 down. They will pay the rest in monthly payments over 1 year at 16% interest. Estimate the Tallchiefs' monthly payment.

_____

Circle the best answer for each item.

<u>Items 19 – 21</u> refer to the following information.

Dayna is the manager of the clothing departments at Shop-Wise. She is scheduled to work 40 hours each week. The table shows what parts of her total week she spends working at different tasks.

Task	% of Time
Supervising	40%
Planning	25%
Selling	20%
Customer relations	15%

19. Which is the correct expression to find how many hours Dayna spends on customer relations each week?

    (1) 15 × 40%
    (2) 15 ÷ 40%
    (3) 40% × 15
    (4) 40 × 15%
    (5) 40 ÷ 15%

20. Which is the correct expression to find the total rate of time Dayna spends on supervising and planning each week?

    (1) 40% × 25%
    (2) 40% + 25%
    (3) 40% − 25%
    (4) 40 × 40% × 25%
    (5) 40 × 40% + 25%

21. How many hours does Dayna spend selling each week?

    (1)   8
    (2) 10
    (3) 20
    (4) 40
    (5) 80

<u>Items 22 – 24</u> refer to the following table.

Wagner Family Budget

Rent and utilities	35%
Food	25%
Transportation	20%
Clothes	15%
Other	5%

22. Mrs. Wagner wants to make a circle graph of the family budget. Find the number of degrees in each section of the graph.

    Rent and utilities _____

    Food   _____

    Transportation   _____

    Clothes   _____

    Other   _____

Circle the best answer for each item.

23. For which item do the Wagners budget the least amount?

    (1) rent and utilities
    (2) food
    (3) transportation
    (4) clothes
    (5) other

24. The Wagners' total monthly income is $2,200. How much do they budget for rent and utilities?

    (1) $35
    (2) $350
    (3) $550
    (4) $570
    (5) $770

Check your answers on pages 294–295.

Solving for the Rate (r)

The Percent Formula

Jan drove from Nashville, Tennessee to Houston, Texas—a distance of 780 miles. The first day of her trip she drove 234 miles. What percent of the total distance did she drive the first day?

In this example you are given two amounts: 780 miles and 234 miles. The question at the end of the problem asks you to find the percent. The percent is the rate, *r*.

Before you can solve for the rate, *r*, you need to identify the base, *b*, and the part, *p*. Read the question at the end of the problem again:

▌ **What percent of the total distance did she drive the first day?**

You have learned that the base often follows the word *of*. In this question you are asked to find the percent *of* the total distance. The quantity that represents the *total distance* is the base. The base, *b*, is 780 miles, the distance between Nashville and Houston.

The distance Jan drove the first day is part of the total distance. The part, *p*, is 234 miles.

You can use the percent formula to solve the problem. Remember, whenever you know two of the elements in a percent problem, you can solve for the unknown element.

$$base \times rate = part$$
$$780 \times ? = 234$$

Using the percent triangle, you can rewrite the formula to solve for the rate. Cover the letter *r*. The other elements, the part and the base, are separated by the division sign.

part ÷ base = rate
234 ÷ 780 = ?

$$\begin{array}{r} 0.30 = 30\% \\ 780\overline{)\ 234.00} \\ -\ 234\ 0 \\ \hline 00 \end{array}$$

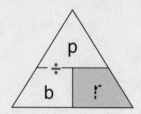

Jan drove 30% of the total distance on the first day; 234 miles is 30% of 780 miles.

Payroll

Bill earns $1,100 per month. The amount he earns before taxes or other deductions are taken out of his paycheck is called his **gross pay**.

Bill can see from his payroll check stub that amounts are taken out of each check to pay federal and state income taxes. His federal income tax deduction is $132, and his state income tax deduction is $15.40. Bill wants to find what percent of his gross pay is used to pay federal and state income taxes.

Bill Mitchell	
Gross pay	$1,100.00
Deductions:	
Federal income tax	132.00
State income tax	15.40
Other	84.13
Total deductions	$ 231.53
Net pay	$ 868.47

First, Bill wants to find what percent of his gross pay is used to pay federal income tax. His gross pay is $1,100. Since the gross pay is the whole amount he earns, $1,100 is the base. The part is $132, the amount of the gross pay used for federal income tax. Bill must solve for the percent or rate, r.

Which is the correct expression to find the percent of Bill's gross pay used to pay federal income tax?

(1) $1,100 × $132
(2) $132 ÷ $1,100
(3) $1,100 ÷ $132
(4) $132 + $1,100
(5) $1,100 − $132

Answer 2 is the correct choice. Bill uses the percent triangle. He covers the letter r because he needs to solve for the rate. He needs to divide the part, $132, by the base, $1,100.

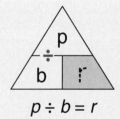

$$p \div b = r$$

He divides, carrying the division out to two decimal places. Then he changes the decimal to a percent.

```
        0.12
1,100 ) 132.00
      − 110 0
        22 00
      − 22 00
            0
```

Bill finds that 12% of his gross pay is taken out of each check to pay federal income tax.

$0.12 = 0.12. = 12\%$

Now Bill wants to find what percent of his gross pay is used to pay state income tax. His gross pay of $1,100 is still the base or whole amount. From his check stub, he can see that $15.40 is taken out of his check to pay state income tax. The amount, $15.40, is part of the base. Bill needs to solve for the rate, r.

Which is the correct expression to find the percent of Bill's gross pay used to pay state income tax?

(1) $15.40 ÷ $1,100.00
(2) $1,100.00 × $15.40
(3) $15.40 + $1,100.00
(4) $1,100.00 ÷ $15.40
(5) $1,100.00 − $15.40

Answer 1 is the correct choice. To solve for the rate, Bill divides the part, $15.40, by the base, $1,100.

He divides.

$$\begin{array}{r} 0.014 \\ 1,100{\overline{)\,15.400}} \\ -\ 11\ 00 \\ \hline 4\ 400 \\ -\ 4\ 400 \\ \hline 0 \end{array}$$

Then he changes the decimal to a percent.

$0.014 = 0.01.4 = 1.4\%$

Bill finds that 1.4% of his gross pay is used to pay state income tax.

Bill wants to put 2% of his gross pay, $1,100, in a company savings plan. Which is the correct expression to find how much money he will put into savings each month?

(1) 2% ÷ $1,100
(2) $1,100 × 200
(3) $1,100 ÷ 2%
(4) $1,100 × 2%
(5) 200 ÷ $1,100

Answer 4 is the correct choice. The gross pay, $1,100, is the base. The rate is 2%. Bill needs to solve for the part. Using the percent triangle, he knows he must multiply the base and the rate to find the part.

$b \times r = p$

$2\% = 0.02. = 0.02$

$$\begin{array}{r} \$1,100 \\ \times\ 0.02 \\ \hline \$22.00 \end{array}$$

Bill will put $22 of each check into the savings plan.

Practice ■ Circle the best answer for each item.

Items 1–3 refer to the following payroll check stub.

Items 4–6 refer to the following payroll check stub.

```
Leona Hill

Gross pay                    $600.00

Deductions:

  Federal income tax      $  84.00
  State income tax            12.60
  Health insurance           30.00
  Total deductions        $126.60

Net pay                    $473.40
```

```
Sylvia Sanchez

Gross pay                  $1,250.00

Deductions:

  Federal income tax      $  143.75
  State income tax            23.75
  Retirement fund            62.50
  Insurance                  25.00
  Total deductions        $  255.00

Net pay                    $  995.00
```

1. Which is the correct expression to find the percent of Leona's gross pay used for health insurance?

   (1) $30.00 ÷ $473.40
   (2) $30.00 ÷ $600.00
   (3) $600.00 − $30.00
   (4) $600.00 × $30.00
   (5) $600.00 ÷ $30.00

2. Which is the correct expression to find the percent of Leona's gross pay used for taxes?

   (1) ($84.00 + $12.60) ÷ $600.00
   (2) $84.00 + $12.60 ÷ $600.00
   (3) $84.00 ÷ $600.00
   (4) $600.00 − ($84.00 + $12.60)
   (5) $600.00 ÷ ($84.00 + $12.60)

3. Leona contributes 3% of her gross pay to a retirement fund. Which is the correct expression to find how much she contributes each pay period?

   (1) 3% ÷ $600.00
   (2) 3 × $600.00
   (3) $600.00 × 3%
   (4) $600.00 ÷ 3%
   (5) $600.00 ÷ 300

4. Which is the correct expression to find the percent of Sylvia's gross pay used for federal income tax?

   (1) $230.00 ÷ $1,250.00
   (2) $143.75 × $1,250.00
   (3) $143.75 ÷ $1,250.00
   (4) $1,250.00 ÷ $143.75
   (5) $1,250.00 − $143.75

5. Sylvia saves 5% of her gross pay. Which is the correct expression to find how much she saves each pay period?

   (1) 5% ÷ $995.00
   (2) 5% ÷ $1,250.00
   (3) $995.00 × 5%
   (4) $1,250.00 × 5%
   (5) $1,250.00 ÷ 5%

6. Which is the correct expression to find the percent of Sylvia's gross pay used for deductions other than taxes?

   (1) ($62.50 + $25.00) ÷ $995.00
   (2) ($62.50 + $25.00) ÷ $1,250.00
   (3) $255.00 ÷ $1,250.00
   (4) $995.00 ÷ $1,250.00
   (5) $1,250.00 × ($62.50 + $25.00)

Check your answers on page 295.

Solving for the Rate (r)

Example

What percent of 62 is 31?

To solve the problem, first identify the elements. The word *of* often comes before the base, so you know that 62 is the base. The number 31 cannot be the rate because it does not have a percent sign, %. So, the number 31 is the part.

You are ready to solve for the rate. Use the percent triangle to help you remember the formula. Cover the letter r because you need to solve for the rate. The other two elements, the part and the base, are separated by the division sign.

$$p \div b = r$$

Divide the part (p) by the base (b) to find the rate. Change the decimal to a percent.

```
     0.5
62) 31.0
  − 31 0
        0
```

$0.5 = 0.50. = 50\%$

The number 31 is 50% of 62.

Example

What percent of 50 is 300?

In this problem, the part, 300, is greater than the base. When the part is greater than the base, the rate will be greater than 100%. Divide the part by the base, and change the decimal to a percent.

```
      6
50) 300
  − 30
      0
```

$6 = 6.00. = 600\%$

The number 300 is 600% of 50.

Example

To the nearest whole percent, what percent of 16 is 9?

The number 16 is the base and 9 is the part. Divide 9 by 16 to find the rate. Carry the division out to three decimal places. Then round to the nearest hundredth. Finally, change the decimal to a percent.

```
       0.562
16) 9.000
   − 8 0
      1 00
    −  96
        40
      − 32
         8
```

0.562 rounds to 0.56
$0.56 = 0.56. = 56\%$

The number 9 is about 56% of 16.

Practice ▎ Solve. Show your work. Round your answers to the nearest whole percent.

1. What percent of 76 is 19?

$$\begin{array}{r} 0.25 \\ 76\overline{)19.00} \\ -15\,2 \\ \hline 3\,80 \\ -3\,80 \\ \hline 0 \end{array}$$

0.25 = 25%

2. What percent of 360 is 36?

3. What percent of 45 is 180?

4. What percent of 95 is 57?

5. What percent of 200 is 4?

6. What percent of 6 is 15?

7. What percent of 84 is 70?

8. What percent of 64 is 40?

▎ Write your answers in the blanks. Show your work. Round your answers to the nearest whole percent.

9. Lyle answered 32 out of 40 questions on a test correctly. What percent of the questions did he answer correctly?

_____

10. Disk Company employs 74 people. Of the employees, 42 are female. What percent of the employees are female?

_____

11. Bev saved $9 on a sweater that regularly sells for $36. What percent of the regular price did she save?

_____

12. Dwayne's weekly gross pay is $260.00. Deductions of $41.60 are taken out of his paycheck each week. What percent of Dwayne's gross pay is taken out of his paycheck for deductions?

_____

Problem-Solving Strategy:

Using Proportions to Solve Percent Problems

Andrew is trying to decrease the amount of fat in his diet. His doctor told him to avoid foods in which more than 30% of the calories come from fat. Andrew wants to compare several foods to decide which have a lower fat content.

In the afternoon, Andrew likes to have a snack. He compares popcorn and potato chips to see which has the lower percent of calories from fat.

He compares the labels on a box of microwave popcorn and a bag of potato chips. Both products are advertised as "low in fat." Andrew wants to figure out how low the fat content really is. The labels from the products are shown below.

MICROWAVE *LITE* POPCORN	RANCH STYLE LIGHT CHIPS
SERVING SIZE ....4 CUPS	SERVING SIZE ....14 CHIPS
CALORIES 150	CALORIES 130
PROTEIN, grams 5	PROTEIN, grams 1
FAT, grams 5	FAT, grams 6
CARBOHYDRATE, grams 21	CARBOHYDRATE, grams 18
SODIUM, milligrams 180	SODIUM, milligrams 110

Andrew knows there are 9 calories in every gram of fat. He can figure out how many calories come from fat by multiplying the grams of fat by 9.

 1 gram of fat = 9 calories

Andrew is ready to find the percent of calories that come from fat for each snack. The popcorn contains 5 grams of fat. He multiplies 5 by 9 and finds that 45 of the calories in the popcorn come from fat.

$$5 \text{ grams} \times 9 = 45 \text{ calories}$$

From the label Andrew knows that there are 150 calories in a serving of popcorn. He needs to find what percent 45 calories is of 150 calories. Andrew knows that 150 calories represents the whole amount or base. The part is 45 calories. He needs to find the rate.

Using the percent triangle, Andrew knows to divide the part, 45, by the base, 150.

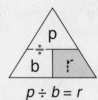

$$p \div b = r$$

However, there is another way to solve the problem. Andrew can use his understanding of ratio and proportion to find the answer.

Percents are actually ratios. *Percent* means "for every 100" or "out of 100." A percent is a ratio comparing an amount to 100. In a percent problem, the rate can be written with a percent sign or as a ratio.

$$\text{rate} = ?\% \longrightarrow 25\%$$

$$\text{rate} = \frac{?}{100} \longrightarrow \frac{25}{100}$$

A ratio can also be written comparing the part to the base.

$$\frac{\text{part}}{\text{base}}$$

To solve a percent problem, set up a proportion using the two ratios.

$$\frac{\text{part}}{\text{base}} = \frac{\text{rate}}{100}$$

You can solve percent problems by putting the elements you know in the proportion. Then solve the proportion to find the missing element.

Example

Andrew needs to find what percent 45 calories is of 150 calories. He knows 150 is the base and 45 is the part. He does not know the rate. He sets up a proportion and solves.

$$\frac{45}{150} = \frac{?}{100}$$

Cross-multiply: $\dfrac{45}{150} \searrow \dfrac{?}{100}$ $45 \times 100 = 4,500$

Divide by the remaining number, 150:

$$150 \overline{)\, 4,500} \quad \begin{array}{r} 30 \\ \hline \end{array}$$
$$\underline{-\,4\,50}$$
$$00$$

So, $\dfrac{45}{150} = \dfrac{30}{100}$.

Write $\dfrac{30}{100}$ as a percent: 30%.

Andrew knows that 45 calories is 30% of 150 calories. Thirty percent of the calories in popcorn come from fat.

You get the same answer using the percent formula.

part ÷ base = rate   Divide: $\begin{array}{r} 0.3 \\ 150 \overline{)\, 45.0} \end{array}$ Change
$45 \div 150 = ?$ $\underline{-\,45\,0}$ to a
                     0 percent: $0.3 = 0.30. = 30\%$

Now Andrew is ready to figure out the percent of fat in potato chips. He reads the label on the bag. One serving has 130 calories and 6 grams of fat. He wants to figure out what percent of calories come from fat.

RANCH STYLE LIGHT CHIPS
SERVING SIZE ....14 CHIPS
CALORIES 130
PROTEIN, grams 1
FAT, grams 6
CARBOHYDRATE, grams 18
SODIUM, milligrams 110

Andrew multiplies 6 grams of fat by 9 to find the number of calories in the chips that come from fat: $6 \times 9 = 54$ calories. So, 54 of the 130 calories come from fat. He wants to know what percent 54 calories is of 130 calories. Andrew sets up a proportion to find the rate.

$$\frac{\text{part}}{\text{base}} = \frac{\text{rate}}{100} \qquad \frac{54}{130} = \frac{?}{100}$$

Using the proportion, what percent of 130 calories is 54 calories? Round your answer to the nearest whole percent.

(1) 30%
(2) 36%
(3) 40%
(4) 42%
(5) 43%

Answer 4 is the correct choice.

First, cross-multiply: $\frac{54}{130} = \frac{?}{100}$ $\qquad \frac{54}{130} \searrow \frac{?}{100}$ $\qquad \begin{array}{r} 54 \\ \times\ 100 \\ \hline 5,400 \end{array}$

Divide by the remaining number:
$$\begin{array}{r} 41.5 \\ 130\overline{)5,400.0} \\ \underline{-\ 5\ 20} \\ 200 \\ \underline{-\ 130} \\ 70\ 0 \\ \underline{-\ 65\ 0} \\ 5\ 0 \end{array}$$

Round to the nearest whole percent: 41.5 rounds to 42.

Write the answer as a percent: 42%.

Of the 130 calories in a serving of potato chips, 42% come from fat. Andrew's doctor told him to avoid foods with a fat content higher than 30%. He decides not to eat these potato chips even though the bag reads "low in fat." The popcorn meets the limits set by his doctor. Even though a serving of the popcorn has more calories than the potato chips, popcorn has a lower fat content. Andrew decides to eat the popcorn.

Practice ◆ For each food, find the number of calories that come from fat and the percent of calories that come from fat. Show your work.

1.

> SPAGHETTI
> SERVING SIZE ....2 OUNCES (DRY)
> CALORIES 200
> PROTEIN, grams 7
> FAT, grams 1
> CARBOHYDRATE, grams 41
> SODIUM, milligrams 0

Number of calories: _____

Percent of calories: _____

3.

> OAT CEREAL
> SERVING SIZE ....1 OUNCE
> CALORIES 120
> PROTEIN, grams 4
> FAT, grams 2
> CARBOHYDRATE, grams 21
> SODIUM, milligrams 290

Number of calories: _____

Percent of calories: _____

2.

> MACARONI AND CHEESE
> SERVING SIZE ....$\frac{3}{4}$ CUP
> CALORIES 300
> PROTEIN, grams 9
> FAT, grams 13
> CARBOHYDRATE, grams 36
> SODIUM, milligrams 530

Number of calories: _____

Percent of calories: _____

4.

> LIGHT MAYONNAISE
> SERVING SIZE ....1 TABLESPOON
> CALORIES 50
> PROTEIN, grams 0
> FAT, grams 5
> CARBOHYDRATE, grams 1
> SODIUM, milligrams 115

Number of calories: _____

Percent of calories: _____

5. Andrew was told to avoid foods in which over 30% of the calories come from fat. Which of the foods in items 1–4 should he avoid?

Reading a Circle Graph

Ella works for the Conrad Chemical Company. She is helping her boss, Paula, collect information on the company's yearly budget. Paula gives Ella the following circle graph.

Conrad Chemical Company Yearly Budget

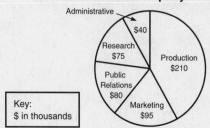

Ella notices that the sections in the graph contain dollar amounts instead of percents. The key at the bottom of the graph tells her that each dollar on the graph represents one thousand dollars.

Paula wants Ella to find the answers to the following questions:

■ What is the total amount of the company's budget for the year?

■ What percent of the budget is spent on marketing?

■ What is the total percent spent on research and production?

Ella can answer all the questions using the graph.

■ What is the total amount of the company's budget for the year?

To answer the question, Ella needs to find the total dollar amount for all the areas on the graph. She adds the amounts on the graph to find the total. Because one dollar on the graph represents one thousand dollars, she multiplies the total by 1,000. The company's yearly budget is $500,000.

$$\begin{array}{r} \$210 \\ 95 \\ 80 \\ 75 \\ +\ 40 \\ \hline \$500 \end{array} \qquad \begin{array}{r} \$500 \\ \times\ 1{,}000 \\ \hline \$500{,}000 \end{array}$$

■ What percent of the budget is spent on marketing?

Ella needs to find a percent to answer this question. The amount spent on marketing is $95,000, or $95 × 1,000. The amount of the whole budget is $500,000.

The whole budget, $500,000, is the base. Ella will use the amount $500 to do the math since it is easier to work with a smaller number. The marketing budget amount, $95,000, is part of the whole budget. For the part she uses the figure $95.

Ella uses the percent formula to find the rate.

She divides the part by the base.

$$500 \overline{)95.00} \quad \begin{array}{l} 0.19 \end{array}$$

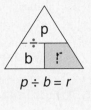

$$p \div b = r$$

```
        0.19
500) 95.00
   - 50 0
     45 00
   - 45 00
         0
```

Then Ella changes the decimal to a percent: 0.19 = 0.19. = 19%.

The amount spent on marketing is 19% of the company budget.

■ What is the total percent spent on research and production?

The amount in the section labeled *Production* is $210. The amount in the *Research* section is $75.

To answer the question, Ella needs to do two things:

1. She must find the total of the two amounts.
2. She must find what percent the total is of the base or whole budget.

What is the total percent spent on research and production?

(1) 47%
(2) 54%
(3) 57%
(4) 63%
(5) 75%

Answer 3 is the correct choice. The amounts spent on research and production are 57% of the total budget.

Ella adds the amount from the two sections on the graph:

```
 $210
+ 75
$285
```

She knows the base is $500, and $285 is the part. Ella needs to solve for the rate.

part ÷ base = rate

Ella divides the part by the base.

```
         0.57
500) 285.00
   - 250 0
      35 00
    - 35 00
          0
```

Finally, she changes the decimal to a percent: 0.57 = 0.57. = 57%.

Practice ■ Circle the best answer for each item.

Items 1– 3 refer to the following graph.

The Morenos' Monthly Budget

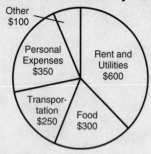

1. What is the total amount of the Morenos' monthly budget?

   (1) $100
   (2) $360
   (3) $1,500
   (4) $1,600
   (5) $5,760

2. To the nearest whole percent, what percent of the Morenos' budget is for rent and utilities?

   (1) 3%
   (2) 17%
   (3) 38%
   (4) 60%
   (5) 600%

3. To the nearest whole percent, what percent of the budget is for personal expenses and other?

   (1) 4%
   (2) 22%
   (3) 28%
   (4) 45%
   (5) 450%

■ Write your answers in the blanks. Show your work.

Items 4– 6 refer to the following graph.

Annual Sales of Team-Wear, Inc., 1992

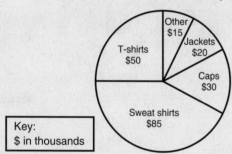

4. What were Team-Wear, Inc.'s total sales in 1992?

5. To the nearest whole percent, what percent of the sales came from T-shirts and sweat shirts?

6. How much larger is the percent of sales from caps than from jackets?

_____

_____

_____

Using Your Math Skills

Solve. Show your work. Round your answers to the nearest whole percent.

1. What percent of 10 is 16?

2. What percent of 72 is 54?

3. What percent of 300 is 12?

4. What percent of 15 is 75?

5. What percent of 80 is 25?

6. What percent of 90 is 33?

Write your answers in the blanks. Show your work. Round your answers to the nearest whole percent.

7. Sedika took a 600-mile trip. She drove 240 miles before stopping for lunch. What percent of the total trip did she drive before lunch?

9. Curtis paid $80 for a jacket that originally cost $96. What percent of the original price did Curtis pay?

_____

8. The Hillside Neighborhood Association has 450 members. In May, 360 members attended the annual meeting. What percent of the association members attended the meeting?

10. Chiang bought a car that cost $8,000. She made a down payment of $500. What percent of the total cost did she pay down on the car?

_____

_____

Circle the best answer for each item.

11. Of the 220 employees at Adams Department Store, 125 work part-time. Which is the correct expression to find the percent of employees that work part-time?

    (1) 125×220
    (2) $125 \div 220$
    (3) $(125 + 220) \div 220$
    (4) $220 - 125$
    (5) $220 \div 125$

12. Of 800 people surveyed, 52% named baseball as their favorite spectator sport. Which is the correct expression to find how many people named baseball?

    (1) $52\% \div 800$
    (2) $800 - 52\%$
    (3) $800 \times 52\%$
    (4) $800 \div 52\%$
    (5) $800\% \div 52$

13. Sarah works 40 hours per week as assistant manager of a hotel. She spends an average of 12 hours each week responding to guest comments and complaints. What percent of her time does Sarah spend responding to guests?

    (1) 3%
    (2) 12%
    (3) 28%
    (4) 30%
    (5) 48%

14. A set of tires regularly sells for $200. Lamont saved 15% by buying the tires on sale. How much did he save by buying the tires on sale?

    (1) $7.50
    (2) $13.30
    (3) $15.00
    (4) $30.00
    (5) $185.00

Items 15–17 refer to the following payroll check stub.

Tony Marquez	
Gross pay	$500.00
Deductions:	
Federal income tax	$ 63.40
State income tax	6.60
Credit union	25.00
Total deductions	$ 95.00
Net pay	$405.00

15. Which is the correct expression to find the percent of Tony's gross pay deducted for his credit union account?

    (1) $\$25.00 \times \$500.00$
    (2) $\$25.00 \div \$500.00$
    (3) $\$500.00 - \$25.00$
    (4) $\$500.00 \times \$25.00$
    (5) $\$500.00 \div \$25.00$

16. What percent of Tony's gross pay is deducted for taxes?

    (1) 7%
    (2) 12%
    (3) 14%
    (4) 35%
    (5) 70%

17. Tony wants to contribute 4% of his gross pay to his employer's savings plan. How much would Tony contribute each pay period?

    (1) $4.00
    (2) $20.00
    (3) $16.20
    (4) $125.00
    (5) $200.00

Check your answers on page 296.

For each food, find the number and the percent of calories that come from fat. Show your work.

18.

WHEAT BREAD	
SERVING SIZE ....1 SLICE	
CALORIES 90	
PROTEIN, grams 3	
FAT, grams 1	
CARBOHYDRATE, grams 17	
SODIUM, milligrams 140	

Number of calories: _____

Percent of calories: _____

19.

YOGURT	
SERVING SIZE ....8 OUNCES	
CALORIES 180	
PROTEIN, grams 11	
FAT, grams 5	
CARBOHYDRATE, grams 23	
SODIUM, milligrams 125	

Number of calories: _____

Percent of calories: _____

Write your answers in the blanks. Show your work.

Items 20 – 22 refer to the following graph.

Favorite Mealtime Beverage Survey
(in thousands of adults)

20. What is the total number of adults surveyed?

_____

21. What percent of those surveyed prefer milk?

_____

22. What percent of those surveyed prefer coffee or tea?

_____

Check your answers on pages 296–297.

Section 14

Solving for the Base (b)

The Percent Formula

Ellen works at a furniture store. Her boss asks her to put a price tag on a new sofa. The amount the furniture store paid for the sofa is called the original price, or the cost. Ellen needs to price the sofa 45% higher than the cost.

But Ellen has a problem. She does not know what the store paid for the sofa. Her boss tells her she should add $112.50 to the cost. If $112.50 represents 45% of the cost, how can Ellen find the cost?

In this example, Ellen knows two of the elements of a percent problem. She knows that the rate is 45% and that $112.50 is part of the cost. The cost is the whole amount, or base. She needs to solve for the base.

Because Ellen knows two of the elements, she can solve the problem using the percent formula. To rewrite the formula to solve for the base, she divides the part by the rate.

base × rate = part
?   × 45% = $112.50

part   ÷ rate = base
$112.50 ÷ 45% = ?

Ellen uses the percent triangle to remember the formula. She covers the letter *b* because she needs to solve for the base. The other elements, the part and the rate, are separated by the division sign.

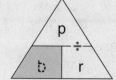

part ÷ rate = base
$112.50 ÷ 45% = ?

45% = .45. = 0.45

$$\begin{array}{r} 2\ 50. \\ 0.45{\overline{\smash{\big)}\,112.50.}} \\ -\ 90 \\ \hline 22\ 5 \\ -\ 22\ 5 \\ \hline 0 \end{array}$$

The base or cost is $250.00. Since 45% of $250.00 is $112.50, Ellen needs to increase the cost by 45%. She adds $112.50 to $250.00. Ellen puts on the sofa a price tag for $362.50.

$250.00
+ 112.50
$362.50

Discount Prices

Paul works at Discount Fashions, a clothing store. The store buys clothes in large quantities at low prices and sells the clothes at a discount. For example, the store might buy a shirt for $7.00. The price is raised to $10.50 so the store can make a profit. However, the price of $10.50 is still much lower than the shirt's regular price of $15.00 at a department store. In fact, the customer saves $4.50, or 30% off the regular department store price.

The price tags on the clothes do not show how much the store paid for the clothes. Each price tag shows the item's regular price, the sale price, the discount rate, and how much the customer saves.

Sometimes customers return clothes to the store. If the tags have been taken off, Paul must print out new tags and attach them to the clothing. Today, Paul needs to print new tags for a pair of pants and a jacket that were returned.

Discount Fashions	
Shirt	
Discount	30%
You save	$4.50
Regular price	$15.00
Sale price	$10.50

The pants and jacket were given as a gift, so the bottom parts of the tags were torn off by the customer. However, Paul can figure out the regular price and the sale price using the information on the top of the tags.

Paul knows the discount rate for the pair of pants is 40%. He also knows the rate represents a discount of $13.60. The regular price of the pair of pants is the whole amount, or base. The amount of the discount, $13.60, is part of the whole. The rate is 40%. Since Paul does not know the regular price, he needs to solve for the base.

Discount Fashions
Pants

Discount   40%
You save $13.60

Which is the correct expression to find the regular price of the pair of pants?

(1) $13.60 × 60%
(2)   40% ÷ $13.60
(3) $13.60 ÷ 40%
(4) $13.60 × 40%
(5)   60% ÷ $13.60

Answer 3 is the correct choice. Paul uses the percent triangle. He covers the letter *b* because he needs to solve for the base. He needs to divide the part, $13.60, by the rate, 40%, to find the base.

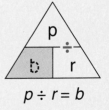

$p \div r = b$

Paul changes the percent to a decimal and divides. The regular price of the pants is $34.00.

$$40\% = 0.40.$$

$$
\begin{array}{r}
\$3\ 4.00 \\
0.4.\overline{)\$13.6.00} \\
-\ 12 \\
\hline
1\ 6 \\
-\ 1\ 6 \\
\hline
0
\end{array}
$$

Paul needs to figure out the sale price. He knows the regular price of the pants is $34.00. He knows the customer will save $13.60. Paul can find the sale price by subtracting $13.60 from $34.00. The sale price is $20.40. He prints this tag for the pair of pants.

$$
\begin{array}{r}
\$34.00 \\
-\ 13.60 \\
\hline
\$20.40
\end{array}
$$

Discount Fashions
Pants

Discount	40%
You save	$13.60
Regular price	$34.00
Sale price	$20.40

Now Paul needs to print a tag for the jacket. From the top of the tag, he knows that the discount rate is 25%, and the amount of customer savings is $15.50. First, Paul needs to solve for the regular price.

Discount Fashions
Jacket

| Discount | 25% |
| You save | $15.50 |

Which is the correct expression to find the regular price of the jacket?

(1) $15.50 × 25%
(2) $15.50 × 75%
(3) 75% ÷ $15.50
(4) 25% ÷ $15.50
(5) $15.50 ÷ 25%

Answer 5 is the correct choice. The regular price of the jacket is the base. The customer savings, $15.50, is part of the base. The rate of discount is 25%. Using the percent formula, Paul divides the part, $15.50, by the rate, 25%, to find the base.

Paul changes the percent to a decimal and divides. The regular price of the jacket is $62.00.

$$25\% = 0.25.$$

$$
\begin{array}{r}
\$\ \ 62. \\
0.25.\overline{)\$15.50.} \\
-\ 15\ 0 \\
\hline
50 \\
-\ 50 \\
\hline
0
\end{array}
$$

Finally, Paul finds the sale price by subtracting. The sale price is $46.50. He prints this tag for the jacket.

$$
\begin{array}{r}
\$62.00 \\
-\ 15.50 \\
\hline
\$46.50
\end{array}
$$

Discount Fashions
Jacket

Discount	25%
You save	$15.50
Regular price	$62.00
Sale price	$46.50

Practice ◤ Circle the best answer for each item.

1. Which is the correct expression to find the regular price of this sweater?

(1) $7.20 × 30%
(2) $7.20 ÷ 30%
(3) $7.20 × 70%
(4) 30% × $7.20
(5) 70% ÷ $7.20

2. Which is the correct expression to find the regular price of this coat?

(1) 45% × $54.00
(2) 45% ÷ $54.00
(3) $54.00 ÷ 45%
(4) $54.00 × 55%
(5) $54.00 ÷ 55%

3. Which is the correct expression to find the sale price of these jeans?

(1) $12.60 × 35%
(2) $12.60 ÷ 35%
(3) $36.00 ÷ 35%
(4) $36.00 + $12.60
(5) $36.00 − $12.60

4. Which is the correct expression to find the regular price of this sweat shirt?

(1) $5.60 × 40%
(2) $5.60 ÷ 40%
(3) $5.60 × 60%
(4) $5.60 ÷ 60%
(5) 40% ÷ $5.60

5. Which is the correct expression to find the amount you save on this dress?

(1) 25% ÷ $64.00
(2) $64.00 × 25%
(3) $64.00 ÷ 25%
(4) $64.00 × 75%
(5) 75% ÷ $64.00

6. Which is the correct expression to find the discount rate for this skirt?

(1) $6.50 × $32.50
(2) $6.50 ÷ $32.50
(3) $32.50 + $6.50
(4) $32.50 − $6.50
(5) $32.50 ÷ $6.50

Check your answers on page 297.

Solving for the Base (*b*)

Example

The number 28 is 20% of what number?

To find the answer, you first need to identify the elements in the problem. You know that 20% is the rate because of the percent sign. Remember that the word *of* usually comes before the base. In this problem the word *of* comes before the words *what number*. The unknown number is the base. The number 28 is the part.

You are ready to solve for the base. Use the percent triangle. Cover the letter *b*, because you need to solve for the base. The other two elements, the part and the rate, are separated by a division sign.

$p \div r = b$

Divide the part *p* by the rate *r* to find the base. First change the percent to a decimal. To divide by a decimal, move the decimal point to the right to make the decimal into a whole number. Then move the decimal point the same number of places to the right in the number you are dividing.

part ÷ *rate* = *base*   20% = .20. = 0.20

28 ÷ 20% = ?

$$0.20\overline{)28.00.}$$
$$140.$$
$$-20$$
$$80$$
$$-80$$
$$0$$

The number 28 is 20% of 140.

You can also solve a percent problem using a proportion.

Example

The number 50 is 125% of what number?

The base is unknown. The number 50 is the part, and 125% ($\frac{125}{100}$) is the rate. Set up the proportion: $\frac{part}{base} = rate$ $\frac{50}{?} = \frac{125}{100}$

Cross-multiply: $\frac{50}{?}$ $\frac{125}{100}$ 50 × 100 = 5,000

Divide by the remaining number: $125\overline{)5,000}$ 40   − 5 00   0

The number 50 is 125% of 40. Remember, when the rate is greater than 100%, the part will be greater than the base.

Practice ◼ Solve. Show your work.

1. 24 is 25% of what number?
   25% = 0.25

   $$\begin{array}{r} 96. \\ 0.25\overline{\smash{)}24.00.} \\ \underline{-22\ 5} \\ 1\ 50 \\ \underline{-1\ 50} \\ 0 \end{array}$$

2. 36 is 40% of what number?

3. $9 is 75% of what amount?

4. 57 is 300% of what number?

5. 40 is 8% of what number?

6. 16 is 32% of what number?

7. $66 is 80% of what amount?

8. 35 is 175% of what number?

◼ Write your answers in the blanks. Show your work.

9. For a sale, Earl's Furniture has discounted all items by 30%. The tag on a chair shows that a customer can save $22.50. What is the regular price of this chair?

   _____

11. Vern spent 35% of his income last month for rent and utilities. He spent $490 for rent and utilities. What was Vern's income last month?

   _____

10. Ladonna's softball team won 14 games this season. The team won 70% of the games played. How many games did Ladonna's team play this season?

   _____

12. Elvia deposited money in a savings account that pays 5% annual interest. She earned $34.25 interest in one year. How much did she deposit?

   _____

Check your answers on page 297.

Commissions

Problem-Solving Strategy: Making a Chart

Kim works in the office at Franklin Auto. Today he is completing some records for Keiko, who does the payroll for the company.

Franklin Auto sells new and used cars. The salespeople at Franklin Auto earn a percent of the profits on the cars they sell. Imagine that the company buys a used car for $8,500. Then it spends another $1,500 fixing up the car. The car cost the company $10,000.

$8,500
+ 1,500
$10,000 ← cost to company

If one of the salespeople can sell the car for $11,000, the company makes a profit of $1,000. The person who sold the car earns a percent of the profit, which is called a **commission.**

$11,000 ← sales price
− 10,000 ← cost
$ 1,000 ← profit

Kim needs to complete the payroll records for four salespeople. For a record to be complete, Kim has to know the amount of profit, the salesperson's rate of commission, and the amount of commission that should be paid. Commission rates vary depending on the type of car sold. Keiko gives Kim the following information:

- Janet Carlson earns a 25% commission on profits on the cars she sells. During the last pay period, she brought in $4,800 in profits for the company.

- Ben Ivey earned $1,350 in commission for the last pay period according to Keiko. Ben's commission rate is 20% for the cars he sells.

- Max Pace earned a $1,675 commission on $6,700 in profits.

Kim knows that he can use the percent formula to complete the records. To organize the information, he decides to make a chart.

Kim knows that the amount of commission the salesperson earns is part of the profit. Therefore, he knows the amount of commission is the part, and the profit is the base. The percent of commission is the rate. He puts headings for the elements of a percent problem along the top of the chart. Down the left side of the chart, he writes the names of the salespeople. Then Kim writes the information in the chart.

Salesperson	Base (Profit)	Rate	Part (Commission)
J. Carlson	$4,800	25%	
B. Ivey		20%	$1,350
M. Pace	$6,700		$1,675

Now Kim is ready to use the percent formula to complete the records. He starts with Janet Carlson's record. He knows the base and the rate; he needs to find the part.

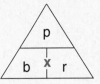

Using the percent triangle, Kim sees he should multiply the base by the rate to find the part. He changes the rate to a decimal and multiplies. Janet's commission is $1,200. Kim writes the commission in the chart.

25% = .25. = 0.25

$$
\begin{array}{r}
\$ \ \ 4,800 \\
\times \ 0.25 \\
\hline
240\ 00 \\
+ \ 960\ 0 \\
\hline
\$1,200.00
\end{array}
$$

Salesperson	Base (Profit)	Rate	Part (Commission)
J. Carlson	$4,800	25%	$1,200

Kim goes to Ben Ivey's record. Kim knows the rate and the part; he needs to find the base. Using the percent triangle, Kim sees he should divide the part by the rate to find the base. He changes the rate to a decimal and divides. Ben brought in $6,750 in profits during the pay period. Kim records the profit in the chart.

20% = .20. = 0.20 = 0.2

$$
\begin{array}{r}
\$675\ 0. \\
0.2.)\ \$1,350.0.0 \\
-\ 1\ 2 \\
\hline
15 \\
-\ 14 \\
\hline
10 \\
-\ 10 \\
\hline
0
\end{array}
$$

Salesperson	Base (Profit)	Rate	Part (Commission)
B. Ivey	$6,750	20%	$1,350

Finally, Kim is ready to complete the third record. He knows the base and the part. He needs to figure out the rate of commission that Max Pace earns. Using the percent triangle, he sees he needs to divide the part by the base to find the rate. He divides and then changes the decimal to a percent. Max earns a 25% commission. Kim writes the rate of commission in the chart.

$$
\begin{array}{r}
0.25 \\
\$6,700)\ \$1,675.00 \\
-\ 1\ 340\ 0 \\
\hline
335\ 00 \\
-\ 335\ 00 \\
\hline
0
\end{array}
$$

0.25 = 0.25. = 25%

Salesperson	Base (Profit)	Rate	Part (Commission)
J. Carlson	$4,800	25%	$1,200
B. Ivey	$6,750	20%	$1,350
M. Pace	$6,700	25%	$1,675

Practice ◼ Circle the best answer for each item.

Items 1–3 refer to the following chart.

Salesperson	Base (Profit)	Rate	Part (Commission)
R. Montoya	$1,320.00	24%	
M. Quan		20%	$425.00
T. Simon	$1,320.00		$290.40

1. What is the amount of commission Roberto Montoya earned?

(1) $31.68
(2) $216.00
(3) $316.80
(4) $3,168.00
(5) $5,500.00

2. What amount of profit did Mary Quan make for her company?

(1) $85.00
(2) $855.00
(3) $1,855.00
(4) $2,125.00
(5) $2,500.00

3. What is Tara Simon's rate of commission?

(1)   22%
(2)   24%
(3)   25%
(4)   26%
(5)   30%

Items 4–6 refer to the following information. Write the information in the chart. Then complete the chart. Show your work.

◼ Lou Morgan earned an $870.00 commission on $4,350.00 in profits.

◼ Bill Whitefeather earned $1,891.00 in commissions. His commission rate is 25%.

◼ Sue Chapa brought in profits of $5,427.00. She earns a 23% commission rate.

	Salesperson	Base (Profit)	Rate	Part (Commission)
4.	L. Morgan			
5.	B. Whitefeather			
6.	S. Chapa			

Using Your Math Skills

Solve. Show your work.

1. 27 is 30% of what number?

2. 60 is 3% of what number?

3. $40.80 is 68% of what amount?

4. 4 is 20% of what number?

5. $35 is 125% of what amount?

6. 36 is 75% of what number?

7. 63 is 350% of what number?

8. $3.40 is 8% of what amount?

Circle the best answer for each item.

9. The Rileys' health insurance pays 80% of all medical expenses. The insurance paid $120 for Mona Riley's x-rays. Which is the correct expression to find the charge for the x-rays?

    (1) 20% × $120
    (2) 80% ÷ $120
    (3) $120 ÷ 20%
    (4) $120 × 80%
    (5) $120 ÷ 80%

10. *Consumer's Digest* reported that 9,610 of people surveyed prefer to drive a sedan. This number represents 62% of those surveyed. Which is the correct expression to find the number of people surveyed?

    (1) 9,610 ÷ 38%
    (2) 9,610 × 62%
    (3) 9,610 ÷ 62%
    (4) 38% × 9,610
    (5) 62% ÷ 9,610

Write your answers in the blanks. Show your work.

Items 11 and 12 refer to the following part of a price tag for a shirt.

11. What is the regular price of the shirt?

_____

12. What is the sale price of the shirt?

_____

Items 13 and 14 refer to the following part of a price tag for a jacket.

13. How much do you save by buying the jacket?

_____

14. What is the sale price of the jacket?

_____

15. Dustin answered 22 questions correctly on a test. His score was 88%. How many questions were on the test?

_____

16. Clara puts 6% of her gross pay in the credit union each pay period. This pay period she put $17.52 in the credit union. What is Clara's gross pay?

_____

17. Michael found that 75% of the people who come into his hardware store make a purchase. Michael expects 360 customers today. How many sales should he expect to make?

_____

18. Attendance at this year's opening game was 16,313. This number is 110% of last year's attendance. What was last year's attendance?

_____

Circle the best answer for each item.

19. Of the 40 hours Curtis worked this week, 45% of his time was spent taking inventory. How many hours did Curtis spend taking inventory?

    (1) 5
    (2) 18
    (3) 22
    (4) 45
    (5) 89

20. Lenora made 20% of the sales at Super Sporting Goods this week. She made 85 sales. How many sales did Super Sporting Goods have this week?

    (1)   17
    (2) 105
    (3) 170
    (4) 425
    (5) 510

21. Transport Movers needs to load 150 boxes onto a moving van. By noon, 129 boxes have been loaded. What percent of the boxes have been loaded?

    (1) 51%
    (2) 62%
    (3) 79%
    (4) 86%
    (5) 93%

22. At CR Fashions, 31% of the daily sales are of children's clothes. Today's sales of children's clothes are $2,356. What are the total sales for the day?

    (1) $4,600
    (2) $5,575
    (3) $6,000
    (4) $7,025
    (5) $7,600

Write the information in the chart. Then complete the chart. Show your work.

Items 23 – 26 refer to the following information.

- Val Murphy brought in profits of $6,352.00 this week. Her commission rate is 22%.

- Sal Santino earned $874.23 in commissions this week. His commission rate is 21%.

- Darwin Hill earned $1,310.00 in commissions on profits of $5,240.00 this week.

- Pat Moreno brought in a profit of $3,250.00 on each of two sales this week. Her commission rate is 24%.

	Salesperson	Base (Profit)	Rate	Part (Commission)
23.	V. Murphy			
24.	S. Santino			
25.	D. Hill			
26.	P. Moreno			

Check your answers on page 298.

Percent of Change

Consumer Math

Pay Raises

Joel works for the parks department and currently earns $5.60 per hour. His boss reviews Joel's work and gives him a raise. His new hourly wage will be $5.88. Joel wants to figure out the percent of increase in his wages.

A percent of change problem is a type of percent problem. To solve the problem, Joel needs to identify the base and find the part. Then he can solve for the rate—the percent of increase.

Joel knows two amounts. His current wage, $5.60, is the original amount, or the **base.** The original amount is the amount before any change has taken place.

Since the other amount, $5.88, is greater than the original amount, you know there has been an increase. The difference between the new amount and the original amount is the **part.**

Joel subtracts his current wage from the new wage to find the difference. The amount of increase (the part) is $0.28.

$$\begin{array}{r} \$5.88 \\ -\ 5.60 \\ \hline \$0.28 \end{array}$$

Joel knows the part and the base. Now he can use the percent formula to solve for the rate.

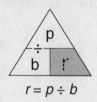

$r = p \div b$

▌
rate	=	part	÷	base
percent of change	=	amount of change	÷	original amount

Joel divides the part, $0.28, by the base, $5.60, to find the rate or percent of increase. Joel changes the decimal to a percent. His wages have increased 5%.

$$\begin{array}{r} 0.05 \\ 5.60\overline{)0.28.00} \\ -\ 28\ 00 \\ \hline 0 \end{array} = 0.05. = 5\%$$

A percent of change problem requires two operations: subtraction and division. The following expression shows how to solve for the percent of increase in Joel's wages.

$$(\$5.88 - \$5.60) \div \$5.60$$

Rosa works on the grounds crew at Lincoln Park. She is thinking of changing jobs, but she will have to take a cut in pay. Even though she will earn less, she will have more chances to move up and earn more.

Her current wage is $7.50 per hour. The new job pays $7.05 per hour. Rosa wants to find the percent of decrease in her hourly wage if she takes the new job.

Which is the correct expression to find the percent of decrease in her wages?

(1) ($7.05 ÷ $7.50) ÷ $7.50
(2) ($7.50 − $7.05) ÷ $7.50
(3) ($7.05 ÷ $7.50) − $7.05
(4) ($7.05 − $7.50) ÷ $7.05
(5) ($7.50 ÷ $7.05) − $7.50

Answer 2 is the correct choice. First Rosa finds the amount of change. She subtracts the smaller amount, $7.05, from the greater amount, $7.50. The result, $0.45, is the part.

$$\begin{array}{r} \$7.50 \\ -\ 7.05 \\ \hline \$0.45 \end{array}$$

The original amount, her current wage of $7.50, is the base. She divides the part by the base.

$$\begin{array}{r} 0.06 \\ 7.50\overline{)0.45.00} \\ -\ 45\ 00 \\ \hline 0 \end{array}$$

Rosa changes the decimal to a percent. The rate of decrease in her wages if she takes the new job will be 6%.

$$0.06 = 0.06. = 6\%$$

Santana works for the parks department as a file clerk. Her current hourly wage is $6.00. Her boss reviews her work and gives her a raise. Her new hourly wage is $6.78. Santana wants to find the rate of change in her wages.

Which is the correct expression to find the percent of increase in Santana's wages?

(1) ($6.78 − $6.00) ÷ $6.00
(2) ($6.00 + $6.78) ÷ $6.00
(3) ($6.78 ÷ $6.00) − $6.78
(4) ($6.00 − $6.78) ÷ $6.78
(5) ($6.78 ÷ $6.00) − $6.00

Answer 1 is the correct choice. Santana subtracts to find the part. Then she divides the part, $0.78, by the base, $6.00, to find the rate of increase. The percent of increase in Santana's wages is 13%.

$$\begin{array}{r} \$6.78 \\ -\ 6.00 \\ \hline \$0.78 \end{array} \qquad \begin{array}{r} 0.13 \\ 6\overline{)0.78} \\ -\ 78 \\ \hline 0 \end{array}$$

$$0.13 = 0.13. = 13\%$$

Practice ■ Circle the best answer for each item.

1. Tanya just started work as a clerk typist. Her current wage is $5.75 per hour. After completing three months on the job, her new hourly wage will be $6.21. Which is the correct expression to find the percent of increase in her wages?

   (1) ($5.75 − $6.21) ÷ $5.75
   (2) ($5.75 − $6.21) ÷ $6.21
   (3) ($6.21 + $5.75) ÷ $5.75
   (4) ($6.21 − $5.75) ÷ $5.75
   (5) ($6.21 − $5.75) ÷ $6.21

2. Tony works at a fast-food restaurant. His current hourly wage is $5.40. He is planning to take a new job at a restaurant that is closer to his home. His new hourly wage will be $5.13. Which is the correct expression to find the percent of decrease in his wages?

   (1) ($5.13 − $5.40) ÷ $5.13
   (2) ($5.13 + $5.40) ÷ $5.40
   (3) $5.40 − $5.13
   (4) ($5.40 − $5.13) ÷ $5.13
   (5) ($5.40 − $5.13) ÷ $5.40

3. Carla is a construction worker. She currently earns $11.50 per hour. After a review of her work, her boss tells her that her new hourly wage will be $12.19. Which is the correct expression to find the amount of increase in her wages?

   (1) $11.50 − $12.19
   (2) $12.19 + $11.50
   (3) $12.19 − $11.50
   (4) ($12.19 − $11.50) ÷ $11.50
   (5) ($12.19 − $11.50) ÷ $12.19

4. Laura works nights as a nurse's aide. Her current wage is $6.40 per hour. She has decided to take a job on the day shift, although her hourly wage will be $6.20. Which is the correct expression to find the percent of decrease in her wages?

   (1) ($6.20 − $6.40) ÷ $6.20
   (2) ($6.20 ÷ $6.40) ÷ $6.40
   (3) ($6.40 − $6.20) ÷ $6.20
   (4) ($6.40 + $6.20) ÷ $6.40
   (5) ($6.40 − $6.20) ÷ $6.40

5. Ike is a welder. He earns $13.25 per hour. His boss told him that he will be getting a raise of $1.06 per hour. Which is the correct expression to find the percent of increase in his wages?

   (1) $1.06 ÷ $13.25
   (2) $1.06 ÷ ($13.25 + $1.06)
   (3) $13.25 + $1.06
   (4) ($13.25 − $1.06) ÷ $1.06
   (5) ($13.25 − $1.06) ÷ $13.25

6. Marcus works at a small factory. His current hourly wage is $7.24. Yesterday the manager announced that it will be necessary to cut everyone's wages to keep the factory in business. Marcus's new wage will be $6.95. Which is the correct expression to find the percent of decrease in his wages?

   (1) ($6.95 − $7.24) ÷ $6.95
   (2) ($7.24 − $6.95) ÷ $6.95
   (3) ($7.24 − $6.95) ÷ $7.24
   (4) ($7.24 ÷ $6.95) − $6.95
   (5) ($7.24 ÷ $6.95) − $7.24

Finding the Percent of Change

Finding the Percent of Increase

Follow these steps to find the percent of increase:

Step 1. Identify the **original amount** (the base).

Step 2. Identify the **new amount**. Find the **amount of change** (the part) by subtracting the original amount from the new amount.

Step 3. Use the percent formula. Divide the part by the base to find the rate.

Step 4. Change the decimal to a percent.

Example

In January, Warren's landlord raised his rent from $450.00 to $486.00 per month. What is the percent of increase in Warren's rent?

Step 1. The original amount, or base, is $450.00.

Step 2. His new rent is $486.00. Subtract to find the amount of change, or the part.

$$\begin{array}{r} \$486.00 \\ -\ 450.00 \leftarrow \text{base} \\ \hline \$36.00 \leftarrow \text{part} \end{array}$$

Step 3. Divide the part, $36.00, by the base, $450.00, to find the rate.

$$\begin{array}{r} 0.08 \\ \$450)\overline{\$36.00} \\ -\ 36\ 00 \\ \hline 0 \end{array}$$

Step 4. Change the decimal to a percent.

$0.08 = 0.08. = 8\% \leftarrow$ rate

There was an 8% increase in Warren's rent in January.

You can also use a proportion to solve a percent of change problem.

Step 1. Set up the proportion.

$$\frac{\text{part (amount of change)}}{\text{base (original amount)}} = \text{rate of change (\%)}$$

$$\frac{\$36}{\$450} = \frac{?}{100}$$

Step 2. Cross-multiply.

Step 3. Divide by the remaining number.

$$\frac{\$36}{\$450} \searrow \frac{?}{100}$$

$\$36 \times 100 = \$3{,}600$
$\$3{,}600 \div \$450 = 8$

Step 4. Write the percent sign. $\frac{8}{100} = 8\%$

Finding the Percent of Decrease

The steps are almost the same to find the percent of decrease.

Example   Chris's Deli lowered the price of its Club Sandwich Combo from $4.00 to $3.20. What is the percent of decrease?

You can solve this problem using the percent formula.

Step 1. The original price of the combo was $4.00, so $4.00 is the base.

Step 2. The new price is $3.20. Subtract the smaller new amount from the original amount to find the amount of change (the part).

$$
\begin{array}{r}
\$4.00 \\
- \ 3.20 \\
\hline
\$0.80
\end{array}
\quad
\begin{array}{l}
\leftarrow \text{ base} \\
\\
\leftarrow \text{ part}
\end{array}
$$

Step 3. Divide the part ($0.80) by the base ($4.00) to find the rate.

$$
\begin{array}{r}
0.20 \\
4\overline{)\,\$0.80} \\
-\ 80 \\
\hline
0
\end{array}
$$

Step 4. Change the decimal to a percent. $0.20 = 0.20. = 20\%$ ⟵ rate

There was a 20% decrease in the price of the combo.

You can get the same answer using a proportion to solve the problem.

Step 1. Set up the proportion. $\dfrac{\text{part (amount of change)}}{\text{base (original amount)}} = \text{rate of change (\%)}$

$$\frac{\$0.80}{\$4.00} = \frac{?}{100}$$

Step 2. Cross-multiply. $\dfrac{\$0.80}{\$4.00} \searrow \dfrac{?}{100}$ $\$0.80 \times 100 = \$80.00$

Step 3. Divide by the remaining number.

$$
\begin{array}{r}
20 \\
\$4.00\overline{)\,\$80.00} \\
-\ 80\ 00 \\
\hline
0
\end{array}
$$

Step 4. Write the percent sign. $\dfrac{20}{100} = 20\%$

Practice ■ Find the percent of increase or decrease. Show your work.

Original Amount	New Amount	Percent of Change
1. $575.00	$690.00	_20%_

$690.00
− 575.00
$115.00

$$\begin{array}{r} 0.2 \\ \$575\overline{)\,115.00} \\ -\,115\,0 \\ \hline 0 \end{array}$$

0.2 = 20%

2. $8.80 $6.60   _____

3. 25 pounds   15 pounds   _____

4. 4,800 people   5,376 people   _____

5. 70 gallons   63 gallons   _____

6. $24.00 $22.56   _____

■ Write your answers in the blanks. Show your work.

7. Last year Michael's car insurance premium was $750.00. His car insurance premium this year is $1,125.00. What is the percent of increase in the premium?

8. A bus ticket from Mesa to Beaverton was $28.00. To attract more customers, the bus company reduced the fare to $23.80. What is the percent of decrease in the fare?

_____   _____

Using a Double Bar Graph

Acorn Business Systems has offices in four states. The company sells office machines to other businesses. The following graph shows company sales by state for the first and second quarters of the year. A quarter is three months.

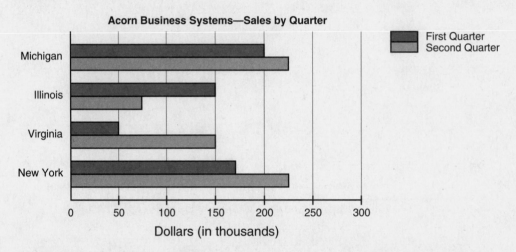

Acorn Business Systems—Sales by Quarter

This graph is called a **double bar graph** because there are two bars for each state. From the key, you learn that the blue bars show the first quarter sales, and the gray bars show the second quarter sales.

The length of the bars is measured using the scale at the bottom of the graph. The numbers on the scale represent thousands of dollars.

Example

The first-quarter bar (blue) for Michigan reaches the mark labeled *200* on the scale. Sales for the Michigan stores for the first quarter equal $200,000.

Carol Todd works at the main office in New York. Her boss, Jorge Ruiz, wants her to use the graph to find some information for him. Jorge wants to know the percent of change from the first quarter to the second quarter for Illinois, Virginia, and New York.

Carol reads the graph to find the sales figures for both quarters in Illinois. The blue bar, representing the first quarter, reaches the mark labeled *150* on the scale. The gray bar, representing the second quarter, reaches halfway between the marks labeled *50* and *100*. The gray bar represents 75 thousand dollars. Carol needs to find the percent of decrease from 150 to 75.

The base is 150. Carol subtracts 75 from 150 to find the part. The part is the difference, 75.

```
  150
−  75
   75
```

Then she uses the percent formula to solve for the rate. She divides the part, 75, by the base, 150, to find the rate.

```
      0.50          0.50 = 0.50. = 50%
150) 75.00
   − 75 0
        0
```

There was a 50% decrease in sales in Illinois from the first quarter to the second quarter.

Then Carol reads the graph for Virginia. The blue bar reaches the mark labeled *50*. The gray bar reaches the mark labeled *150*. What is the percent of increase from 50 to 150?

(1) $66\frac{2}{3}\%$
(2) 75%
(3) 100%
(4) 200%
(5) 250%

Answer 4 is the correct choice. Carol subtracts to find the part. Then she divides the part, 100, by the base, 50, to find the rate. There was a 200% increase in sales in Virginia from the first quarter to the second quarter.

```
  150
−  50
  100
```

```
      2.00  = 2.00. = 200%
50) 100.00
  − 100
       0
```

Carol reads the graph for New York. The blue bar represents 175. The gray bar represents 225. To the nearest whole percent, what is the percent of increase from 175 to 225?

(1) 22%
(2) 29%
(3) 33%
(4) 50%
(5) 72%

Answer 2 is the correct choice. Carol subtracts to find the part. Then she uses the percent formula to solve for the rate. There was a 29% increase in sales in New York.

```
  225
− 175
   50
```

```
      0.285  rounds to 0.29
175) 50.000        0.29 = 29%
   − 35 0
     15 00
   − 14 00
      1 000
    −   875
        125
```

Practice Use the following graph to answer items 1–6.

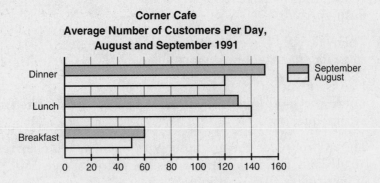

Circle the best answer for each item.

1. How many more customers did the Corner Cafe have each day for dinner in September than in August?

   (1) 15
   (2) 20
   (3) 30
   (4) 40
   (5) 270

2. To the nearest whole percent, what is the percent of increase in the number of customers each day for dinner from August to September?

   (1) 13%
   (2) 20%
   (3) 25%
   (4) 44%
   (5) 56%

Write your answers in the blanks. Show your work.

3. To the nearest whole percent, what percent of the total customers each day during September were breakfast customers?

5. To the nearest whole percent, what is the percent of decrease in the number of customers each day for lunch from August to September?

_____

4. To the nearest whole percent, what is the percent of increase in the number of customers each day for breakfast from August to September?

6. To the nearest whole percent, what is the percent of increase in the total number of customers each day from August to September?

_____

Weight Changes

Problem-Solving Strategy: Too Much Information

Risa Chapa works at a health care clinic. She writes information in the patient files and makes sure the files are complete. Two of the patients the doctor will see today are on weight-loss programs. To complete the charts for each patient, Risa will write the patient's current weight in the chart and calculate the percent of change in weight to the nearest whole percent.

Silvia Torres is the first patient. When she first came to the clinic, she weighed 166 pounds. Ms. Torres is 5 feet 4 inches tall. Using a chart, the doctor found that her ideal weight is 140 pounds. Dr. Martin told her she needed to lose 26 pounds. One month later, she had lost 5 pounds. On her next visit, she was down to 153 pounds. Today, she weighs 146 pounds.

Risa needs to calculate the percent of change in Ms. Torres' weight. To the nearest whole percent, what is the percent of decrease in Ms. Torres' weight since her first visit?

(1)   8%
(2)   10%
(3)   12%
(4)   14%
(5)   16%

Answer 3 is the correct choice. The percent of decrease from the patient's original weight of 166 pounds to her current weight of 146 pounds is 12%.

Find the difference.	Solve for the rate.	Round and change to a percent.
166	0.120	0.120 rounds to 0.12.
− 146	166) 20.000	0.12 = 0.12. = 12%
20 pounds	− 16 6	
	3 40	
	− 3 32	
	80	

Risa records the percent of decrease in the patient's chart.

This problem contained too much information. What information do you need to find the percent of change? You need to know only the original weight and the current weight. The other quantities are extra information.

Joe Ludlow is 6 feet 1 inch tall. According to the chart, his ideal weight is 178 pounds. Three months ago, Joe weighed 214 pounds. Today he weighs 224 pounds. Dr. Martin puts Joe on a diet to help him get down to his ideal weight.

To the nearest whole percent, what would be the percent of decrease from his current weight to his ideal weight?

(1) 14%
(2) 16%
(3) 19%
(4) 21%
(5) 26%

Answer 4 is the correct choice. Joe's current weight of 224 is the original amount, or base. His ideal weight of 178 pounds is the new amount.

Find the difference.	Solve for the rate.	Round and change to a percent.

$$\begin{array}{r} 224 \\ -\ 178 \\ \hline 46 \text{ pounds} \end{array}$$

$$\begin{array}{r} 0.205 \\ 224\overline{)46.000} \\ -\ 44\ 8 \\ \hline 1\ 200 \\ -\ 1\ 120 \\ \hline 80 \end{array}$$

0.205 rounds to 0.21.
0.21 = 0.21. = 21%

Now Risa needs to find the percent of increase in Joe's weight over the last three months. Three months ago, he weighed 214 pounds. Now he weighs 224 pounds. What is the percent of increase to the nearest whole percent?

(1) 4%
(2) 5%
(3) 6%
(4) 8%
(5) 10%

Answer 2 is the correct choice. The original amount is 214 pounds. His current weight is 224 pounds.

Find the difference.	Solve for the rate.	Round and change to a percent.

$$\begin{array}{r} 224 \\ -\ 214 \\ \hline 10 \text{ pounds} \end{array}$$

$$\begin{array}{r} 0.046 \\ 214\overline{)10.000} \\ -\ 8\ 56 \\ \hline 1\ 440 \\ -\ 1\ 284 \\ \hline 156 \end{array}$$

0.046 rounds to 0.05.
0.05 = 0.05. = 5%

Risa writes the information on the patient's chart.

Practice ◤ Circle the best answer for each item.

Items 1–2 refer to the following information.

Vanessa is 5 feet 6 inches tall. Her ideal weight is 150 pounds. Before getting sick, Vanessa weighed 160 pounds. Today Vanessa is well and weighs 142 pounds.

1. To the nearest whole percent, what was the percent of decrease in Vanessa's weight while she was sick?

   (1)   5%
   (2)   6%
   (3)   7%
   (4) 11%
   (5) 13%

2. To the nearest whole percent, what would be the percent of increase from Vanessa's current weight to her ideal weight?

   (1)   5%
   (2)   6%
   (3)   7%
   (4) 11%
   (5) 13%

Items 3–4 refer to the following information.

John is 6 feet 2 inches tall. Two months ago, he weighed 240 pounds. He is exercising to reach his ideal weight of 185 pounds. Today he weighs 225 pounds.

3. To the nearest whole percent, what would be the percent of decrease from John's weight two months ago to his ideal weight?

   (1) 18%
   (2) 22%
   (3) 23%
   (4) 25%
   (5) 30%

4. To the nearest whole percent, what is the percent of decrease in John's weight from two months ago to his current weight?

   (1)   3%
   (2)   6%
   (3)   7%
   (4) 18%
   (5) 23%

◤ Write your answers in the blanks. Show your work.

Items 5–6 refer to the following information.

Toya is 5 feet 2 inches tall. Although her ideal weight is 120 pounds, two months ago Toya weighed only 95 pounds. Her doctor put her on a program to gain weight. After the first month, Toya weighed 102 pounds. Today, Toya weighs 108 pounds.

5. To the nearest whole percent, what is the percent of increase in Toya's weight during the last two months?

6. To the nearest whole percent, what would be the percent of increase from Toya's current weight to her ideal weight?

Using Your Math Skills

Circle the best answer for each item.

1. Willis worked at Value-Mart for $5.76 per hour. When Value-Mart closed, Willis went to work at Major's Department Store for $5.40 per hour. Which is the correct expression to find the percent of decrease in his wages?

   (1) ($5.76 + $5.40) ÷ $5.76
   (2) ($5.40 − $5.76) ÷ $5.40
   (3) ($5.40 ÷ $5.76) ÷ $5.76
   (4) ($5.76 − $5.40) ÷ $5.40
   (5) ($5.76 − $5.40) ÷ $5.76

2. Last year, the Hassans paid $216.00 each month for health insurance. This year, their monthly premium is $233.28. What is the percent of increase in their monthly premium?

   (1) 7%
   (2) 8%
   (3) 17%
   (4) 21%
   (5) 93%

3. Stan works as a data entry operator. His current wage is $6.50 per hour. Because of Stan's excellent performance, his boss gave him a raise. His new hourly wage will be $7.15. What is the percent of increase in Stan's wages?

   (1) 8%
   (2) 9%
   (3) 10%
   (4) 65%
   (5) 91%

4. Last year, Atlas Company had sales of $526,000. This year, Atlas had sales of $550,000. Which is the correct expression to find the percent of increase in sales?

   (1) ($526,000 − $550,000) ÷ $526,000
   (2) ($526,000 − $550,000) ÷ $550,000
   (3) ($550,000 − $526,000) − $526,000
   (4) ($550,000 − $526,000) ÷ $526,000
   (5) ($550,000 − $526,000) ÷ $550,000

Write your answers in the blanks. Show your work.

Items 5–7 refer to the following information.

Jan is 5 feet 3 inches tall. Her ideal weight is 128 pounds. Two months ago, she weighed 150 pounds. One month ago, she weighed 156 pounds. Then she started a weight-loss program. Today she weighs 146 pounds.

5. To the nearest whole percent, what was the percent of increase in Jan's weight during the month before she started her weight-loss program?

6. To the nearest whole percent, what was the percent of decrease in Jan's weight during the past month?

7. To the nearest whole percent, what would be the percent of decrease from Jan's weight one month ago to her ideal weight?

8. At Cinema 2, opening night attendance for *The Mysterious Silence* was 980 people. Three weeks later, 245 people attended the showing of this movie. What is the percent of decrease in attendance for the movie?

_____

9. Each year, Max flies to New York City to visit his mother. Last year, he paid $450 for airfare. This year, he paid $470. To the nearest whole percent, what is the percent of increase in Max's airfare?

_____

10. Consuella's old car got 15 miles per gallon of gas. Her new car gets 24.6 miles per gallon. What is the percent of increase in mileage with the new car?

_____

11. Last year, United Wholesalers employed 350 people throughout the country. Now the company employs 320. To the nearest whole percent, what is the percent of decrease in the number of employees?

_____

Items 12–14 refer to the following graph.

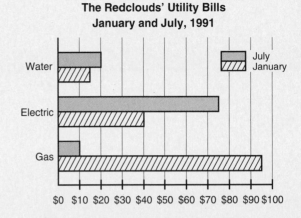

**The Redclouds' Utility Bills
January and July, 1991**

12. To the nearest whole percent, what is the percent of decrease in the gas bill from January to July?

_____

13. To the nearest whole percent, what is the percent of increase in the electric bill from January to July?

_____

14. To the nearest whole percent, what is the percent of increase in the water bill from January to July?

_____

Unit 4 Review:
Ratio, Proportion, and Percent

Solve. Show your work.

1. $\frac{8}{20} = \frac{?}{35}$

2. What is 450% of 72?

3. What percent of 320 is 8?

4. $4.05 is 9% of what amount?

Find the percent of increase or decrease. Show your work.

5. Original Amount   New Amount   Percent of Change

       $12.50 $17.50   _____

Write your answers in the blanks. Show your work.

<u>Items 6 and 7</u> refer to the following information.

Donita bought a washing machine that cost $520. She paid $100 down. She will pay the rest in monthly payments over 2 years at 18% interest.

6. Estimate how much interest Donita will pay.

     _____

7. Estimate what Donita's monthly payment will be.

     _____

8. Auto Needs has oil on sale at 3 quarts for $2.85. Minh wants to buy 8 quarts. How much will he pay for the oil?

     _____

9. Carlos is 6 feet 4 inches tall. His ideal weight is 205 pounds. One month ago, he weighed 250 pounds. Today he weighs 237 pounds. To the nearest whole percent, what is the percent of decrease in Carlos' weight during the last month?

     _____

Circle the best answer for each item.

10. Marvin's gross pay for one week is $340.00. His federal income tax deduction is $40.80. Which is the correct expression to find the percent of Marvin's gross pay that is deducted for federal income tax?

    (1) $40.80 + $340.00
    (2) $40.80 ÷ $340.00
    (3) $340.00 − $40.80
    (4) $340.00 ÷ $40.80
    (5) ($340.00 − $40.80) ÷ $340.00

11. Kelly bought a sweater. She saved $6.40 or 25% off the regular price. What was the regular price of this sweater?

    (1) $1.60
    (2) $16.00
    (3) $19.20
    (4) $25.60
    (5) $32.00

12. The Wilsons want to make a circle graph of their family budget. They budget 30% of their take-home pay each month for rent. How many degrees should be in the section representing rent?

    (1) 30°
    (2) 70°
    (3) 108°
    (4) 120°
    (5) 130°

13. Wanda, a school bus driver, earns $8.50 per hour. After a new contract is signed, her hourly wage will be $8.84. Which is the correct expression to find the percent of increase in her wages?

    (1) ($8.50 − $8.84) ÷ $8.50
    (2) ($8.50 − $8.84) ÷ $8.84
    (3) ($8.84 + $8.50) ÷ $8.50
    (4) ($8.84 − $8.50) ÷ $8.50
    (5) ($8.84 − $8.50) ÷ $8.84

Write your answers in the blanks. Show your work.

Item 14 refers to the following map.

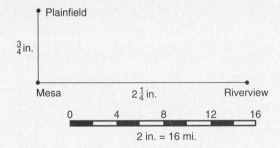

14. What is the actual distance in miles from Riverview to Mesa?

_____

Items 15 and 16 refer to the following graph.

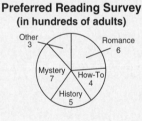

15. What is the total number surveyed?

_____

16. What percent of those surveyed preferred mysteries?

_____

Cumulative Review

Write each number in words.

1. 6,030,017 _____

2. 7.096 _____

Compare each pair of numbers. Write >, <, or = between the two numbers.

3. 54,277 _____ 54,227

4. 0.083 _____ 0.83

5. 5.10 _____ 5.1

Solve. Show your work.

6.
$$5\frac{2}{3}$$
$$+\;3\frac{3}{4}$$

7.
$$7\frac{1}{6}$$
$$-\;4\frac{4}{5}$$

8. $5 \times 4 - 2 + 9 \div 3 =$

9. $\sqrt{25} =$

10. $25 \div 0.8 =$

11. $\$27.36 \div 9 =$

12. $76 \times 60 =$

13. $0.097 \times 0.05 =$

14. $457 + 32 + 619 =$

15. $\$9.00 - \$3.48 =$

16. $3\frac{3}{8} \times 3\frac{1}{3} =$

17. $2\frac{1}{2} \div 3\frac{1}{4} =$

18. $2.54 + 3.408 + 53.1 =$

19. $8.4 - 3.726 =$

Check your answers on page 302.

Circle the best answer for each item.

20. Ben is building a rectangular dog pen that is 4.3 meters long and 2.5 meters wide. Which is the correct expression to find the perimeter of the dog pen?

(1) 2.5^2
(2) 4.3^2
(3) $4.3 + 2.5$
(4) 4.3×2.5
(5) $4.3 + 4.3 + 2.5 + 2.5$

21. A one-ounce serving of cereal has 120 calories and 2 grams of fat. What percent of the calories come from fat? (Reminder: 1 gram of fat contains 9 calories.)

(1) 8%
(2) 10%
(3) 12%
(4) 15%
(5) 25%

Item 22 refers to the following table.

Funship Park Admission

	1-Day Pass	2-Day Pass
Children (18 and under)	$ 9.95	$11.95
Adults	$19.95	$26.95
Senior Citizens (over 65)	$14.95	$21.95

22. Marti, who is 32, wants to buy a 2-day pass for herself and her 3 school-age children. How much will the passes cost?

(1) $35.85
(2) $47.80
(3) $49.80
(4) $62.80
(5) $99.60

Write your answers in the blanks. Show your work.

Items 23 and 24 refer to the following information.

During one week, the employees at RV Sales worked the following hours: 46, 39.5, 41.5, 38.5, 39, 41.5.

23. What is the mean number of hours worked?

_____

24. What is the median of the data?

Item 25 refers to the following graph.

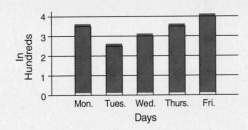

Crosstown Courier Service Deliveries, 3/24–3/28

25. What is the difference between the number of deliveries made on the busiest day and the number of deliveries made on the slowest day?

_____

Unit 5

SPECIAL TOPICS

These people are waiting to buy lottery tickets. All lotteries depend on the laws of probability.

Imagine you buy a lottery ticket. You have to pick 6 numbers out of 49 possible numbers. The chances that you will choose the right numbers are about 1 out of 14 million. The probability is very low (much less than 1%) that you will pick the right 6 numbers to win the lottery.

Probability uses numbers to show how likely it is that an event will happen. When you cannot control how an event will turn out, the outcome or result is left to **chance**.

Now imagine you are playing a board game. You throw a 6-sided die to find how many spaces to move. When you land on a red space, you draw a card from a deck of 50 cards. When you land on a blue space, you spin a spinner to see how many points you earn. The spinner can stop in 1 of 8 sections.

The outcome of throwing the die, drawing a card, or spinning the spinner is left to chance. The outcome is random. Any side of the die is just as likely to come up. Any card is just as likely to be drawn, and the arrow is just as likely to stop in any of the sections on the spinner.

Although the outcomes are random, you can calculate the probability of drawing a certain card, throwing a certain number with a die, or having a spinner stop on a certain space. In Section 16, you will learn more about probability.

You will learn about triangles and circles in this unit. A **triangle** is a figure with three sides and three angles. In Section 17, you will identify different kinds of triangles.

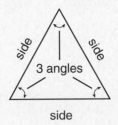

A **circle** is different from the other figures in this book because it has a curved edge. The distance around this curved edge is called the **circumference** of the circle. You can solve for the circumference using a formula given in Section 17. The **area** is the measure of the surface of the circle. You will learn a formula to solve for the area of a circle in Section 17.

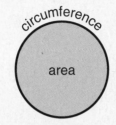

Another special topic involves the use of **integers**. Suppose John has $30.00 in the bank. What will John's balance be if he writes a check for $35.00? His new balance will be –$5.00. In other words, he will be $5.00 overdrawn.

John's balance of –$5.00 is a negative number and represents an amount less than 0. His original balance of $30.00 can also be written +$30.00. It is a positive number and represents an amount greater than 0.

All whole numbers—including positive numbers, negative numbers, and zero—are called integers. One way to show a range of integers is on a number line.

A number line has equally spaced points marked on the line. One point is labeled *0*. The numbers to the right of *0* are positive numbers. The numbers to the left of *0* are negative numbers. All of the numbers on the number line are integers.

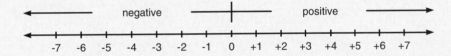

You will learn more about integers and how to solve problems using a number line in Section 18.

Here are a few of the problem-solving situations presented in Unit 5:

- finding the probability of choosing a certain name in an office drawing

- finding the probability of winning a certain prize on a game show

- identifying right, acute, isosceles, and equilateral triangles

- finding the circumference of a fountain

- finding the area of a circular pond in order to buy tiling

- reading a thermometer

- using a number line with positive and negative numbers

Section 16

Probability Theory

Facts About Probability

Scott is organizing the holiday office party. He writes the names of ten employees, including the name of the boss, Molly, on separate cards. Then he folds each card the same way and puts the ten cards in a box. Each person will pick a name and buy that coworker a gift. Wanda chooses first. She reaches into the box without looking and takes one card.

The name that Wanda picks is left to **chance.** In other words, Scott and Wanda cannot **control** how the drawing will turn out, and they cannot predict with certainty what will happen.

An **outcome** is a result. There are ten cards in the box. When Wanda picks a card, there are ten possible outcomes. Each of the ten outcomes is equally likely to occur.

■ Probability is the study of chance and outcome.

You can express probability using the numbers from 0 to 1 or using percents from 0% to 100%. A probability of 1 or 100% means that you are sure that a certain outcome will occur. A probability of 0 or 0% means that a certain outcome cannot possibly happen.

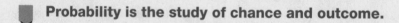

■ Example

What is the probability that Wanda will pick the name of one of the ten office employees?

The probability is 1 or 100% that the paper will have the name of an employee on it. There is no other possibility.

■ Example

What is the probability that the card Wanda picks will be blank?

The probability that Wanda will pick a blank card is 0 or 0%. None of the cards is blank, so there is no possibility that the card she chooses will be blank.

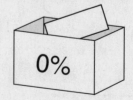

Finding the Probability of an Outcome

You can write probabilities that are greater than 0 but less than 1 either as a fraction or as a percent.

Example   What is the probability that Wanda will pick Molly's name?

Because there are 10 cards in the box, there are 10 equally likely outcomes. Since Molly's name is written on only one of the cards, the chance is 1 in 10 that Wanda will draw Molly's name.

You can write the probability as a fraction. The top number is the number of ways an outcome can occur. The bottom number is the number of possible outcomes. Reduce the fraction to lowest terms.

$$\text{Probability of an outcome} = \frac{\text{number of ways an outcome can occur}}{\text{number of possible outcomes}} = \frac{1}{10}$$

You can also express the probability as a percent by changing the fraction to a percent. The probability that Wanda will pick Molly's name is $\frac{1}{10}$ or 10%.

$$\begin{array}{r} 0.1 = 10\% \\ 10\overline{)1.0} \\ -\,1\,0 \\ \hline 0 \end{array}$$

Practice   Write each probability as a fraction and as a percent.

Items 1–4 refer to the following information.

A die (one of a pair of dice) is a cube with six sides marked as shown.

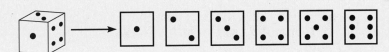

1. If you roll a die, what is the probability that you will roll a 4?

    Fraction: _____   Percent: _____

2. If you roll a die, what is the probability that you will roll a 9?

    Fraction: _____   Percent: _____

3. If you roll a die, what is the probability that you will roll a number less than 7?

    Fraction: _____   Percent: _____

4. If you roll a die, what is the probability that you will roll an even number (2, 4, 6)?

    Fraction: _____   Percent: _____

Items 5 and 6 refer to the following information.

A box contains 5 marbles: a red, a green, a blue, an orange, and a yellow marble. You take one marble out of the box without looking.

5. What is the probability that you will choose a colored marble?

    Fraction: _____   Percent: _____

6. What is the probability that you will choose a blue marble?

    Fraction: _____   Percent: _____

More Than One Chance for the Same Outcome

Sometimes there is more than one way for an outcome to occur.

Example

On a TV game show, a player spins a wheel to win a prize. The wheel has eight equal sections. Since the sections are the same size, there is an equal chance that the wheel will stop on any one section.

Only one section is marked *New Car*. A player has a 1 in 8 chance of winning a new car. The probability that the wheel will stop on the section marked *New Car* is $\frac{1}{8}$ or 12.5%.

Four sections are marked *$100*. A player has four chances of winning $100. What is the probability that the wheel will stop on *$100*?

There are four ways to win $100. There are eight sections on the wheel.

$$\text{Probability of an outcome} = \frac{\text{number of ways an outcome can occur}}{\text{number of possible outcomes}} = \frac{4}{8} = \frac{4 \div 4}{8 \div 4} = \frac{1}{2}$$

Change the fraction to a percent: $\frac{1}{2} = 50\%$

The probability of a player winning $100 is $\frac{1}{2}$ or 50%.

Example

A box contains 12 marbles. Nine marbles are black. Three marbles are white. If you take one marble from the box without looking, what is the probability that you will choose a white marble?

(1) $\frac{1}{12}$ or $8\frac{1}{2}\%$

(2) $\frac{1}{4}$ or 25%

(3) $\frac{1}{3}$ or $33\frac{1}{3}\%$

(4) $\frac{1}{2}$ or 50%

(5) $\frac{3}{4}$ or 75%

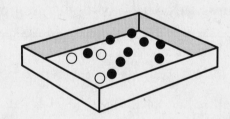

Answer 2 is the correct choice. You have 3 chances of choosing a white marble. There are 12 marbles in the box. The probability of choosing a white marble is $\frac{1}{4}$ or 25%.

$$\text{Probability of an outcome} = \frac{\text{number of ways an outcome can occur}}{\text{number of possible outcomes}} = \frac{3}{12} = \frac{3 \div 3}{12 \div 3} = \frac{1}{4}$$

Change the fraction to a percent: $\frac{1}{4} = 25\%$

Practice ▮ Circle the best answer for each item.

<u>Items 1– 4</u> refer to the following information.

The carnival game spinner shown contains 10 equal sections.

1. What is the probability that the wheel will stop on a shaded section?

   (1) $\frac{1}{10}$ or 10%

   (2) $\frac{3}{10}$ or 30%

   (3) $\frac{3}{8}$ or 37.5%

   (4) $\frac{1}{2}$ or 50%

   (5) $\frac{7}{10}$ or 70%

2. What is the probability that the wheel will stop on an even number (2, 4, 6, 8, 10)?

   (1) $\frac{1}{4}$ or 25%

   (2) $\frac{3}{10}$ or 30%

   (3) $\frac{1}{2}$ or 50%

   (4) $\frac{2}{3}$ or 66$\frac{2}{3}$%

   (5) 1 or 100%

3. What is the probability that the wheel will stop on a number greater than 4?

   (1) 0 or 0%

   (2) $\frac{1}{4}$ or 25%

   (3) $\frac{2}{5}$ or 40%

   (4) $\frac{1}{2}$ or 50%

   (5) $\frac{3}{5}$ or 60%

4. What is the probability that the wheel will stop on a number less than 12?

   (1) 0 or 0%

   (2) $\frac{1}{5}$ or 20%

   (3) $\frac{3}{5}$ or 60%

   (4) $\frac{9}{10}$ or 90%

   (5) 1 or 100%

▮ Write your answers in the blanks. Show your work.

<u>Items 5–7</u> refer to the following information.

A box contains 8 marbles: 3 black, 3 gray, and 2 white. You take one marble out of the box without looking.

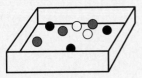

5. What is the probability that you will choose a gray marble?

_____

6. What is the probability that you will choose a black or gray marble?

_____

7. What is the probability that you will not choose a black marble?

_____

Check your answers on page 303.   *Section 16: Probability Theory*   233

Finding a Dependent Probability

Sometimes the chance of something happening depends on another outcome. To find a **dependent probability**, you have to consider the other outcomes.

M & M Furniture is having a drawing for its employees. The names of the six employees with the best attendance records will be written on cards and a drawing will be held. Two names will be drawn and the two employees drawn will win a vacation. Of the six employees in the drawing, two work in shipping and four work in sales.

The office manager wants to answer two questions:

■ What is the probability that the first name drawn will be an employee from the shipping department?

■ What is the probability that the second name drawn will be an employee from sales?

Two of the six employees work in shipping. The probability that an employee from shipping will be chosen first is $\frac{1}{3}$ or $33\frac{1}{3}\%$.

$$\frac{\text{number of ways an outcome can occur}}{\text{number of possible outcomes}} = \frac{2}{6} = \frac{2 \div 2}{6 \div 2} = \frac{1}{3} \qquad \frac{1}{3} = 33\frac{1}{3}\%$$

The probability that the second name drawn will be an employee from sales depends on which employee is chosen first. It is a **dependent probability**. There are two possible outcomes:

■ If the first name drawn is from shipping, there will be 5 names left: 1 name from shipping and 4 names from sales. In this case, the probability that the second name drawn will be from sales is $\frac{4}{5}$ or 80%.

First card drawn	These cards are left:				
Shipping	Shipping	Sales	Sales	Sales	Sales

■ If the first name drawn is from sales, there will be 2 names left from shipping and 3 names left from sales. In this case, the probability that the second name drawn will be from sales is $\frac{3}{5}$ or 60%.

First card drawn	These cards are left:				
Sales	Shipping	Shipping	Sales	Sales	Sales

Practice ◼ Circle the best answer for each item.

Items 1–3 refer to the following information.

Five friends are planning a fishing trip. To decide who will drive, they place five cards of the same size in a bag. *Drive* is written on one card. The other cards are blank. Each person will draw a card until someone draws the card with *Drive* on it.

1. What is the probability that the first card drawn will have *Drive* written on it?

   (1) $\frac{1}{5}$ or 20%

   (2) $\frac{1}{4}$ or 25%

   (3) $\frac{3}{4}$ or 75%

   (4) $\frac{4}{5}$ or 80%

   (5) 1 or 100%

2. The first card drawn is blank. What is the probability that the second card drawn will have *Drive* written on it?

   (1) $\frac{1}{5}$ or 20%

   (2) $\frac{1}{4}$ or 25%

   (3) $\frac{3}{4}$ or 75%

   (4) $\frac{4}{5}$ or 80%

   (5) 1 or 100%

3. The first card drawn is blank. What is the probability that the second card drawn will also be blank?

   (1) $\frac{1}{5}$ or 20%

   (2) $\frac{1}{4}$ or 25%

   (3) $\frac{3}{5}$ or 60%

   (4) $\frac{3}{4}$ or 75%

   (5) $\frac{4}{5}$ or 80%

◼ Write your answers in the blanks. Show your work.

Items 4–6 refer to the following information.

As part of Food Basket's grand opening, nine bills are placed in a box; six $20 bills and three $100 bills. Each hour, a customer will be selected to draw one bill from the box without looking.

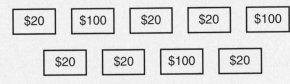

4. What is the probability that the first bill drawn will be a $100 bill?

_____

5. The first bill drawn is a $100 bill. What is the probability that the second bill drawn will also be a $100 bill?

_____

6. The first bill drawn is a $20 bill. What is the probability that the second bill drawn will be a $100 bill?

_____

Using Your Math Skills

<u>Items 1–8</u> refer to the following information.

A box contains 10 marbles: 6 black, 1 gray, and 3 white. You take one marble out of the box without looking.

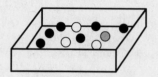

Circle the best answer for each item.

1. What is the probability that you will choose a black marble?

   (1) $\frac{2}{5}$ or 40%

   (2) $\frac{3}{5}$ or 60%

   (3) $\frac{2}{3}$ or 66$\frac{2}{3}$%

   (4) 1 or 100%

   (5) $\frac{3}{2}$ or 150%

2. What is the probability that you will choose a green marble?

   (1) 0 or 0%

   (2) $\frac{1}{10}$ or 10%

   (3) $\frac{1}{9}$ or 11$\frac{1}{9}$%

   (4) $\frac{2}{5}$ or 40%

   (5) 1 or 100%

3. What is the probability that you will choose a gray marble?

   (1) 0 or 0%

   (2) $\frac{1}{10}$ or 10%

   (3) $\frac{1}{9}$ or 11$\frac{1}{9}$%

   (4) $\frac{9}{10}$ or 90%

   (5) 1 or 100%

4. What is the probability that you will not choose a white marble?

   (1) 0 or 0%

   (2) $\frac{3}{10}$ or 30%

   (3) $\frac{2}{5}$ or 40%

   (4) $\frac{3}{5}$ or 60%

   (5) $\frac{7}{10}$ or 70%

Write your answers in the blanks. Show your work.

5. The first marble drawn is gray. A second marble is drawn. What is the probability that it is white?

   _____

6. The first marble drawn is gray. A second marble is drawn. What is the probability that it is also gray?

   _____

7. The first marble drawn is white. A second marble is drawn. What is the probability that it is black?

   _____

8. The first two marbles drawn are white. A third marble is drawn. What is the probability that it is also white?

   _____

Check your answers on page 304.

Section 17

Triangles and Circles

Identifying Triangles

A **triangle** has three sides and three angles. You can identify a triangle by the lengths of its sides and the measures of its angles.

Right triangle
One angle is a right angle. A right angle measures 90°.

Acute triangle
Each angle measures less than 90°.

Isosceles triangle
Two sides are the same length. Two angles have the same measure.

Equilateral triangle
All sides are equal. Each angle is 60°.

Example

Kafia is building a fence around a triangular garden. Each side of the garden measures 4 feet. What is the perimeter of the garden?

Kafia's garden is an equilateral triangle. Each side is the same length. The perimeter is 12 feet because 4 feet × 3 = 12 feet.

Practice Write the term or terms that describe each triangle. Use *right, acute, isosceles,* or *equilateral.* Some triangles can be described by more than one term.

1.

2.

3.

_____   _____   _____

4.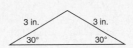

5.

6.

_____   _____   _____

Check your answers on page 304.

Finding the Circumference of a Circle

A **circle** differs in two ways from the other figures you have worked with in this book.

- A circle has a curved edge.

- Every point on the edge is the same distance from the center of the circle.

Example

Roger is building a low wall around a circular fountain. He needs to know the **circumference,** or the distance around the fountain, to buy materials for the job. If the diameter of the fountain is 8 feet, what is the circumference to the nearest foot?

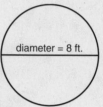

Because the edge of a circle is curved, you cannot measure the length of its edge in the same way that you measure the perimeter of squares, rectangles, and triangles. Instead, you can use information about the parts of the circle to find the circumference.

This diagram shows the parts of a circle:

The **diameter** is a straight line drawn from the edge of the circle, through the center, to the other edge.

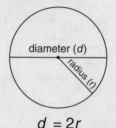

The **radius** is a straight line connecting the center of the circle to any point on the edge. The diameter is twice as long as the radius.

$$d = 2r$$

Roger needs to find the **circumference,** or the distance around the circle. He knows the diameter of the circle is 8 feet. He can use the diameter to find the circumference.

For all circles, the ratio of the circumference to the diameter is the same. The ratio is represented by the Greek letter π (pi). The value of π is about $\frac{22}{7}$, which is about 3.14. This means that for all circles, the distance around the circle is about three times the distance across the circle.

Using the ratio, we can write a formula for finding the circumference, C, of a circle.

 $C = \pi d$, where $\pi = 3.14$ and d = diameter

Since Roger knows the value of π, 3.14, and the diameter of the fountain, 8 feet, he can solve for the circumference.

Roger multiplies the diameter by the value of pi to find the circumference.

$C = \pi d$ 3.14   25.12 feet rounds to 25 feet.
$ = 3.14 \times 8$ $\underline{\times\ \ 8}$
$ = 25.12$ feet   25.12

The circumference of the fountain is about 25 feet.

Example

Karen wants to put a fence around a circular garden. She needs to calculate the circumference of the garden. The radius of the garden is 12 feet. What is the distance around the garden to the nearest foot?

The diameter of a circle is two times the length of the radius. Karen needs to calculate the diameter of the garden. The radius of the garden is 12 feet. Karen multiplies the radius by 2 to find the diameter ($12 \times 2 = 24$ feet).

Now she uses the formula to solve for circumference.

$C = \pi d$
$= 3.14 \times 24$
$= 75.36$ feet

```
  3.14
×  24
12 56
62 8
75.36
```

75.36 feet rounds to 75 feet.

The circumference of the garden is about 75 feet.

Practice Find the circumference of each circle. Round your answer to the nearest whole number. Show your work.

1.
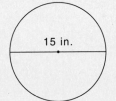

15 in.

2.
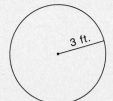

3 ft.

3.
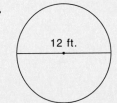

12 ft.

_____   _____   _____

Write your answers in the blanks. Show your work.

4. Raul is building a deck around a circular pool. The diameter of the pool is 24 feet. What is the circumference of the pool to the nearest foot?

5. Keesha is buying lace trim to sew on a round tablecloth. The radius of the tablecloth is 32 inches. What is the circumference of the tablecloth to the nearest inch?

_____   _____

Check your answers on page 304.

Finding the Area of a Circle

Lin is putting tiles on the floor of a circular pond. To buy tiles, he needs to know the area of the pond. If the radius of the pond is 3 feet, what is the area to the nearest square foot?

Lin uses a formula to find the area, *A*, of a circle.

$$A = \pi r^2, \text{ where } \pi = 3.14 \text{ and } r = \text{radius}$$

Lin multiplies 3.14 by the square of the radius ($r \times r$). Then he rounds the answer to the nearest square foot.

The area of the pond is about 28 square feet.

$$A = 3.14 \times 3 \times 3$$
$$= 3.14 \times 9$$
$$= 28.26 \text{ square feet}$$
28.26 sq. ft. rounds to 28 sq. ft.

Example

Another circular pond to be tiled has a diameter of 8 feet. What is the area to the nearest square foot? To find the radius, divide the diameter by 2 ($8 \div 2 = 4$). Then use the formula to find the area of a circle.

$$A = \pi r^2$$
$$= 3.14 \times 4 \times 4$$
$$= 50.24 \text{ sq. ft.}$$
50.24 sq. ft. rounds to 50 sq. ft.

Practice Find the area of each circle. Round your answer to the nearest whole square unit. Show your work.

1.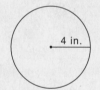
   4 in.

2.
   10 ft.

3.
   9 ft.

_____   _____   _____

Write your answers in the blanks. Show your work.

4. Rita is having a circular pool installed. The diameter of the pool is 18 feet. How much area to the nearest square foot will the pool cover?

5. Artemis is planting a circular rose garden that has a radius of 7 yards. What is the area of the garden to the nearest square yard?

_____   _____

Using Your Math Skills

Find the circumference and area of each circle. Round your answer to the nearest whole number. Show your work.

1.

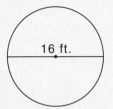

16 ft.

2.

10 yd.

3.

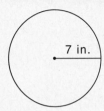

7 in.

Circumference: _____   Circumference: _____   Circumference: _____

Area: _____   Area: _____   Area: _____

Circle the best answer for each item.

4. Which terms best describe the triangle?

    (1)   acute; equilateral
    (2)   acute; isosceles
    (3)   acute; right
    (4)   right; equilateral
    (5)   right; isosceles

5. A flower bed is in the shape of an equilateral triangle. One side is 6 feet long. Which is the correct expression to find the perimeter of the flower bed?

    (1) $6 + 6 + 3$
    (2) 6×2
    (3) 6×3
    (4) 6×4
    (5) 6^3

Write your answers in the blanks. Show your work.

6. Marcus is planning to lay a sidewalk around the circular fountain in City Park. The radius of the fountain is 13 feet. What is the circumference of the fountain to the nearest foot?

_____

7. Andrea is placing mulch in circles around the young trees she has just planted. The radius of each mulched area is 9 inches. What is the area covered by each tree and its surrounding mulch to the nearest square inch?

_____

Check your answers on page 305.

Section 18

Integers

Problem-Solving Strategy: Reading a Thermometer

Laura lives in Duluth, Minnesota. On January 11, Laura looked at the outdoor thermometer and saw that the temperature was 4 degrees above 0. The next day, Laura heard on the radio that the temperature had dropped 12 degrees. What was the temperature on the second day?

In places where the weather gets very cold, you need positive and negative numbers to talk about the temperature. Temperature is measured in degrees above or below 0 using a thermometer. Positive numbers on the thermometer show a temperature greater than 0. Negative numbers show a temperature less than 0.

All whole numbers—positive numbers, negative numbers, and zero—are called **integers**.

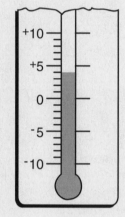

Integers that are greater than 0 are called **positive numbers**. Positive numbers are often written with a + in front of the number. A number (other than zero) that does not have a sign in front of it is always a positive number. Integers that are less than 0 are **negative numbers**. Negative numbers are written with a − in front of the number. A **number line** shows the relationship of the positive and negative numbers and zero. On a number line, positive numbers are to the right of 0 or greater than 0, and negative numbers are to the left of 0 or less than 0. The integer 0 is the starting point on a number line.

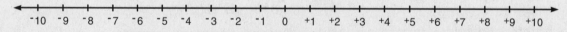

To solve problems using a number line, count to the right to find an increase or gain. Count to the left to find a decrease or loss.

A thermometer contains a vertical number line. Laura uses the number line to find the temperature on the second day. She starts at +4 and counts 12 units to the left because the temperature decreased 12 degrees. She ends at −8. The temperature on the second day was −8 degrees.

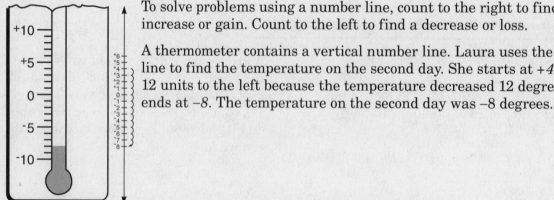

12 units

The radio announcer also said the temperature would increase 10 degrees by the third day. The temperature was –8 degrees on the second day. If the temperature increases 10 degrees, what will the temperature be on the third day?

(1) –10
(2) –8
(3) –2
(4) +2
(5) +4

Answer 4 is the correct choice. Start at *–8* on the number line and count 10 units to the right. Count to the right because the temperature increases 10 degrees. You end at *+2*. The temperature on the third day is +2 degrees.

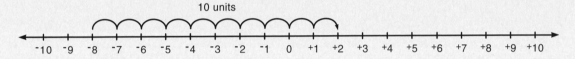

Practice ◆ Write your answers in the blanks. Refer to the number line below if necessary.

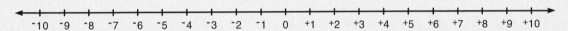

1. When Darius went to bed, the outdoor temperature was +6 degrees. The next morning, the temperature was 9 degrees lower. What was the morning temperature?

   _____

2. When Elena left for work in the morning, the temperature was –6 degrees. During the morning, the temperature increased +8 degrees. What was the temperature when Elena left work to go to lunch?

   _____

3. The morning low for Tuesday in the city was –5 degrees. During the day, the temperature increased 4 degrees. What was the high temperature for the day?

   _____

4. Jesse is a farmer. During very cold weather, he checks the temperature hourly. Before dinner, he saw that the temperature was –2 degrees. During the next hour, the temperature fell 3 degrees. What was the temperature at that time?

   _____

Unit 5 Review:
Special Topics

Circle the best answer for each item.

<u>Items 1–2</u> refer to the following information.

The carnival game spinner shown contains 8 equal sections.

1. What is the probability that the wheel will stop on a 3?

    (1) 0 or 0%

    (2) $\frac{1}{4}$ or 25%

    (3) $\frac{1}{3}$ or 33$\frac{1}{3}$%

    (4) $\frac{3}{8}$ or 37.5%

    (5) 1 or 100%

2. What is the probability that the wheel will stop on a number less than 5?

    (1) 0 or 0%

    (2) $\frac{1}{8}$ or 12.5%

    (3) $\frac{1}{2}$ or 50%

    (4) $\frac{5}{8}$ or 62.5%

    (5) 1 or 100%

3. A box contains 6 marbles: 4 black and 2 white. You take one marble out of the box without looking. The first marble you choose is black. Then you choose a second marble. What is the probability that it will also be black?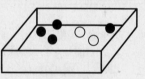

    (1) $\frac{2}{5}$ or 40%

    (2) $\frac{1}{2}$ or 50%

    (3) $\frac{3}{5}$ or 60%

    (4) $\frac{2}{3}$ or 66$\frac{2}{3}$%

    (5) $\frac{4}{5}$ or 80%

4. Which terms best describe this triangle?

    (1) right; acute
    (2) right; isosceles
    (3) right; equilateral
    (4) acute; equilateral
    (5) acute; right

<u>Items 5–6</u> refer to this circle.

5. What is the circumference of this circle to the nearest whole foot?

    (1) 19
    (2) 38
    (3) 48
    (4) 113
    (5) 452

6. What is the area of this circle to the nearest square foot?

    (1) 19
    (2) 38
    (3) 113
    (4) 144
    (5) 452

7. This pennant is an isosceles triangle. Which is the correct expression to find the perimeter?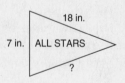

    (1) 18 + 7
    (2) 18 − 7
    (3) 18 × 7
    (4) 18 + 7 + 7
    (5) 18 + 18 + 7

Write your answers in the blanks. Show your work.

Items 8– 9 refer to the following number line.

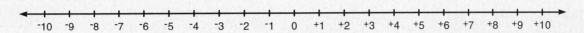

8. Yesterday's high temperature was +3 degrees. By midnight, the temperature had dropped 7 degrees. What was the temperature at midnight?

_____

9. The early morning low temperature was –5 degrees. By noon, the temperature had increased 8 degrees. What was the temperature at noon?

_____

10. You roll a die. What is the probability that you will roll an 8?

_____

11. Marge built a circular fish pond in her backyard. The radius of the pond is 7 feet. What is the area of the bottom of the pond to the nearest square foot?

_____

12. A round dining room table has a radius of 30 inches. What is the circumference to the nearest whole inch?

_____

Items 13–15 refer to the following information.

A bag contains 3 nickels and 2 dimes. You choose one coin without looking.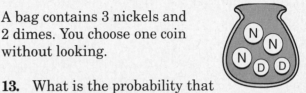

13. What is the probability that you will choose a nickel?

_____

14. The first coin you choose is a nickel. You choose another coin without looking. What is the probability that the second coin you choose will be a nickel also?

_____

15. The first coin you choose is a dime. You choose another coin without looking. What is the probability that the second coin you choose will be a nickel?

_____

Item 16 refers to the following information.

Six coworkers, 4 women and 2 men, decide to exchange gifts for the holidays. They each write their name on a card and place the cards in a box. Then each person will choose a name.

Man	Man	Woman
Woman	Woman	Woman

16. The first name chosen is a woman's name. What is the probability that the second name chosen will be a man's name?

_____

Check your answers on page 306.

Cumulative Review

Solve. Show your work.

1. $26 + 459 + 52 =$

2. $5,568 \div 27 =$

3. $9.2 - 6.487 =$

4. $0.048 \times 0.06 =$

5.
$$\begin{array}{r} 8 \\ -\ 3\frac{5}{8} \\ \hline \end{array}$$

6. $2\frac{2}{5} \times 3\frac{1}{8} =$

7. $9^2 =$

8. $\dfrac{9}{12} = \dfrac{?}{40}$

9. What percent of 32 is 40?

10. $378 \times 504 =$

11. $800 - 157 =$

12. $4.26 + 36.1 + 572.174 =$

13. $7 \div 0.16 =$

14.
$$\begin{array}{r} 2\frac{5}{6} \\ +\ 3\frac{3}{4} \\ \hline \end{array}$$

15. $4\frac{1}{2} \div 6\frac{3}{4} =$

16. $5^3 =$

17. What is 5% of $240?

18. 18 is 30% of what number?

                                   Check your answers on pages 306–307.

Circle the best answer for each item.

19. The Davises are putting a fence around their yard. The yard is 90 feet wide and 100 feet long. Which is the correct expression to find the perimeter of the yard?

(1) 90 + 100
(2) 90 × 100
(3) 90 + 90 + 90 + 90
(4) 90 + 90 + 100 + 100
(5) 100 + 100 + 100 + 100

20. Al works at a shoe store. Last week he sold 63 pairs of tennis shoes, 78 pairs of flats, and 35 pairs of boots. Estimate the total number of shoes and boots Al sold last week.

(1) 155 – 165
(2) 165 – 175
(3) 175 – 185
(4) 185 – 195
(5) 195 – 205

21. Latrice works as an accounting clerk for an appliance store. Her current wage is $6.20 per hour. After a review of her work, her boss tells her that her new hourly wage will be $6.60. Which is the correct expression to find the percent of increase in Latrice's wages?

(1) ($6.20 + $6.60) ÷ $6.20
(2) ($6.20 – $6.60) ÷ $6.20
(3) ($6.20 – $6.60) ÷ $6.60
(4) ($6.60 – $6.20) ÷ $6.20
(5) ($6.60 – $6.20) ÷ $6.60

22. Amy borrowed $5,600 from her aunt for 3 years at 14% interest to buy a used car. What is the interest on Amy's loan?

(1) $220.89
(2) $784.00
(3) $952.00
(4) $2,352.00
(5) $7,952.00

Write your answers in the blanks. Show your work.

23. John's recipe for date bars calls for $1\frac{3}{4}$ cups of chopped dates. He wants to double the recipe for a bake sale at the community center. How many cups of chopped dates should John use?

_____

24. What is the regular price of this sweater?

_____

25. Maria's personal record in the high jump is 1.98 meters. How many centimeters is this?

_____

Item 26 refers to the following diagram.

26. Hector needs mulch for a circular flower bed that is 6 feet in diameter. One bag of mulch covers 25 square feet. What is the area of the garden to the nearest square foot?

_____

POSTTEST

Write the value of the underlined digit in words.

1. 2,043,109 _____

2. 4.0<u>5</u>6 _____

Compare each pair of numbers. Write >, <, or = between the two numbers.

3. 25,744 _____ 25,447

4. 0.83 _____ 0.083

5. Round 420,536 to the nearest thousand.

6. Round 7.839 to the nearest tenth.

_____

_____

7. Write the mixed number that names the shaded portion.

 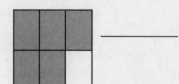

_____

Solve. Reduce answers to lowest terms.

8. $7.05
   − 3.88

9. 9.3
   − 4.654

10. 954
    × 307

11. 38) 7,925

12. $3\frac{3}{4}$
   $+ 5\frac{4}{5}$

13. $7\frac{1}{6}$
   $- 3\frac{3}{8}$

14. $8 + 2 \times 9 \div (7 - 4) =$

15. $76 + 58 + 429 =$

Go on to the next page.

16. $7.29 + 28.306 + 4.6 =$

17. $800 - 416 =$

18. $0.067 \times 0.08 =$

19. $2\frac{2}{3} \times 2\frac{1}{10} =$

20. $\$27.68 \div 8 =$

21. $2.5 \div 0.04 =$

22. $6\frac{2}{5} \div 5\frac{1}{3} =$

23. $6^3 =$

24. Change $3\frac{1}{2}\%$ to a decimal.

25. Change 6.5 to a percent.

26. Change 75% to a fraction.

27. Change $\frac{3}{5}$ to a percent.

28. What is 40% of $36?

29. What percent of 16 is 20?

30. 8 is 2% of what number?

31. $\frac{12}{40} = \frac{9}{?}$

Go on to the next page.

Circle the best answer for each item.

32. Shirley is the attendance secretary at Lincoln Junior High. There are 276 seventh graders and 287 eighth graders enrolled at Lincoln. On Monday, 542 students attended classes. What is the total enrollment at Lincoln?

    (1) 21
    (2) 563
    (3) 818
    (4) 829
    (5) 1,105

33. Jose is fencing a rectangular garden that is 4.8 meters long and 2.3 meters wide. Which is the correct expression to find the perimeter of the garden?

    (1) 4.8 + 2.3
    (2) 4.8 × 2.3
    (3) $4.8^2 + 2.3^2$
    (4) 4.8 + 4.8 + 2.3 + 2.3
    (5) 4.8 × 4.8 × 2.3 × 2.3

34. Rita wants to tile a rectangular floor that is 8 feet wide and 18 feet long. What is the area of Rita's floor in square feet?

    (1) 26
    (2) 52
    (3) 64
    (4) 144
    (5) 324

35. Of 121 customers who made a purchase at Sports World on Thursday, 63 paid cash. Estimate the number of charge customers.

    (1) 40
    (2) 50
    (3) 60
    (4) 175
    (5) 185

36. A company that makes lawn chairs ships the chairs in boxes of 4. Which is the correct expression to find the number of boxes needed to ship 36 chairs?

    (1) 4 + 36
    (2) 4 ÷ 36
    (3) 36 − 4
    (4) 36 × 4
    (5) 36 ÷ 4

37. A box has 10 marbles in it: 5 black, 4 white, and 1 blue. What is the probability of choosing a white marble?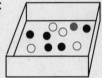

    (1) $\frac{1}{10}$ or 10%
    (2) $\frac{2}{5}$ or 40%
    (3) $\frac{1}{2}$ or 50%
    (4) $\frac{3}{5}$ or 60%
    (5) 1 or 100%

38. Karen's recipe for pudding uses $2\frac{1}{2}$ cups of milk. Karen is doubling the recipe. Which is the correct expression to find the number of cups of milk she needs?

    (1) $\frac{1}{2} \div 2\frac{1}{2}$
    (2) $2 \div 2\frac{1}{2}$
    (3) $2\frac{1}{2} \times \frac{1}{2}$
    (4) $2\frac{1}{2} \times 2$
    (5) $2\frac{1}{2} \div 2$

39. Which terms best describe this triangle?

    (1) acute; equilateral
    (2) acute; isosceles
    (3) acute; right
    (4) right; equilateral
    (5) right; isosceles

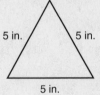

5 in.   5 in.

5 in.

40. Charlene works 8 hours per day as a salesperson. She spends 25% of her time preparing sales reports. How many hours each day does she spend preparing sales reports?

(1) 0.25
(2) 2
(3) 4
(4) 8
(5) 20

41. At birth, Sue and Ron's baby measured 46 centimeters long. How many meters long was the baby?

(1) 0.046
(2) 0.46
(3) 46
(4) 460
(5) 4,600

42. A department store is having a summer clearance sale. Men's sport shirts are on sale at 3 for $25.98. Rudy wants to buy one shirt. Which is the correct expression to find the cost of one shirt?

(1) 3 × $25.98
(2) 3 ÷ $25.98
(3) $25.98 × 3
(4) $25.98 ÷ 0.3
(5) $25.98 ÷ 3

43. Lisa's gross pay is $1,200.00 each month. She has $75.40 deducted for health insurance. Which is the correct expression to find the percent of Lisa's gross pay that is deducted for health insurance?

(1) $75.40 × $1,200.00
(2) $75.40 ÷ $1,200.00
(3) $75.40 − $1,200.00
(4) $1,200.00 − $75.40
(5) $1,200.00 ÷ $75.40

44. Ray bought a sweater for his son at Discount Fashions. The price tag is shown below. What is the original price of the sweater?

(1) $2.72
(2) $9.52
(3) $10.20
(4) $17.00
(5) $23.80

45. Value City has tube socks on sale at 6 pairs for $4.98. Darrell wants to buy 10 pairs. Which is the correct expression to find the cost of 10 pairs?

(1) $\dfrac{6}{?} = \dfrac{\$4.98}{10}$

(2) $\dfrac{6}{10} = \dfrac{?}{\$4.98}$

(3) $\dfrac{6}{\$4.98} = \dfrac{?}{10}$

(4) $\dfrac{6}{\$4.98} = \dfrac{10}{?}$

(5) $\dfrac{10}{\$4.98} = \dfrac{6}{?}$

46. Marge works the third shift at Capital Products. She earns $8.60 per hour. If she were to switch to first shift, her wages would be $8.30 per hour. Which is the correct expression to find the percent of decrease in her wages?

(1) ($8.30 − $8.60) ÷ $8.30
(2) ($8.30 + $8.60) ÷ $8.60
(3) ($8.60 − $8.30) ÷ $8.30
(4) ($8.60 − $8.30) ÷ $8.60
(5) ($8.60 ÷ $8.30) − $8.60

Go on to the next page.

Write your answers in the blanks. Show your work.

---

47. What is the volume in cubic inches of the shipping carton shown?

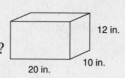

12 in.
10 in.
20 in.

_____

48. Gloria delivers newspapers. She drives $2\frac{1}{5}$ miles on Broad Street, $3\frac{9}{10}$ miles through a housing subdivision, and $1\frac{3}{10}$ miles on Hilltop Road. Estimate how many miles Gloria drives on her route.

_____

Item 49 refers to the following table.

Northbrook Hotel
Banquet Reservations, Week of 4/15

	Ballroom	Salon	Terrace
Friday	416	184	112
Saturday	504	224	136

49. Banquet guests are seated 8 guests to a table. How many tables must be set up for a banquet on Saturday in the ballroom?

_____

50. Mike is planning to reseal his driveway. His driveway is $27\frac{2}{3}$ yards long. How many feet are in $27\frac{2}{3}$ yards?

_____

Item 51 refers to the timecard below.

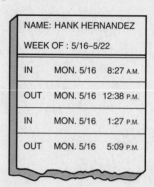

NAME: HANK HERNANDEZ
WEEK OF : 5/16–5/22

IN	MON. 5/16	8:27 A.M.
OUT	MON. 5/16	12:38 P.M.
IN	MON. 5/16	1:27 P.M.
OUT	MON. 5/16	5:09 P.M.

51. Approximately how many hours did Hank work in the afternoon?

_____

52. The Chans bought a circular pool for their children. The radius of the pool is 7 feet. What is the area to the nearest square foot covered by this pool?

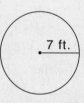

7 ft.

_____

53. George works at a hardware store. His customer bought a gallon of paint for $11.37 and a paintbrush for $2.89. Sales tax on this purchase was $0.72. The customer gave George $20.00 in cash. How much change should George have given his customer?

_____

Item 54 refers to the following graph.

Plainview Rainfall

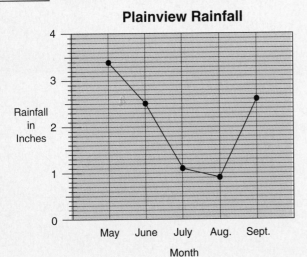

Month

54. What was the total amount of rainfall for August and September?

_____

55. Find the circumference of this circle to the nearest inch.

20 in.

_____

Item 56 refers to the following data.

Vehicles serviced by a mechanic during the 4 weeks in September: 42, 36, 19, 31

56. What is the mean of the data?

_____

57. At Good's Supply, 18 employees work in the warehouse and 12 drive delivery trucks. What is the ratio in lowest terms of warehouse employees to drivers?

_____

Item 58 refers to the following graph.

Swansons' Monthly Budget (in hundreds of dollars)

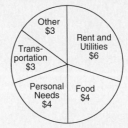

58. What percent of the Swansons' budget is for transportation?

_____

59. Conrad borrowed $7,300 from his parents. He will pay this back after 4 years at 11% interest. How much interest will he pay?

_____

Item 60 refers to the following number line.

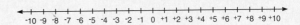

-10 -9 -8 -7 -6 -5 -4 -3 -2 -1 0 +1 +2 +3 +4 +5 +6 +7 +8 +9 +10

60. In the morning, the temperature was –3 degrees. By noon the temperature had increased 6 degrees. What was the temperature at noon?

_____

POSTTEST
Correlation Chart

Mathematics

The chart below will help you determine your strengths and weaknesses in the math skills presented in this book. Circle the number of each item you answered correctly. Count the number of items you answered correctly in each row. Write the amount in the *Total Correct* space for each row. (For example, in the *Whole Number Theory* row, write the number correct in the blank before *out of 4*). Complete this process for the remaining rows. Then add the 18 totals to get your Total Correct for the whole test. If you answered fewer than 54 items correctly, refer to the page numbers in the right-hand column for further practice on the skills.

Section/Skill	Item Numbers	Total Correct	Pages
1. Whole Number Theory	1, 3, 5, 14	_____ out of 4	10–15
2. Adding and Subtracting Whole Numbers	8, 15, 17, 32, 35	_____ out of 5	18–29
3. Multiplying and Dividing Whole Numbers	10, 11, 20, 34, 36, 49	_____ out of 6	32–43
4. Squares, Cubes, and Square Roots	23, 47	_____ out of 2	46–53
5. Fraction Theory	7	_____ out of 1	60–67
6. Adding and Subtracting Fractions	12, 13, 48, 51	_____ out of 4	70–82
7. Multiplying and Dividing Fractions	19, 22, 38, 50	_____ out of 4	86–98
8. Adding and Subtracting Decimals	2, 4, 6, 9, 16, 33, 53, 54	_____ out of 8	108–120
9. Multiplying and Dividing Decimals	18, 21, 41, 42, 56	_____ out of 5	124–135
10. Ratio and Proportion	31, 45, 57	_____ out of 3	144–158
11. Percent Theory	24, 25, 26, 27	_____ out of 4	162–165
12. Solving for the Part (p)	28, 40, 59	_____ out of 3	167–178
13. Solving for the Rate (r)	29, 43, 58	_____ out of 3	182–194
14. Solving for the Base (b)	30, 44	_____ out of 2	198–206
15. Percent of Change	46	_____ out of 1	210–221
16. Probability Theory	37	_____ out of 1	230–235
17. Triangles and Circles	39, 52, 55	_____ out of 3	237–240
18. Integers	60	_____ out of 1	242–243

TOTAL CORRECT FOR POSTTEST _____ out of 60

ANSWERS AND EXPLANATIONS

INVENTORY

PAGES 1–6

1. **three hundred thousand**
2. **seven thousandths**
3. **46,0̲23 < 46,2̲03**   Zero is less than 2.
4. **0.7̲6 > 0.4̲56**   Add a zero: 0.7̲60 0.4̲56
   Then compare. 0.760 is greater than 0.456.
5. **530,000**
   5③4,108 The number to the right of the 3 is less than 5. Do not change the circled digit.
6. **3.73**
   3.7②5 The number to the right of the 2 is 5; add 1 to the circled digit.
7. **$2\frac{1}{4}$**   Each figure is divided into 4 equal parts. Two figures are completely shaded, and 1 of the 4 parts of the last figure is shaded.
8. **272**
$$\begin{array}{r} {\overset{5\ 9\ 10}{\cancel{600}}} \\ -\ 328 \\ \hline 272 \end{array}$$
9. **2.854**
$$\begin{array}{r} {\overset{5\ 16\ 9\ 10}{\cancel{6.700}}} \\ -\ 3.846 \\ \hline 2.854 \end{array}$$
10. **451,744**
$$\begin{array}{r} 743 \\ \times\ 608 \\ \hline 5\ 944 \\ +\ 445\ 80 \\ \hline 451,744 \end{array}$$
11. **\$3.07**
$$\begin{array}{r} \$\ 3.07 \\ 4\overline{)\$12.28} \\ -\ 12\ \ \ \ \ \\ \hline 0\ 28 \\ -\ 28 \\ \hline 0 \end{array}$$
12. **$7\frac{5}{24}$**
$$\begin{array}{r} 4\frac{7}{8} = 4\frac{21}{24} \\ +\ 2\frac{1}{3} = 2\frac{8}{24} \\ \hline 6\frac{29}{24} = 6 + 1\frac{5}{24} = 7\frac{5}{24} \end{array}$$
13. **$1\frac{11}{15}$**
$$\begin{array}{r} 6\frac{2}{5} = 6\frac{6}{15} = \overset{5\ \ 21}{\cancel{6}\frac{\cancel{6}}{15}} \\ -\ 4\frac{2}{3} = 4\frac{10}{15} = 4\frac{10}{15} \\ \hline 1\frac{11}{15} \end{array}$$

14. **20**
$$\begin{array}{c} 12 \div (2 + 1) \times 6 - 4 \\ 12 \div \ \ \ \ 3 \ \ \ \ \times 6 - 4 \\ 4 \ \ \ \ \ \ \ \times 6 - 4 \\ 24 \ \ \ \ \ \ \ \ \ - 4 \\ 20 \end{array}$$
15. **475**
$$\begin{array}{r} {\overset{1\ 1}{42}} \\ 376 \\ +\ 57 \\ \hline 475 \end{array}$$
16. **38.201**
$$\begin{array}{r} {\overset{1\ 1\ 1}{3.270}} \\ 26.400 \\ +\ 8.531 \\ \hline 38.201 \end{array}$$
17. **\$2.09**
$$\begin{array}{r} {\overset{4\ \ 9\ 18}{\$\cancel{5.08}}} \\ -\ 2.99 \\ \hline \$2.09 \end{array}$$
18. **0.0162**
$$\begin{array}{r} 0.054 \\ \times\ \ 0.3 \\ \hline 0.0162 \end{array}$$
19. **$16\frac{1}{2}$** $4\frac{2}{5} \times 3\frac{3}{4} = \frac{\overset{11}{\cancel{22}}}{5} \times \frac{\overset{3}{\cancel{15}}}{\cancel{4}_{2}} = \frac{33}{2} = 16\frac{1}{2}$
20. **182 r14**
$$\begin{array}{r} 182\ \text{r}14 \\ 42\overline{)7,658} \\ -\ 42\ \ \ \ \ \\ \hline 3\ 45\ \ \\ -\ 3\ 36\ \ \\ \hline 98 \\ -\ 84 \\ \hline 14 \end{array}$$
21. **520**
$$\begin{array}{r} 5\ 20 \\ 0.06.\overline{)31.20.} \\ -\ 30\ \ \ \ \\ \hline 1\ 2\ \ \\ -\ 1\ 2\ \ \\ \hline 0 \end{array}$$
22. **$\frac{4}{5}$** $3\frac{1}{2} \div 4\frac{3}{8} = \frac{7}{2} \div \frac{35}{8} = \frac{\overset{1}{\cancel{7}}}{\cancel{2}} \times \frac{\overset{4}{\cancel{8}}}{\cancel{35}_{5}} = \frac{4}{5}$
23. **49** $7^2 = 7 \times 7 = 49$
24. **3.75** $375\% = 3.75. = 3.75$

25. **7%** $0.07 = 0.07 = 7\%$

26. $\frac{4}{5}$ $80\% = \frac{80}{100} = \frac{80 \div 20}{100 \div 20} = \frac{4}{5}$

27. **75%**
$$\begin{array}{r} 0.75 \\ 4\overline{)3.00} \\ \underline{-2\,8} \\ 20 \\ \underline{-\,20} \\ 0 \end{array}$$
$0.75 = 75\%$

28. **12** $8\% = 0.08$
$$\begin{array}{r} 150 \\ \times\ 0.08 \\ \hline 12.00 \end{array}$$

29. **25%**
$$\begin{array}{r} 0.25 \\ \$72\overline{)\$18.00} \\ \underline{-\,14\,4} \\ 3\,60 \\ \underline{-\,3\,60} \\ 0 \end{array}$$
$0.25 = 25\%$

30. **36** $150\% = 1.5$
$$\begin{array}{r} 3\,6 \\ 1.5\,)\overline{54.0.} \\ \underline{-\,45} \\ 9\,0 \\ \underline{-\,9\,0} \\ 0 \end{array}$$

31. **14** $8 \times 35 = 280;\ 280 \div 20 = 14$

32. **(3) 144 – 48**   Subtract the number of gallons of interior paint sold (48) from the number of gallons of interior paint in stock (144). You do not need the number of gallons of exterior paint.

33. **(2) 36**   Two sides measure 12 feet, and two sides measure 6 feet. Add all four measurements to find the perimeter.
$12 + 12 + 6 + 6 = 36$

34. **(3) 20²**   The room is a square because all four sides have the same length. Use the formula $A = s^2$, and substitute 20 for s.

35. **(3) 170**   Round the three to the nearest ten, and add to estimate the total.
$$\begin{array}{rll} 79 & \text{rounds to} & 80 \\ 35 & \text{rounds to} & 40 \\ +\ 52 & \text{rounds to} & +\ 50 \\ \hline & & 170 \end{array}$$

36. **(4) 16 x 8**   To find the total amount, multiply the number of packages (16) by the number of buns in each package (8).

37. **(3) $\frac{1}{2}$ or 50%**
$$\frac{\text{number of sections with 2}}{\text{number of sections}} = \frac{3}{6} = \frac{1}{2} \text{ or } 50\%$$

38. **(2) $\frac{3}{4}$**   To make one third of the recipe, divide the amount of broth ($2\frac{1}{4}$ cups) by 3.
$$2\frac{1}{4} \div 3 = \frac{9}{4} \div \frac{3}{1} = \frac{\overset{3}{\cancel{9}}}{4} \times \frac{1}{\underset{1}{\cancel{3}}} = \frac{3}{4}$$

39. **(2) $\frac{3}{\$1.56} = \frac{5}{?}$**   Both ratios are in the same order. The first ratio means that 3 pounds cost $1.56. The second ratio means that 5 pounds cost an unknown amount.

40. **(4) 40 x 15%**   Multiply the base (40) times the rate (15%) to find the part.

41. **(4) 200**   Multiply by 1,000 to convert kilograms to grams.
$0.2 \times 1,000 = 0.200 = 200$

42. **(4) $2.08 x 4**   Find the total cost by multiplying the unit cost ($2.08) by the number of pounds (4).

43. **(2) 6%**   Divide the part ($25.20) by the base ($420.00) to find the rate.
$$\begin{array}{r} 0.06 \\ \$420\overline{)\$25.20} \\ \underline{-\,25\,20} \\ 0 \end{array}$$
$0.06 = 6\%$

44. **(3) $18.60 ÷ 30%**   Divide the part ($18.60) by the rate (30%) to find the base.

45. **(5) right; isosceles**   One angle is a right angle (90°), and two sides have the same length.

46. **(2) 4%**   Subtract Abdul's current wage ($5.25) from his new wage ($5.46) to find the amount of change. Then divide by the original amount, his current wage.
$$\begin{array}{r} \$5.46 \\ -\ 5.25 \\ \hline \$0.21 \end{array} \qquad \begin{array}{r} 0.04 \\ \$5.25.\,)\overline{\$0.21.00} \\ \underline{-\ 21.00} \\ 0 \end{array}$$
$0.04 = 4\%$

47. **1,920 cubic inches**
$$\begin{aligned} V &= l \times w \times h \\ &= 10 \times 12 \times 16 \\ &= 1,920 \end{aligned}$$

48. **18 miles**   Round each distance and subtract.
$$\begin{array}{rll} 36\frac{9}{10} & \text{rounds to} & 37 \\ -\ 19\frac{2}{5} & \text{rounds to} & -\ 19 \\ \hline & & 18 \end{array}$$

49. **345 miles**   Multiply the number of gallons of gas (15) by the miles car B can travel on the highway per gallon of gas (23).

$$\begin{array}{r} 23 \\ \times\ 15 \\ \hline 115 \\ +\ 23 \\ \hline 345 \end{array}$$

50. **$4\frac{17}{24}$ feet**   Since there are 12 inches in a foot and inches are smaller than feet, divide $56\frac{1}{2}$ by 12.

$56\frac{1}{2} \div 12 = \frac{113}{2} \div \frac{12}{1} = \frac{113}{2} \times \frac{1}{12} = \frac{113}{24} = 4\frac{17}{24}$

51. **$3\frac{3}{4}$ hours**   Since 43 is close to 45, think of 8:43 as $8\frac{3}{4}$. Since 36 is close to 30, think of 12:36 as $12\frac{1}{2}$. Then subtract.

$$\begin{array}{r} 12\frac{1}{2} = 12\frac{2}{4} = \overset{11}{\cancel{12}}\overset{6}{\frac{\cancel{2}}{4}} \\ -\ 8\frac{3}{4} = \ \ 8\frac{3}{4} = \ \ 8\frac{3}{4} \\ \hline 3\frac{3}{4} \end{array}$$

52. **50 square feet**   Divide the diameter (8 ft.) by 2 to find the radius ($8 \div 2 = 4$ ft.).

$A = \pi r^2$
$A = 3.14 \times 4 \times 4$
$A = 3.14 \times 16$
$A = 50.24$ square feet

Then 50.24 square feet rounds to 50 square feet.

53. **$4.04**   Add the cost of the statue and the card to find the subtotal. Add the tax to find the total. Then subtract the total from the amount of cash the customer gives Tawanna to find the amount of change.

$$\begin{array}{ccc} \overset{1}{}\$32.50 & \$34.25 & \overset{3\ 9\ 9\ 10}{\$\cancel{40.00}} \\ +\ \ 1.75 & +\ \ 1.71 & -\ 35.96 \\ \hline \$34.25 & \$35.96 & \$\ 4.04 \end{array}$$

54. **1,500**   The bar for Lincoln County ends between the *3* and *4* marks and represents 3,500 customers. The bar for Hamilton County reaches the *2* mark and represents 2,000 customers. Subtract to find the difference.

$$\begin{array}{r} 3,500 \\ -\ 2,000 \\ \hline 1,500 \end{array}$$

55. **28 feet**

$C = \pi d$
$C = 3.14 \times 9$
$C = 28.26$ feet

Then 28.26 feet rounds to 28 feet.

56. **25**   Find the total of the numbers in the set.

$37 + 18 + 21 + 24 = 100$

Then divide by the number of items in the set.

$100 \div 4 = 25$

57. **22.5**   Arrange the numbers in order. Then find the middle numbers.

18, <u>21</u>, <u>24</u>, 37

Then find the mean of the middle numbers.

$21 + 24 = 45; 45 \div 2 = 22.5$

58. **$\frac{5}{9}$**

$\dfrac{20 \text{ in factory}}{36 \text{ employees}} = \dfrac{20 \div 4}{36 \div 4} = \dfrac{5}{9}$

59. **$5,640**

$\begin{aligned} interest &= principal \times rate \times time \\ &= \$9,400 \times 0.12 \times 5 \\ &= \$5,640 \end{aligned}$

60. **$^-$5 degrees**   Start at $^+$2 on the number line. Count 7 units to the left.

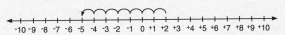

UNIT 1: WHOLE NUMBERS

SECTION 1

PAGE 10

2. ones
3. thousands
4. hundreds
5. ten thousands
6. hundred thousands
7. thousands
8. millions
9. hundreds
10. hundred thousands
11. tens
12. ten thousands
13. ones
14. ten millions
15. thousands
16. hundreds

PAGE 11

2. forty-three thousand, eighteen
3. one hundred fifteen thousand, two hundred
4. five million, four hundred thousand, twelve
6. 250,911
7. 12,016
8. 9,014,560

PAGE 12

2. **38,0̲00 < 38,5̲00**   0 is less than 5.
3. **179 = 179**   The numbers are the same.
4. **210,5̲80 > 218,4̲80**   5 is greater than 4.
5. **1,000,000 < 10,000,000**   10,000,000 has 8 digits; 1,000,000 has only 7 digits.
6. **496 < 4,690**   496 has fewer digits than 4,690.
7. **13,415 = 13,415**   The numbers are the same.
8. **802,1̲65 < 803,9̲80**   2 is less than 3.
9. **5,000 < 50,000**   5,000 has fewer digits than 50,000.
10. **1,3̲45 < 1,4̲35**   3 is less than 4.
11. **10,334 = 10,334**   The numbers are the same.
12. **479̲ > 476̲**   9 is greater than 6.
13. **340,6̲35 < 340,8̲35**   6 is less than 8.
14. **5,01̲0 > 5,00̲1**   1 is greater than 0.
15. **682,489 = 682,489**   The numbers are the same.
16. **3,80̲0 < 3,85̲0**   0 is less than 5.

PAGE 13

2. **1,700**
   1,⑦2̲3 Since 2 is less than 5, do not change the circled digit.
3. **7,000**
   ⑥,5̲09 The number to the right of 6 is 5; add 1 to the circled digit.
4. **900**
   ⑧6̲1 Since 6 is greater than 5, add 1 to the circled digit.
5. **20,000**
   1⑨,5̲80 The number to the right of 9 is 5; add 1 to the circled digit. The 9 becomes a 10. Write a zero and add 1 to the next place value to the left.
6. **210,000**
   2⓪9̲,320 Since 9 is greater than 5, add 1 to the circled digit.
7. **64,000**
   6④,2̲99 Since 2 is less than 5, do not change the circled digit.
8. **5,300,000**
   5,②5̲6,000 The number to the right of 2 is 5; add 1 to the circled digit.

PAGE 15

2. **35** $(4 + 3) \times 5$
            $7 \quad \times 5$
               35

3. **16** $7 + 8 - 9 \div 3 + 4$
            $7 + 8 - \quad 3 \quad + 4$
            $15 \quad - \quad 3 \quad + 4$
               $12 \qquad + 4$
                  16

4. **20** $8 + 6 \times (12 \div 6)$
            $8 + 6 \times \quad 2$
            $8 + \qquad 12$
               20

5. **13** $4 \times 3 - 1 + 6 \div 3$
            $12 \quad - 1 + 6 \div 3$
            $12 \quad - 1 + \quad 2$
            $11 \qquad + \quad 2$
               13

6. **11** $9 \div (4 - 1) + 8$
            $9 \div \quad 3 \quad + 8$
               $3 \quad + 8$
                  11

7. **15** $6 \times 3 + 2 - 10 \div 2$
            $18 \quad + 2 - 10 \div 2$
            $18 \quad + 2 - \quad 5$
               $20 \quad - \quad 5$
                  15

8. **5**
$$\begin{aligned}(8 + 4) \div 3 + 1 \\ 12 \div 3 + 1 \\ 4 + 1 \\ 5\end{aligned}$$

9. **10**
$$\begin{aligned}35 \div 7 + 4 \times 2 - 3 \\ 5 + 4 \times 2 - 3 \\ 5 + 8 - 3 \\ 13 - 3 \\ 10\end{aligned}$$

10. **4**
$$\begin{aligned}3 \times (9 - 5) \div 6 \times 2 \\ 3 \times 4 \div 6 \times 2 \\ 12 \div 6 \times 2 \\ 2 \times 2 \\ 4\end{aligned}$$

11. **19**
$$\begin{aligned}7 \times 2 + 8 - 3 \\ 14 + 8 - 3 \\ 22 - 3 \\ 19\end{aligned}$$

12. **5**
$$\begin{aligned}10 - 7 \times 1 + 4 \div 2 \\ 10 - 7 + 4 \div 2 \\ 10 - 7 + 2 \\ 3 + 2 \\ 5\end{aligned}$$

PAGES 16–17

1. **hundreds**
2. **ten thousands**
3. **millions**
4. **hundred thousands**
5. **twenty-eight thousand, three hundred two**
6. **one million, seventy-six thousand, five hundred**
7. **42,057**
8. **3,400,590**
9. **5,680 > 856**
   5,680 has more digits than 856.
10. **32,457 = 32,457** The numbers are the same.
11. **82,346 < 82,546** 3 is less than 5.
12. **790,300 > 709,300** 9 is greater than 0.
13. **40**
   4⃝3 Since 3 is less than 5, do not change the circled digit.
14. **2,500**
   2,4⃝53 The number to the right of the circled digit is 5; add 1 to the circled digit.
15. **310,000**
   30⃝7,126 Since 7 is greater than 5, add 1 to the circled digit.
16. **4,000,000**
   4⃝,293,785 Since 2 is less than 5, do not change the circled digit.

17. **13**
$$\begin{aligned}5 + 4 \times 3 - 8 \div 2 \\ 5 + 12 - 8 \div 2 \\ 5 + 12 - 4 \\ 17 - 4 \\ 13\end{aligned}$$

18. **23**
$$\begin{aligned}32 \div (5 + 3) \times 6 - 1 \\ 32 \div 8 \times 6 - 1 \\ 4 \times 6 - 1 \\ 24 - 1 \\ 23\end{aligned}$$

19. **(2) Fewer parts were produced during week 1 than during week 3.** 12,4̲35 (week 1) > 12,3̲45 (week 3) because 4 > 3. Therefore, <u>more</u> parts were produced during week 1 than during week 3.
20. **(4) week 4**
   14,814 (week 4) > 12,435 (week 1) because 4 > 2.
   14,8̲14 (week 4) > 14,5̲26 (week 2) because 8 > 5.
   14,814 (week 4) > 12,345 (week 3) because 4 > 2.
   14,814 (week 4) > 13,7̲06 (week 5) because 4 > 3.
21. **(5) week 5**
   13⃝,̲706 Since 7 is greater than 5, add 1 to the circled digit. 13,706 (week 5) rounds to 14,000.
22. **(2) one million, thirty thousand, four hundred two**
23. **(4) 245,603 > 245,306**
   245,6̲03 > 245,3̲06 because 6 is greater than 3.
24. **(4) $1,500**
   $1,4⃝8̲3 Since 8 is greater than 5, add 1 to the circled digit.
25. **(2) 410,308**

SECTION 2

PAGES 19–20

1. **(1) 8 – 2** Find the difference between the length of the side and the break in the fence. Subtract the smaller number from the larger one.
2. **(4) 40 + 40 + 30 + 30** Since it is a rectangle, two sides of the space measure 40 feet and two sides measure 30 feet. Add all four measurements to find the perimeter.
3. **(4) 7 + 7 + 3** The door is a rectangle, but the molding goes along only three of the lengths. The two sides each measure 7 feet. The top of the doorway measures 3 feet. Add the three measurements to find the total molding needed.

Answers and Explanations 259

4. **(5) 20 + 20 + 24 + 24**   Since it is a
rectangle, two sides of the painting measure
20 inches and two sides measure 24 inches.
Add all four measurements to find the
perimeter.

5. **(2) 80 − 3**   Find the difference in the width
of the yard and the opening needed for the
sidewalk. Subtract the smaller number from
the larger one.

6. **(4) 30 + 30 + 6 + 6**   You know that two
sides measure 30 feet and two sides measure
6 feet. Add all four sides to find the perimeter.

7. **(1) 10 + 10 + 18**   The deck is a rectangle,
but the railing goes along only three sides.
Two of the sides each measure 10 feet, and the
third side measures 18 feet. Add the three
measurements to find the total railing length.

8. **(5) 300 + 300 + 200 + 200**   You know
that two sides measure 300 yards and two
sides measure 200 yards. Add all four sides to
find the perimeter.

9. **(1) 10 + 10 + 14 + 14**   You know that
two walls measure 10 feet across and two
walls measure 14 feet across. Add all four wall
measurements to find the perimeter.

10. **(3) 15 + 12**   The room is a rectangle, but
the wood trim goes along only two walls.
One wall measures 15 feet across and one wall
measures 12 feet across. Add the two
measurements to find the total trim length.

PAGE 22

2. **494**

$$
\begin{array}{r} \overset{1}{4}76 \\ +\ 18 \\ \hline 494 \end{array}
$$
Check
$$
\begin{array}{r} \overset{1}{1}8 \\ +\ 476 \\ \hline 494 \end{array}
$$

3. **651**

$$
\begin{array}{r} \overset{1\,1}{3}87 \\ +\ 264 \\ \hline 651 \end{array}
$$
Check
$$
\begin{array}{r} \overset{1\,1}{2}64 \\ +\ 387 \\ \hline 651 \end{array}
$$

4. **$6.55**

$$
\begin{array}{r} \overset{1}{\$4}.73 \\ +\ 1.82 \\ \hline \$6.55 \end{array}
$$
Check
$$
\begin{array}{r} \overset{1}{\$1}.82 \\ +\ 4.73 \\ \hline \$6.55 \end{array}
$$

5. **707**

$$
\begin{array}{r} \overset{1\,1}{1}48 \\ 327 \\ +\ 232 \\ \hline 707 \end{array}
$$
Check
$$
\begin{array}{r} \overset{1\,1}{2}32 \\ 327 \\ +\ 148 \\ \hline 707 \end{array}
$$

6. **$13.75**

$$
\begin{array}{r} \overset{1\,1}{\$1}.35 \\ 4.56 \\ +\ 7.84 \\ \hline \$13.75 \end{array}
$$
Check
$$
\begin{array}{r} \overset{1\,1}{\$7}.84 \\ 4.56 \\ +\ 1.35 \\ \hline \$13.75 \end{array}
$$

7. **735**

$$
\begin{array}{r} \overset{1\,1}{5}42 \\ 125 \\ +\ 68 \\ \hline 735 \end{array}
$$
Check
$$
\begin{array}{r} \overset{1\,1}{\ }68 \\ 125 \\ +\ 542 \\ \hline 735 \end{array}
$$

8. **1,346**

$$
\begin{array}{r} \overset{1\,1}{8}17 \\ 76 \\ +\ 453 \\ \hline 1{,}346 \end{array}
$$
Check
$$
\begin{array}{r} \overset{1\,1}{4}53 \\ 76 \\ +\ 817 \\ \hline 1{,}346 \end{array}
$$

9. **195**

$$
\begin{array}{r} \overset{1}{3}8 \\ +\ 157 \\ \hline 195 \end{array}
$$
Check
$$
\begin{array}{r} \overset{1}{1}57 \\ +\ 38 \\ \hline 195 \end{array}
$$

10. **$9.64**

$$
\begin{array}{r} \overset{1\,1}{\$4}.50 \\ 3.26 \\ +\ 1.88 \\ \hline \$9.64 \end{array}
$$
Check
$$
\begin{array}{r} \overset{1\,1}{\$1}.88 \\ 3.26 \\ +\ 4.50 \\ \hline \$9.64 \end{array}
$$

PAGE 23

2. **653**

$$
\begin{array}{r} 957 \\ -\ 304 \\ \hline 653 \end{array}
$$
Check
$$
\begin{array}{r} 653 \\ +\ 304 \\ \hline 957 \end{array}
$$

3. **$4.74**

$$
\begin{array}{r} \$8.99 \\ -\ 4.25 \\ \hline \$4.74 \end{array}
$$
Check
$$
\begin{array}{r} \$4.74 \\ +\ 4.25 \\ \hline \$8.99 \end{array}
$$

4. **743**

$$
\begin{array}{r} 786 \\ -\ 43 \\ \hline 743 \end{array}
$$
Check
$$
\begin{array}{r} 743 \\ +\ 43 \\ \hline 786 \end{array}
$$

5. **25**

$$
\begin{array}{r} \overset{4\ 13}{\cancel{5}\cancel{3}} \\ -\ 28 \\ \hline 25 \end{array}
$$
Check
$$
\begin{array}{r} \overset{1}{2}5 \\ +\ 28 \\ \hline 53 \end{array}
$$

6. **$1.55**

$$
\begin{array}{r} \overset{3\ 12}{\$\cancel{4}.\cancel{2}6} \\ -\ 2.71 \\ \hline \$1.55 \end{array}
$$
Check
$$
\begin{array}{r} \overset{1}{\$1}.55 \\ +\ 2.71 \\ \hline \$4.26 \end{array}
$$

7. **179**

$$
\begin{array}{r} \overset{2\ 12}{\cancel{3}\cancel{2}9} \\ -\ 150 \\ \hline 179 \end{array}
$$
Check
$$
\begin{array}{r} \overset{1}{1}79 \\ +\ 150 \\ \hline 329 \end{array}
$$

8. 467

$$
\begin{array}{r}
{\scriptstyle 13} \\
{\scriptstyle 7\,8\,13} \\
\cancel{843} \\
-\ 376 \\
\hline
467
\end{array}
$$

Check
$$
\begin{array}{r}
{\scriptstyle 1\,1} \\
467 \\
+\ 376 \\
\hline
843
\end{array}
$$

9. 333

$$
\begin{array}{r}
{\scriptstyle 9} \\
{\scriptstyle 4\,10\,10} \\
\cancel{500} \\
-\ 167 \\
\hline
333
\end{array}
$$

Check
$$
\begin{array}{r}
{\scriptstyle 1\,1} \\
333 \\
+\ 167 \\
\hline
500
\end{array}
$$

10. $3.87

$$
\begin{array}{r}
{\scriptstyle 10} \\
{\scriptstyle 6\,0\,15} \\
\$\cancel{7.15} \\
-\ 3.28 \\
\hline
\$3.87
\end{array}
$$

Check
$$
\begin{array}{r}
{\scriptstyle 1\,1} \\
\$3.87 \\
+\ 3.28 \\
\hline
\$7.15
\end{array}
$$

11. 877

$$
\begin{array}{r}
{\scriptstyle 9} \\
{\scriptstyle 8\,10\,16} \\
\cancel{906} \\
-\ 29 \\
\hline
877
\end{array}
$$

Check
$$
\begin{array}{r}
{\scriptstyle 1\,1} \\
877 \\
+\ 29 \\
\hline
906
\end{array}
$$

12. 38

$$
\begin{array}{r}
{\scriptstyle 4\,11\,10} \\
\cancel{520} \\
-\ 482 \\
\hline
38
\end{array}
$$

Check
$$
\begin{array}{r}
{\scriptstyle 1\,1} \\
38 \\
+\ 482 \\
\hline
520
\end{array}
$$

13. 573

$$
\begin{array}{r}
{\scriptstyle 7\,12} \\
\cancel{827} \\
-\ 254 \\
\hline
573
\end{array}
$$

Check
$$
\begin{array}{r}
{\scriptstyle 1} \\
573 \\
+\ 254 \\
\hline
827
\end{array}
$$

14. $3.18

$$
\begin{array}{r}
{\scriptstyle 7\,10\,17} \\
\$\cancel{8.17} \\
-\ 4.99 \\
\hline
\$3.18
\end{array}
$$

Check
$$
\begin{array}{r}
{\scriptstyle 1\,1} \\
\$3.18 \\
+\ 4.99 \\
\hline
\$8.17
\end{array}
$$

15. 157

$$
\begin{array}{r}
{\scriptstyle 9} \\
{\scriptstyle 6\,10\,10} \\
\cancel{700} \\
-\ 543 \\
\hline
157
\end{array}
$$

Check
$$
\begin{array}{r}
{\scriptstyle 1\,1} \\
157 \\
+\ 543 \\
\hline
700
\end{array}
$$

16. 198

$$
\begin{array}{r}
{\scriptstyle 5\,17\,14} \\
\cancel{684} \\
-\ 486 \\
\hline
198
\end{array}
$$

Check
$$
\begin{array}{r}
{\scriptstyle 1\,1} \\
198 \\
+\ 486 \\
\hline
684
\end{array}
$$

PAGE 26

1. **(3) Williams** The tallest bar represents the greatest number of votes. The bar for Williams is the tallest.

2. **(5) 10,500** The two tallest bars represent the two candidates with the greatest number of votes. The bars for Ortez and Williams are the tallest. The bar for Ortez ends between the 4 and 5 marks and represents 4,500 votes.

The bar for Williams reaches the 6 mark and represents 6,000 votes. Add to find the total number.

$$
\begin{array}{r}
4,500 \\
+\ 6,000 \\
\hline
10,500
\end{array}
$$

3. **(3) 4,500** The tallest bar represents the greatest number of votes. The bar for Williams is the tallest. It reaches the 6 mark and represents 6,000 votes. The smallest bar represents the least number of votes. The bar for Martin is the smallest. It ends between the 1 and 2 marks and represents 1,500 votes. Subtract to find the difference.

$$
\begin{array}{r}
{\scriptstyle 5\,10} \\
\cancel{6,000} \\
-\ 1,500 \\
\hline
4,500
\end{array}
$$

4. **(4) minivan** The smallest bar represents the least number of cars sold. The bar for minivan is the smallest.

5. **(2) 150** The bar for 4-door cars reaches the 4 mark and represents 400 cars. The bar for 2-door cars ends between the 2 and 3 marks and represents 250 cars. Subtract to find the difference.

$$
\begin{array}{r}
{\scriptstyle 3\,10} \\
\cancel{400} \\
-\ 250 \\
\hline
150
\end{array}
$$

6. **(4) 250** The two smallest bars represent the two least popular types of cars sold. The bars for minivan and convertible are the smallest. The bar for minivan reaches the 1 mark and represents 100 cars. The bar for convertible ends between the 1 and 2 marks and represents 150 cars. Add to find the total.

$$
\begin{array}{r}
100 \\
+\ 150 \\
\hline
250
\end{array}
$$

PAGE 29

1. **(1) 56 + 17** Add to find the total number of boxes. Add the boxes collected in the morning (56) and the boxes collected in the afternoon (17).

2. **(3) $75 − $25** The amount Lelia still owes is the amount that is left. Subtract to find how much is left. Option 3 is correct because you need to subtract the amount Lelia paid ($25) from the cost of the coat ($75).

3. **(2) 130** Compare the number of hamburgers sold all day (198) with the number sold after 7:00 P.M. (72). Round the numbers to the nearest ten and subtract to estimate the difference.

$$
\begin{array}{r}
198 \quad \text{is about} \quad \overset{1\ 10}{\cancel{2}\cancel{0}0} \\
-\ 72 \quad \text{is about} \quad -\ 70 \\ \hline
130
\end{array}
$$

The estimate is 130, so Option 2 is correct.

4. **(2) 220** Add to find the total. Round the three numbers to the nearest ten and add to estimate the total.

$$
\begin{array}{r}
67 \quad \text{is about} \quad 70 \\
73 \quad \text{is about} \quad 70 \\
+\ 81 \quad \text{is about} \quad +\ 80 \\ \hline
220
\end{array}
$$

The estimate is 220, so Option 2 is correct.

5. **81 tickets** Subtract to compare the two numbers.

$$
\begin{array}{r}
\overset{0\ 12}{\cancel{1}\cancel{2}7} \\
-\ 46 \\ \hline
81 \text{ tickets}
\end{array}
$$

6. **123 pairs** You need to know the number of pairs of sandals at the start of the sale and the number of pairs of sandals at the end of the sale. You don't need to know the number of pairs of tennis shoes. Find the difference between the number of pairs of sandals by subtracting.

$$
\begin{array}{r}
\overset{4\ 10}{1\cancel{5}\cancel{0}} \\
-\ 27 \\ \hline
123 \text{ pairs}
\end{array}
$$

7. **56 bottles** Subtract to compare the number of bottles delivered on two different days.

$$
\begin{array}{r}
\overset{12}{\underset{}{0\ \cancel{2}\ 12}} \\
\cancel{1}\cancel{3}\cancel{2} \\
-\ 76 \\ \hline
56 \text{ bottles}
\end{array}
$$

8. **52 copies** Since the number of copies will be equal to the number of employees, add to find the total number of employees.

$$
\begin{array}{r}
\overset{1}{}13 \\
22 \\
+\ 17 \\ \hline
52
\end{array}
$$

PAGES 30–31

1. **733**
$$
\begin{array}{r}
\overset{1\ 1}{237} \\
+\ 496 \\ \hline
733
\end{array}
$$

2. **162**
$$
\begin{array}{r}
\overset{4\ 14}{\cancel{5}\cancel{4}7} \\
-\ 385 \\ \hline
162
\end{array}
$$

3. **$7.82**
$$
\begin{array}{r}
\overset{1\ 1}{\$2.95} \\
+\ 4.87 \\ \hline
\$7.82
\end{array}
$$

4. **279**
$$
\begin{array}{r}
\overset{5\ 10\ 10}{\cancel{6}\cancel{0}\cancel{0}} \\
-\ 321 \\ \hline
279
\end{array}
$$

5. **$3.12**
$$
\begin{array}{r}
\overset{5\ 1}{\$\cancel{6}.07} \\
-\ 2.95 \\ \hline
\$3.12
\end{array}
$$

6. **928**
$$
\begin{array}{r}
\overset{1\ 1}{503} \\
58 \\
+\ 367 \\ \hline
928
\end{array}
$$

7. **$6.89**
$$
\begin{array}{r}
\overset{1}{\$2.27} \\
3.17 \\
+\ 1.45 \\ \hline
\$6.89
\end{array}
$$

8. **$6.99**
$$
\begin{array}{r}
\overset{8\ 18\ 13}{\$\cancel{9}.\cancel{9}\cancel{3}} \\
-\ 2.94 \\ \hline
\$6.99
\end{array}
$$

9. **78**
$$
\begin{array}{r}
\overset{6\ 15\ 12}{\cancel{7}\cancel{6}\cancel{2}} \\
-\ 684 \\ \hline
78
\end{array}
$$

10. **1,250**
$$
\begin{array}{r}
\overset{1}{836} \\
+\ 414 \\ \hline
1,250
\end{array}
$$

11. **$8.00**
$$
\begin{array}{r}
\overset{1\ 1}{\$3.42} \\
+\ 4.58 \\ \hline
\$8.00
\end{array}
$$

12. **458**
$$
\begin{array}{r}
\overset{4\ 12\ 14}{\cancel{5}\cancel{3}\cancel{4}} \\
-\ 76 \\ \hline
458
\end{array}
$$

13. **89 people** Subtract the number of deliveries made before Ed's break from the total number of deliveries he needs to make.

$$
\begin{array}{r}
\overset{1\ 12\ 18}{\cancel{2}\cancel{3}\cancel{8}} \\
-\ 149 \\ \hline
89
\end{array}
$$

14. **422 miles**   Add the number of miles driven before lunch and the number of miles driven after lunch. You don't need the number of days they will spend camping or the number of hours they drove.

$$\begin{array}{r} {\scriptstyle 1\;1} \\ 243 \\ +\;179 \\ \hline 422 \end{array}$$

15. **221 customers**   Add the number of each type of customer.

$$\begin{array}{r} {\scriptstyle 1\;1} \\ 153 \\ 26 \\ +\;42 \\ \hline 221 \end{array}$$

16. **$1.15**   Subtract the cost of the hamburger by itself from the cost of the hamburger platter. You don't need the cost of a beverage.

$$\begin{array}{r} {\scriptstyle 5\,10} \\ \$3.\cancel{6}\cancel{0} \\ -\;\;2.45 \\ \hline \$1.15 \end{array}$$

17. **(5) 20 + 20 + 14 + 14**   You know that two sides measure 20 feet and two sides measure 14 feet. Add all four measurements to find the perimeter.

18. **(3) $90**   Add to find a total. Round the three numbers to the nearest ten and add to estimate the total.

$53	is about	$50
28	is about	30
+ 11	is about	+ 10
		$90

19. **(2) 208 – 185**   The difference between Bill's present weight and the weight his doctor advised is the weight Bill should lose. Subtract the smaller amount from the larger one.

20. **(3) $402**   Add the cost of tuition and the cost of books and supplies. You don't need the number of weeks the course lasts.

$$\begin{array}{r} {\scriptstyle 1\;1} \\ \$348 \\ +\;\;\;54 \\ \hline \$402 \end{array}$$

21. **(4) comedy**   The tallest bar represents the greatest number of rentals. The bar for comedy is the tallest.

22. **(4) 250**   The bar for comedy is the tallest. It ends between the *4* and *5* marks and represents 450 rentals. The bar for drama is the smallest. It reaches the *2* mark and represents 200 rentals. Subtract to find the difference.

$$\begin{array}{r} 450 \\ -\;200 \\ \hline 250 \end{array}$$

23. **(1) 43 – 17**   Subtract the number of points made from the free throw line from the total number of points scored. You don't need the number of fouls.

SECTION 3
PAGES 33–34

1. **(4) 36 x 4**   To find the total, Dean needs to multiply the number of students by the number of cookies for each student.

2. **(1) 144 ÷ 12**   To separate a large amount into dozens, Dean needs to divide the number of cookies by the number in a dozen.

3. **(3) 50 – 12**   To find the amount he will have left, Dean needs to subtract the amount he plans to sell from the amount he has.

4. **(5) 38 + 8**   To find the total, Dean needs to add both amounts.

5. **(3) $549 ÷ 3**   To separate an amount into equal payments, divide the full amount by the number of payments.

6. **(1) 144 – 12**   To find the number of miles still remaining, subtract the miles driven from the total miles.

7. **(4) 48 x 6**   To find the total amount, multiply the number of wreaths by the number of yards needed for each wreath.

8. **(3) 4 x 10**   To find the total number of feet, multiply the number of rolls by the number of feet in each roll.

9. **(2) 18 + 30**   To find the total, add the number originally on hand and the number in the shipment.

10. **(1) 12 + 6**   To find the total number of pounds, add the number of pounds of melon and the number of pounds of berries.

11. **(5) 200 ÷ 10**   To separate a large amount into equal parts, divide the number of miles driven by the number of gallons of gas used.

12. **(4) 18 x 24**   To find the total number of planes packed, multiply the number of planes that fit in each carton by the number of cartons packed.

2. **688**
$$\overset{2}{1}72$$
$$\times\quad 4$$
$$688$$

3. **2,304**
$$\overset{5\,2}{3}84$$
$$\times\quad 6$$
$$2,304$$

4. **1,314**
$$\overset{2}{7}3$$
$$\times\ 18$$
$$584$$
$$+\ 73$$
$$1,314$$

5. **1,992**
$$\overset{1}{8}3$$
$$\times\ 24$$
$$332$$
$$+\ 1\ 66$$
$$1,992$$

6. **12,173**
$$\overset{2\,3}{\overset{4\,8}{2}}59$$
$$\times\ 47$$
$$1\ 813$$
$$+\ 10\ 36$$
$$12,173$$

7. **$42.75**
$$\overset{6\ 4}{\$4}.75$$
$$\times\qquad 9$$
$$\$42.75$$

8. **19,200**
$$\overset{1}{6}4$$
$$\times\ 300$$
$$19,200$$

9. **336,474**
$$\overset{1\,2}{\overset{\cancel{1}}{8}}37$$
$$\times\ 402$$
$$1\ 674$$
$$+\ 334\ 80$$
$$336,474$$

10. **35,280**
$$\overset{2\,4}{\overset{\cancel{4}}{1}}26$$
$$\times\ 280$$
$$10\ 080$$
$$25\ 2$$
$$35,280$$

11. **$27.23**
$$\overset{6\ 6}{\$3}.89$$
$$\times\qquad 7$$
$$\$27.23$$

12. **1,920**
$$\overset{3}{4}8$$
$$\times\ 40$$
$$1,920$$

13. **33,201**
$$\overset{4}{\overset{1\,2}{5}}27$$
$$\times\ 63$$
$$1\ 581$$
$$+\ 31\ 62$$
$$33,201$$

14. **475,488**
$$\overset{1\,3}{\overset{2\,4}{9}}36$$
$$\times\ 508$$
$$7\ 488$$
$$+\ 468\ 00$$
$$475,488$$

2. **$2.15**

```
       $ 2.15          $2.15
7) $15.05          ×      7
  − 14             $15.05
    1 0
  −   7
     35
  −  35
      0
```

3. **902 r4**

```
     902 r4          902
6) 5,416          ×    6
 − 5 4            5,412
   016            +   4
 −  12            5,416
     4
```

4. **16 r27**

```
      16 r27          16
28) 475           ×   28
  − 28            128
   195            +  32
 − 168            448
    27            +  27
                  475
```

5. **$3.30**

```
     $ 3.30          $3.30
5) $16.50         ×     5
 − 15             $16.50
   1 5
 − 1 5
    00
```

6. **231 r12**

$$
\begin{array}{r}
231\ r12 \\
42\overline{)9{,}714} \\
-\ 8\,4 \\
\hline
1\,31 \\
-\ 1\,26 \\
\hline
54 \\
-\ 42 \\
\hline
12
\end{array}
\qquad
\begin{array}{r}
231 \\
\times\ \ 42 \\
\hline
462 \\
+\ 9\,24 \\
\hline
9{,}702 \\
+\ \ \ 12 \\
\hline
9{,}714
\end{array}
$$

7. **204 r10**

$$
\begin{array}{r}
204\ r10 \\
36\overline{)7{,}354} \\
-\ 7\,2 \\
\hline
154 \\
-\ 144 \\
\hline
10
\end{array}
\qquad
\begin{array}{r}
204 \\
\times\ \ 36 \\
\hline
1\,224 \\
+\ 6\,12 \\
\hline
7{,}344 \\
+\ \ \ 10 \\
\hline
7{,}354
\end{array}
$$

8. **$3.02**

$$
\begin{array}{r}
\$\ 3.02 \\
4\overline{)\$12.08} \\
-\ \$12 \\
\hline
0\ 08 \\
-\ \ \ 8 \\
\hline
0
\end{array}
\qquad
\begin{array}{r}
\$3.02 \\
\times\ \ \ 4 \\
\hline
\$12.08
\end{array}
$$

PAGE 40

1. **(5) $32.85** Multiply the cost of a large special pizza ($10.95) by the number of pizzas ordered (3).

$$
\begin{array}{r}
\overset{2\ 1}{\$10.95} \\
\times\ \ \ \ \ 3 \\
\hline
\$32.85
\end{array}
$$

2. **(4) $10.40** Add the cost of a small cheese pizza ($3.95) and the cost of a medium pizza with 2 toppings ($6.45).

$$
\begin{array}{r}
\overset{1\ 1}{\$3.95} \\
+\ \ 6.45 \\
\hline
\$10.40
\end{array}
$$

3. **$1.65** Divide the cost of a large pizza with 3 toppings ($8.25) by the number of people sharing the cost (5).

$$
\begin{array}{r}
\$1.65 \\
5\overline{)\$8.25} \\
-\ 5 \\
\hline
3\,2 \\
-\ 3\,0 \\
\hline
25 \\
-\ 25 \\
\hline
0
\end{array}
$$

4. **$21.35** Multiply the number of large cheese pizzas ordered (2) times the cost of each ($6.25). Then add the total and the cost of one medium special pizza ($8.85).
$6.25 \times 2 = \$12.50.$
$\$12.50 + \$8.85 = \$21.35.$

5. **$1.65** Subtract to find the difference between the cost of a small special pizza ($7.25) and the cost of a small pizza with 3 toppings ($5.60). $\$7.25 - \$5.60 = \$1.65.$

6. **$4.85** Subtract the cost of ingredients ($0.95) from the price a customer pays for a medium pizza with one topping ($5.80). $\$5.80 - \$0.95 = \$4.85.$

PAGE 43

1. **(1) 12 x 18** To find the area, multiply the length (18 feet) by the width (12 feet).

2. **(3) 6 x 4 ÷ 3** To find the total number of feet, multiply the number of feet needed for each panel (6) by the number of panels (4). Then divide by the number of feet in a yard (3).

3. **(5) $550 – $75** To find the cost of the carpet, subtract the cost of installation ($75) from the cost of the carpet plus installation ($550).

4. **(2) 12 + 12 + 18 + 18 – 3 – 6** To find the length needed, subtract the door openings (3 feet and 6 feet) from the perimeter (12 + 12 + 18 + 18).

5. **216 square feet**

$$
\begin{array}{r}
\overset{1}{12} \\
\times\ 18 \\
\hline
96 \\
+\ 12 \\
\hline
216
\end{array}
$$

6. **8 yards** $\quad 6 \times 4 \div 3 = 24 \div 3 = 8$

7. **$475**

$$
\begin{array}{r}
\$\overset{41410}{550} \\
-\ \ 75 \\
\hline
\$475
\end{array}
$$

8. **51 feet**

$$
\begin{array}{r}
\overset{2}{12} \\
12 \\
18 \\
+\ 18 \\
\hline
60 \\
-\ 3 \\
\hline
57 \\
-\ 6 \\
\hline
51
\end{array}
$$

PAGES 44–45

1. **1,368**

$$
\begin{array}{r}
\overset{1\ 1}{456} \\
\times\ \ \ 3 \\
\hline
1{,}368
\end{array}
$$

2. 4,067

$$\overset{\overset{1}{2}}{83}$$
$$\times\ 49$$
$$\overline{747}$$
$$+\ 3\ 32$$
$$\overline{4,067}$$

3. $17.82

$$\overset{5\ 4}{\$2.97}$$
$$\times\ \ \ \ \ 6$$
$$\overline{\$17.82}$$

4. 124,956

$$\overset{5\ 5}{\overset{\cancel{1}\ \cancel{1}}{178}}$$
$$\times\ 702$$
$$\overline{356}$$
$$+\ 124\ 60$$
$$\overline{124,956}$$

5. 199,165

$$\overset{\overset{1}{2}\cancel{1}}{653}$$
$$\times\ 305$$
$$\overline{3265}$$
$$+\ 19590$$
$$\overline{199,165}$$

6. 823 r1

$$823\ r1$$
$$4\overline{)3,293}$$
$$-\ 3\ 2$$
$$\overline{\ \ \ 09}$$
$$-\ \ \ 8$$
$$\overline{\ \ \ \ 13}$$
$$-\ \ 12$$
$$\overline{\ \ \ \ \ 1}$$

7. $9.20

$$\$9.20$$
$$7\overline{)\$64.40}$$
$$-\ 63$$
$$\overline{\ \ 1\ 4}$$
$$-\ 1\ 4$$
$$\overline{\ \ \ 00}$$

8. 321 r16

$$321\ r16$$
$$18\overline{)5,794}$$
$$-\ 5\ 4$$
$$\overline{\ \ \ 39}$$
$$-\ 36$$
$$\overline{\ \ \ \ 34}$$
$$-\ 18$$
$$\overline{\ \ \ \ 16}$$

9. 201 r14

$$201\ r14$$
$$43\overline{)8,657}$$
$$-\ 8\ 6$$
$$\overline{\ \ \ 057}$$
$$-\ \ 43$$
$$\overline{\ \ \ \ 14}$$

10. 153

$$153$$
$$27\overline{)4,131}$$
$$-\ 27$$
$$\overline{\ \ 1\ 43}$$
$$-\ 1\ 35$$
$$\overline{\ \ \ \ \ 81}$$
$$-\ \ 81$$
$$\overline{\ \ \ \ \ \ 0}$$

11. 31,200

$$\overset{7}{39}$$
$$\times\ 800$$
$$\overline{31,200}$$

12. $42.10

$$\overset{2\ 1}{\$8.42}$$
$$\times\ \ \ \ \ 5$$
$$\overline{\$42.10}$$

13. $2.05

$$\$\ 2.05$$
$$8\overline{)\$16.40}$$
$$-\ 16$$
$$\overline{\ \ \ 0\ 40}$$
$$-\ \ \ 40$$
$$\overline{\ \ \ \ \ \ 0}$$

14. 143 r27

$$143\ r27$$
$$52\overline{)7,463}$$
$$-\ 5\ 2$$
$$\overline{\ \ 2\ 26}$$
$$-\ 2\ 08$$
$$\overline{\ \ \ \ 183}$$
$$-\ 156$$
$$\overline{\ \ \ \ \ 27}$$

15. **1,152 pencils**   Multiply the number in each gross by the number of gross ordered.

$$\overset{3\ 3}{144}$$
$$\times\ \ \ \ \ 8$$
$$\overline{1,152}$$

16. **180 tiles**   To find the area, multiply the length times the width.

$$\overset{1}{15}$$
$$\times\ 12$$
$$\overline{30}$$
$$+\ 15$$
$$\overline{180}$$

17. **$19.88**   Multiply the price of one pair by the number of pairs bought.

$$\overset{3\ 2}{\$4.97}$$
$$\times\ \ \ \ \ 4$$
$$\overline{\$19.88}$$

18. **22 customers**   Divide the total collected for oil changes by the cost of an oil change.

$$\begin{array}{r} 22 \\ \$15\overline{)\,\$330} \\ -30 \\ \hline 30 \\ -30 \\ \hline 0 \end{array}$$

19. **(2) 94 x 50**   To find the area, multiply the length times the width.

20. **(4) $45.50**   Multiply Lena's hourly wage by the number of hours she worked.

$$\begin{array}{r} \overset{3}{\$6.50} \\ \times 7 \\ \hline \$45.50 \end{array}$$

21. **(3) $7.20 ÷ 6**   To find the price of one quart, divide the total cost by the number of quarts bought.

22. **(4) 1,000**   To find the area, multiply the length times the width.

$$\begin{array}{r} \overset{2}{25} \\ \times 40 \\ \hline 1,000 \end{array}$$

23. **(1) 14 x 28**   To find the total miles, multiply the number of gallons times the number of miles that can be driven on each gallon.

24. **(5) 5,324 – 75**   Find the column for Wednesday and subtract the number of defective parts from the total number of parts produced.

25. **(5) 709**   Divide the total number of parts produced on Thursday (5,672) by the number of inspectors (8).

$$\begin{array}{r} 709 \\ 8\overline{)\,5{,}672} \\ -5\,6 \\ \hline 072 \\ -72 \\ \hline 0 \end{array}$$

SECTION 4

PAGES 47–48

1. **(4) 15^2**   The room is a square because all 4 sides have the same length. Use the formula $A = s^2$ and substitute 15 for s.

2. **(5) 225 ÷ 9**   Divide the number of square feet by the number of square feet in a square yard (9).

3. **(1) 18^2**   The room is a square because all 4 sides have the same length. Use the formula $A = s^2$ and substitute 18 for s.

4. **(2) 36 ÷ 9**   Divide the number of square feet by the number of square feet in a square yard (9).

5. **(5) 20 + 20 + 20 + 20**   To find the perimeter, add the measurements of each side.

6. **(3) $8 x 17**   Multiply the cost of each square yard by the number of square yards.

7. **(2) 10 x 14**   The room is a rectangle, so multiply the length times the width.

8. **(1) $11^2 + 12^2$**   First, find the area of each room. Since the rooms are squares, the area of the first room is 11^2, and the area of the second is 12^2. To find the total area, add the area of the two rooms.

9. **(4) 4 x 18**   Multiply the number of tiles in a square foot by the number of square feet.

10. **(1) 12^2 ÷ 9**   First, find the area of the patio in square feet. Use the formula $A = s^2$ and substitute 12 for s. Then, divide the number of square feet by the number of square feet in a square yard (9).

PAGE 50

2. **5 x 5 = 25**

3. **1 x 1 = 1**

4. **7 x 7 x 7 = 49 x 7 = 343**

5. **64**

6. **121**

7. **324**

8. **256**

9. **11**

10. **4**

11. **17**

12. **14**

PAGE 53

1. **672 cu. in.** $\begin{aligned} V &= l \times w \times h \\ &= 8 \times 7 \times 12 \\ &= 56 \times 12 \\ &= 672 \end{aligned}$

2. **30 cu. ft.** $\begin{aligned} V &= l \times w \times h \\ &= 3 \times 2 \times 5 \\ &= 6 \times 5 \\ &= 30 \end{aligned}$

3. **22,400 cu. in.** $\begin{aligned} V &= l \times w \times h \\ &= 28 \times 40 \times 20 \\ &= 1{,}120 \times 20 \\ &= 22{,}400 \end{aligned}$

4. **24 cu. ft.** $\begin{aligned} V &= l \times w \times h \\ &= 6 \times 4 \times 1 \\ &= 24 \times 1 \\ &= 24 \end{aligned}$

5. **(4) 315** $V = l \times w \times h$
$= 9 \times 7 \times 5$
$= 63 \times 5$
$= 315$

6. **(5) 720** $V = l \times w \times h$
$= 12 \times 10 \times 6$
$= 120 \times 6$
$= 720$

7. **(2) 405**   Subtract the volume of the gift-wrapped box (see the explanation for item 5) from the volume of the shipping carton (see the explanation for item 6).

$$\begin{array}{r} 720 \\ -\ 315 \\ \hline 405 \end{array}$$

PAGES 54–55

1. **8 x 8 = 64**
2. **1 x 1 x 1 = 1**
3. **3 x 3 x 3 = 27**
4. **9 x 9 = 81**
5. **289**
6. **225**
7. **5**
8. **18**
9. **400 sq. ft.**   The room is a square because all 4 sides have the same length. Use the formula $A = s^2$ and substitute 20 for s. $20 \times 20 = 400$

10. **1,800 cu. ft.** $V = l \times w \times h$
$= 15 \times 12 \times 10$
$= 180 \times 10$
$= 1,800$

11. **720 cu. ft.** $V = l \times w \times h$
$= 30 \times 6 \times 4$
$= 180 \times 4$
$= 720$

12. **$126**   Multiply the cost per square yard by the number of square yards bought. $14 \times 9 = 126

13. **64 sq. yd.**   Divide the number of square feet by the number of square feet in a square yard (9). $576 \div 9 = 64$

14. **576 cu. ft.** $V = l \times w \times h$
$= 12 \times 8 \times 6$
$= 96 \times 6$
$= 576$

15. **(2) 14 x 6 x 20**   To find the volume of a rectangular container, multiply the length (14 inches) times the width (6 inches) times the height (20 inches).

16. **(5) 15²**   The room is a square because all 4 sides have the same length. Use the formula $A = s^2$ and substitute 15 for s.

17. **(5) 160** $V = l \times w \times h$
$= 8 \times 5 \times 4$
$= 40 \times 4$
$= 160$ cu. ft.

18. **(3) 42² ÷ 9**   To find the area in square feet, use the formula $A = s^2$ and substitute 42 for s. Then divide the number of square feet by the number of square feet in a square yard (9).

19. **(3) 100 sq. ft.**   The patio will be a square because all 4 sides are to be the same length. Use the formula $A = s^2$ and substitute 10 for s.

20. **(1) 18 x 12 x 3 cu. in.**   To find the volume of a rectangular space, multiply the length (18 inches) times the width (12 inches) times the height (3 inches).

21. **(5) 6,480 cu. in.** $V = l \times w \times h$
$= 18 \times 18 \times 20$
$= 324 \times 20$
$= 6,480$

22. **(2) 12 sq. yd.**   Divide the number of square feet by the number of square feet in a square yard (9). $108 \div 9 = 12$

UNIT 1 REVIEW

PAGES 56–57

1. **ten thousands**
2. **millions**
3. **417 < 1,740**   417 has fewer digits than 1,740.
4. **54,9_7_2 > 54,9_2_7**   7 is greater than 2.
5. **10** $\begin{array}{l} 4 + 2 \times 6 - 12 \div 2 \\ 4 + \quad 12 \quad - 12 \div 2 \\ 4 + \quad 12 \quad - \qquad 6 \\ \quad 16 \qquad\quad - \qquad 6 \\ \qquad\qquad\qquad\qquad 10 \end{array}$

6. **2** $\begin{array}{l} 3 \times (1 + 3) \div 4 - 1 \\ 3 \times \quad 4 \quad \div 4 - 1 \\ \quad 12 \qquad\quad \div 4 - 1 \\ \qquad\qquad\quad 3 \quad - 1 \\ \qquad\qquad\qquad\qquad 2 \end{array}$

7. **763** $\begin{array}{r} \overset{1\ 1}{426} \\ 84 \\ +\ 253 \\ \hline 763 \end{array}$

8. **$9.92** $\begin{array}{r} \overset{1\ 3}{\$2.48} \\ \times \qquad 4 \\ \hline \$9.92 \end{array}$

9. **$5.76**

$$
\begin{array}{r}
{\scriptstyle 8\ 14\ 14} \\
\$9.\cancel{54} \\
-\ \ 3.78 \\
\hline
\$5.76
\end{array}
$$

10. **29 r2**

$$
\begin{array}{r}
29\ \text{r2} \\
27\overline{)785} \\
-\ 54 \\
\hline
245 \\
-\ 243 \\
\hline
2
\end{array}
$$

11. **223,608**

$$
\begin{array}{r}
{\scriptstyle 1} \\
{\scriptstyle \cancel{2}\cancel{4}} \\
726 \\
\times\ 308 \\
\hline
5\ 808 \\
+\ 217\ 80 \\
\hline
223,608
\end{array}
$$

12. **64** $4 \times 4 \times 4 = 16 \times 4 = 64$

13. **257**

$$
\begin{array}{r}
{\scriptstyle 9} \\
{\scriptstyle 4\ \cancel{10}\ 10} \\
\cancel{500} \\
-\ 243 \\
\hline
257
\end{array}
$$

14. **1,188**

$$
\begin{array}{r}
{\scriptstyle 1} \\
32 \\
847 \\
+\ 309 \\
\hline
1,188
\end{array}
$$

15. **26,160**

$$
\begin{array}{r}
{\scriptstyle 2\ 3} \\
436 \\
\times\ \ 60 \\
\hline
26,160
\end{array}
$$

16. **$3.13**

$$
\begin{array}{r}
\$\ 3.13 \\
8\overline{)\$25.04} \\
-\ 24 \\
\hline
1\ 0 \\
-\ \ 8 \\
\hline
24 \\
-\ 24 \\
\hline
0
\end{array}
$$

17. **305 r11**

$$
\begin{array}{r}
305\ \text{r11} \\
13\overline{)3,976} \\
-\ 3\ 9 \\
\hline
076 \\
-\ 65 \\
\hline
11
\end{array}
$$

18. **4,380,000**

4,3⑦5,429 The number to the right of 7 is 5; add 1 to the circled digit.

19. **13**   Because $13^2 = 169$, the square root of 169 is 13.

20. **(5) 48 + 48 + 20 + 20**   Two sides measure 48 feet and two sides measure 20 feet. Add all four measurements to find the perimeter.

21. **(3) $90**   Add to find a total. Round the three numbers to the nearest ten and estimate the total.

$$
\begin{array}{lll}
\$57 & \text{rounds to} & \$60 \\
13 & \text{rounds to} & 10 \\
+\ \ 21 & \text{rounds to} & +\ \ 20 \\
\hline
& & \$90
\end{array}
$$

22. **(4) 350**   The tallest bar is for December. It reaches the *5* mark and represents 500 sweat shirts. The bar for September is the smallest. It ends between the *1* and *2* marks and represents 150 sweat shirts. Subtract to find the difference.

$$
\begin{array}{r}
{\scriptstyle 4\ 10} \\
\cancel{500} \\
-\ 150 \\
\hline
350
\end{array}
$$

23. **(2) $6 x 43**   To find the amount Ramon earned this week, multiply the amount he earns per hour ($6) times the number of hours he worked this week (43). You don't need the number of hours he worked last week.

24. **(4) 196**   The room is a square because all four sides have the same length. Use the formula $A = s^2$ and substitute 14 for *s*.

25. **(5) $19.00**   Use the prices in the column marked *After 6:00*. Add the price of 2 children's tickets ($3.50 each), 1 adult ticket ($7.00), and 1 senior citizen ticket ($5.00).

$$
\begin{array}{r}
{\scriptstyle 1} \\
\$3.50 \\
3.50 \\
7.00 \\
+\ \ 5.00 \\
\hline
\$19.00
\end{array}
$$

UNIT 2: FRACTIONS

SECTION 5

PAGE 62

2. $\frac{2}{3}$ There are 3 circles in the group, and 2 are shaded.

3. $\frac{1}{2}$ The figure is divided into 2 parts, and 1 part is shaded.

4. $\frac{3}{5}$ The figure is divided into 5 parts, and 3 parts are shaded.

5. $\frac{3}{4}$ There are 4 figures in the group, and 3 figures are shaded.

6. $\frac{5}{8}$ The figure is divided into 8 parts, and 5 parts are shaded.

8. $\frac{5}{2}$ Each figure is divided into 2 parts, and there are 5 shaded parts among the figures.

9. $\frac{19}{8}$ Each figure is divided into 8 parts, and there are 19 shaded parts among the figures.

11. $2\frac{1}{6}$ Each figure is divided into 6 parts. Two figures are completely shaded, and 1 part of the last figure is shaded.

12. $4\frac{1}{2}$ Each figure is divided into 2 parts. Four figures are completely shaded, and 1 part of the last figure is shaded.

PAGE 64

2. 3

$$\begin{array}{r} 3 \\ 6)\overline{18} \\ -18 \\ \hline 0 \end{array}$$

3. $2\frac{4}{5}$

$$\begin{array}{r} 2 \\ 5)\overline{14} \\ -10 \\ \hline 4 \end{array} \rightarrow 2\frac{4}{5}$$

4. $3\frac{1}{3}$

$$\begin{array}{r} 3 \\ 3)\overline{10} \\ -9 \\ \hline 1 \end{array} \rightarrow 3\frac{1}{3}$$

5. 5

$$\begin{array}{r} 5 \\ 4)\overline{20} \\ -20 \\ \hline 0 \end{array}$$

6. $1\frac{7}{8}$

$$\begin{array}{r} 1 \\ 8)\overline{15} \\ -8 \\ \hline 7 \end{array} \rightarrow 1\frac{7}{8}$$

8. $\frac{5}{2}$ $2\frac{1}{2} = \frac{(2 \times 2) + 1}{2}$
   $= \frac{4 + 1}{2}$
   $= \frac{5}{2}$

9. $\frac{7}{1}$ $7 = \frac{7}{1}$

10. $\frac{19}{5}$ $3\frac{4}{5} = \frac{(5 \times 3) + 4}{5}$
    $= \frac{15 + 4}{5}$
    $= \frac{19}{5}$

11. $\frac{12}{1}$ $12 = \frac{12}{1}$

12. $\frac{43}{4}$ $10\frac{3}{4} = \frac{(4 \times 10) + 3}{4}$
    $= \frac{40 + 3}{4}$
    $= \frac{43}{4}$

PAGE 66

2. $\frac{2}{3}$ $\frac{8}{12} = \frac{8 \div 4}{12 \div 4} = \frac{2}{3}$

3. $\frac{2}{5}$ $\frac{4}{10} = \frac{4 \div 2}{10 \div 2} = \frac{2}{5}$

4. $\frac{3}{4}$ $\frac{6}{8} = \frac{6 \div 2}{8 \div 2} = \frac{3}{4}$

5. $\frac{4}{5}$ $\frac{20}{25} = \frac{20 \div 5}{25 \div 5} = \frac{4}{5}$

6. $\frac{1}{3}$ $\frac{12}{36} = \frac{12 \div 12}{36 \div 12} = \frac{1}{3}$

7. $\frac{2}{3}$ $\frac{6}{9} = \frac{6 \div 3}{9 \div 3} = \frac{2}{3}$

8. $\frac{1}{2}$ $\frac{8}{16} = \frac{8 \div 8}{16 \div 8} = \frac{1}{2}$

9. $\frac{4}{5}$ $\frac{16}{20} = \frac{16 \div 4}{20 \div 4} = \frac{4}{5}$

10. $\frac{5}{7}$ $\frac{10}{14} = \frac{10 \div 2}{14 \div 2} = \frac{5}{7}$

11. $\frac{1}{3}$ $\frac{5}{15} = \frac{5 \div 5}{15 \div 5} = \frac{1}{3}$

12. $\frac{5}{6}$ $\frac{20}{24} = \frac{20 \div 4}{24 \div 4} = \frac{5}{6}$

PAGE 67

2. $\frac{8}{12}$ $\frac{2}{3} = \frac{2 \times 4}{3 \times 4} = \frac{8}{12}$

3. $\frac{3}{18}$ $\frac{1}{6} = \frac{1 \times 3}{6 \times 3} = \frac{3}{18}$

4. $\frac{14}{20}$ $\frac{7}{10} = \frac{7 \times 2}{10 \times 2} = \frac{14}{20}$

5. $\frac{15}{24}$ $\frac{5}{8} = \frac{5 \times 3}{8 \times 3} = \frac{15}{24}$

6. $\frac{12}{30}$ $\frac{2}{5} = \frac{2 \times 6}{5 \times 6} = \frac{12}{30}$

7. $\frac{8}{18}$ $\frac{4}{9} = \frac{4 \times 2}{9 \times 2} = \frac{8}{18}$

8. $\frac{3}{12}$ $\frac{1}{4} = \frac{1 \times 3}{4 \times 3} = \frac{3}{12}$

9. $\frac{28}{32}$ $\frac{7}{8} = \frac{7 \times 4}{8 \times 4} = \frac{28}{32}$

10. $\frac{15}{25}$ $\frac{3}{5} = \frac{3 \times 5}{5 \times 5} = \frac{15}{25}$

11. $\frac{21}{36}$ $\frac{7}{12} = \frac{7 \times 3}{12 \times 3} = \frac{21}{36}$

12. $\frac{12}{40}$ $\frac{3}{10} = \frac{3 \times 4}{10 \times 4} = \frac{12}{40}$

1. $\frac{5}{6}$ The figure is divided into 6 parts, and 5 parts are shaded.

2. $\frac{3}{5}$ There are 5 circles in the group, and 3 are shaded.

3. $\frac{7}{2}$ Each figure is divided into 2 parts, and 7 parts are shaded.

4. $\frac{14}{9}$ Each figure is divided into 9 parts, and 14 parts are shaded.

5. $1\frac{1}{3}$ Each figure is divided into 3 parts. One figure is completely shaded, and 1 of the 3 parts of the last figure is shaded.

6. $2\frac{3}{4}$ Each figure is divided into 4 parts. Two figures are completely shaded, and 3 of the 4 parts of the last figure are shaded.

7. $1\frac{5}{6}$
$$6)\overline{11} \;\rightarrow\; 1\frac{5}{6}$$
$$\underline{-\;6}$$
$$5$$

8. 5
$$5)\overline{25}$$
$$\underline{-\;25}$$
$$0$$

9. $2\frac{3}{8}$
$$8)\overline{19} \;\rightarrow\; 2\frac{3}{8}$$
$$\underline{-\;16}$$
$$3$$

10. $\frac{7}{1}$ $7 = \frac{7}{1}$

11. $\frac{15}{8}$ $1\frac{7}{8} = \frac{(8 \times 1) + 7}{8}$
$$= \frac{8 + 7}{8}$$
$$= \frac{15}{8}$$

12. $\frac{23}{5}$ $4\frac{3}{5} = \frac{(5 \times 4) + 3}{5}$
$$= \frac{20 + 3}{5}$$
$$= \frac{23}{5}$$

13. $\frac{1}{2}$ $\frac{5}{10} = \frac{5 \div 5}{10 \div 5} = \frac{1}{2}$

14. $\frac{3}{4}$ $\frac{9}{12} = \frac{9 \div 3}{12 \div 3} = \frac{3}{4}$

15. $\frac{2}{3}$ $\frac{16}{24} = \frac{16 \div 8}{24 \div 8} = \frac{2}{3}$

16. $\frac{9}{18}$ $\frac{1}{2} = \frac{1 \times 9}{2 \times 9} = \frac{9}{18}$

17. $\frac{20}{24}$ $\frac{5}{6} = \frac{5 \times 4}{6 \times 4} = \frac{20}{24}$

18. $\frac{24}{32}$ $\frac{3}{4} = \frac{3 \times 8}{4 \times 8} = \frac{24}{32}$

19. $\frac{7}{25}$

20. $\frac{9}{16}$

21. $\frac{13}{40}$

22. $\frac{5}{36}$

23. (3) $\frac{3}{4}$ $\frac{6}{8} = \frac{6 \div 2}{8 \div 2} = \frac{3}{4}$

24. (3) $3\frac{3}{4}$
$$4)\overline{15} \;\rightarrow\; 3\frac{3}{4}$$
$$\underline{-\;12}$$
$$3$$

25. (1) $\frac{7}{1}$ $7 = \frac{7}{1}$

26. (4) $\frac{8}{12}$
$$\frac{2}{3} \;\times\; \frac{8}{12} \qquad 2 \times 12 = 24$$
$$3 \times 8 = 24$$
The fractions $\frac{2}{3}$ and $\frac{8}{12}$ are equal.

27. (2) 2
$$5)\overline{10}$$
$$\underline{-\;10}$$
$$0$$

28. (2) $\frac{21}{16}$ $1\frac{5}{16} = \frac{(16 \times 1) + 5}{16}$
$$= \frac{16 + 5}{16}$$
$$= \frac{21}{16}$$

SECTION 6

PAGE 72

1. (2) $1\frac{7}{8} + 2\frac{5}{8}$ Use the column for size 12. Add the number of yards needed for jacket B ($1\frac{7}{8}$) and the number of yards needed for a skirt ($2\frac{5}{8}$).

2. (4) $(2\frac{1}{4} + 2\frac{5}{8}) - (1\frac{7}{8} + 2\frac{5}{8})$ Use the column for size 10. Add the number of yards needed for jacket A ($2\frac{1}{4}$) and the skirt ($2\frac{5}{8}$) and the number of yards needed for jacket B ($1\frac{7}{8}$) and the skirt ($2\frac{5}{8}$). Then subtract the smaller total from the larger total.

3. (5) $2\frac{1}{2} + 2\frac{5}{8}$ Use the column for size 14. Add the number of yards needed for jacket A ($2\frac{1}{2}$) and the skirt ($2\frac{5}{8}$).

4. (3) $1\frac{3}{4} + 2$ Use the row for jumper. Add the number of yards needed for size 4 ($1\frac{3}{4}$) and for size 6 (2).

5. (2) $1\frac{7}{8} + 1\frac{1}{8} + \frac{3}{4}$ Use the column for size 5. Add the number of yards needed for the jumper ($1\frac{7}{8}$); blouse B ($1\frac{1}{8}$); and facing, blouse B ($\frac{3}{4}$).

6. (4) $5 - (1\frac{3}{4} + 1\frac{1}{8})$ Use the column for size 4. Add the number of yards needed for the jumper ($1\frac{3}{4}$) and blouse A ($1\frac{1}{8}$). Then subtract this total from the number of yards of fabric Russ has (5).

PAGE 74

2. $1\frac{3}{5}$ $\frac{7}{10} + \frac{9}{10} = \frac{16}{10} = 1\frac{6}{10} = 1\frac{3}{5}$

3. $\frac{17}{20}$ $\frac{1}{4} + \frac{3}{5} =$
   $\frac{5}{20} + \frac{12}{20} = \frac{17}{20}$

4. $1\frac{1}{2}$ $\frac{5}{6} + \frac{2}{6} =$
   $\frac{5}{6} + \frac{4}{6} = \frac{9}{6} = 1\frac{3}{6} = 1\frac{1}{2}$

5. $5\frac{3}{5}$ $\begin{array}{r} 2\frac{1}{5} \\ + 3\frac{2}{5} \\ \hline 5\frac{3}{5} \end{array}$

6. 7 $\begin{array}{r} 4\frac{5}{12} \\ + 2\frac{7}{12} \\ \hline 6\frac{12}{12} = 6 + 1 = 7 \end{array}$

7. $4\frac{11}{12}$ $\begin{array}{r} 1\frac{1}{4} = 1\frac{3}{12} \\ + 3\frac{2}{3} = 3\frac{8}{12} \\ \hline 4\frac{11}{12} \end{array}$

8. $8\frac{1}{15}$ $\begin{array}{r} 5\frac{2}{3} = 5\frac{10}{15} \\ + 2\frac{2}{5} = 2\frac{6}{15} \\ \hline 7\frac{16}{15} = 7 + 1\frac{1}{15} = 8\frac{1}{15} \end{array}$

9. $6\frac{19}{24}$ $\begin{array}{r} 6\frac{5}{8} = 6\frac{15}{24} \\ + \frac{1}{6} = \frac{4}{24} \\ \hline 6\frac{19}{24} \end{array}$

10. $6\frac{5}{12}$ $\begin{array}{r} 3\frac{2}{3} = 3\frac{8}{12} \\ + 2\frac{3}{4} = 2\frac{9}{12} \\ \hline 5\frac{17}{12} = 5 + 1\frac{5}{12} = 6\frac{5}{12} \end{array}$

PAGE 76

2. $\frac{11}{24}$ $\frac{5}{6} - \frac{3}{8} =$
   $\frac{20}{24} - \frac{9}{24} = \frac{11}{24}$

3. $\frac{5}{16}$ $\frac{9}{16} - \frac{1}{4} =$
   $\frac{9}{16} - \frac{4}{16} = \frac{5}{16}$

4. $3\frac{2}{5}$ $\begin{array}{r} 6 = 6\frac{5}{5} \\ - 2\frac{3}{5} = 2\frac{3}{5} \\ \hline 3\frac{2}{5} \end{array}$

5. $3\frac{1}{2}$ $\begin{array}{r} 4\frac{7}{8} \\ - 1\frac{3}{8} \\ \hline 3\frac{4}{8} = 3\frac{1}{2} \end{array}$

6. $5\frac{1}{12}$ $\begin{array}{r} 7\frac{3}{4} = 7\frac{9}{12} \\ - 2\frac{2}{3} = 2\frac{8}{12} \\ \hline 5\frac{1}{12} \end{array}$

7. $2\frac{7}{9}$ $\begin{array}{r} 8 = 8\frac{9}{9} \\ - 5\frac{2}{9} = 5\frac{2}{9} \\ \hline 2\frac{7}{9} \end{array}$

8. $2\frac{1}{3}$ $\begin{array}{r} 6\frac{1}{6} = 6\frac{7}{6} \\ - 3\frac{5}{6} = 3\frac{5}{6} \\ \hline 2\frac{2}{6} = 2\frac{1}{3} \end{array}$

9. $\frac{5}{8}$ $\begin{array}{r} 9\frac{1}{4} = 9\frac{2}{8} = 9\frac{10}{8} \\ - 8\frac{5}{8} = 8\frac{5}{8} = 8\frac{5}{8} \\ \hline \frac{5}{8} \end{array}$

10. $5\frac{11}{15}$ $\begin{array}{r} 7\frac{2}{5} = 7\frac{6}{15} = 7\frac{21}{15} \\ - 1\frac{2}{3} = 1\frac{10}{15} = 1\frac{10}{15} \\ \hline 5\frac{11}{15} \end{array}$

PAGE 79

1. **(4) 17**   Jose drives $6\frac{3}{10}$ miles from Myer Vending Co. to Precision Auto, $6\frac{4}{5}$ miles from Precision Auto to the city pool, and $4\frac{2}{5}$ miles from the city pool to the hospital. To estimate the total distance, round each distance and add.

   $\begin{array}{ll} 6\frac{3}{10} & \text{rounds to} \quad 6 \\ 6\frac{4}{5} & \text{rounds to} \quad 7 \\ + 4\frac{2}{5} & \text{rounds to} \quad 4 \\ \hline & \qquad\qquad\quad 17 \text{ miles} \end{array}$

2. **(5) $17\frac{1}{2}$**   Add each distance to find the total. See the explanation for Item 1.

   $\begin{array}{l} 6\frac{3}{10} = 6\frac{3}{10} \\ 6\frac{4}{5} = 6\frac{8}{10} \\ + 4\frac{2}{5} = 4\frac{4}{10} \\ \hline 16\frac{15}{10} = 16 + 1\frac{5}{10} = 17\frac{5}{10} = 17\frac{1}{2} \text{ miles} \end{array}$

3. **$1\frac{1}{10}$ miles**   One-Stop Gas and Food is located between the city pool and the hospital. Jose drives $3\frac{3}{10}$ miles from the city pool to One-Stop Gas and Food and $4\frac{2}{5}$ miles from the city pool to the hospital. Subtract to find the distance from One-Stop Gas and Food to the hospital.

   $\begin{array}{r} 4\frac{2}{5} = 4\frac{4}{10} \\ - 3\frac{3}{10} = 3\frac{3}{10} \\ \hline 1\frac{1}{10} \end{array}$

4. 9 miles Jose drives $1\frac{1}{10}$ miles from the hospital to the city hall, $1\frac{9}{10}$ miles from the city hall to the junior college, and $5\frac{7}{10}$ miles from the junior college back to Myer Vending Company. To estimate the total distance, round each distance and add.

$1\frac{1}{10}$ rounds to $\ \ 1$
$1\frac{9}{10}$ rounds to $\ \ 2$
$+\ 5\frac{7}{10}$ rounds to $\ \underline{\ \ 6}$
$\phantom{+\ 5\frac{7}{10}\text{ rounds to }}9$

5. $8\frac{7}{10}$ miles Add each distance to find the total. See the explanation for Item 4.

$1\frac{1}{10}$
$1\frac{9}{10}$
$\underline{+\ 5\frac{7}{10}}$
$7\frac{17}{10} = 7 + 1\frac{7}{10} = 8\frac{7}{10}$

PAGE 82

1. $3\frac{3}{4}$ hours Think of 9:00 as 9. Since 42 is close to 45, think of 12:42 as $12\frac{3}{4}$. Then subtract.

$12\frac{3}{4}$
$\underline{-\ \ \ 9}$
$\ \ 3\frac{3}{4}$

2. $4\frac{1}{4}$ hours Since 48 is close to 45, think of 1:48 as $1\frac{3}{4}$. Since 2 is close to 0, think of 6:02 as 6. Then subtract.

$6\ \ = \overset{5}{\cancel{6}}\frac{4}{4}$
$\underline{-\ 1\frac{3}{4} = 1\frac{3}{4}}$
$\ \ \ \ \ \ \ \ 4\frac{1}{4}$

3. 8 hours Add the hours Vlady worked in the morning (see the explanation for Item 1) and the hours he worked in the afternoon (see the explanation for Item 2).

$3\frac{3}{4}$
$\underline{+\ 4\frac{1}{4}}$
$7\frac{4}{4} = 7 + 1 = 8$

4. (3) $3\frac{3}{4}$ Since 50 is close to 45, think of 8:50 as $8\frac{3}{4}$. Since 32 is close to 30, think of 12:32 as $12\frac{1}{2}$. Then subtract.

$12\frac{1}{2} = 12\frac{2}{4} = \overset{11\ \ 6}{\cancel{12}\frac{2}{4}}$
$\underline{-\ 8\frac{3}{4} = \ \ 8\frac{3}{4} = \ \ 8\frac{3}{4}}$
$\ 3\frac{3}{4}\text{ hours}$

5. (1) $3\frac{3}{4}$ Since 24 is close to 30, think of 1:24 as $1\frac{1}{2}$. Since 10 is close to 15, think of 5:10 as $5\frac{1}{4}$. Then subtract.

$5\frac{1}{4} = 5\frac{1}{4} = \overset{4\ \ 5}{\cancel{5}\frac{1}{4}}$
$\underline{-\ 1\frac{1}{2} = 1\frac{2}{4} = 1\frac{2}{4}}$
$\ \ \ \ \ \ \ \ \ \ \ \ \ \ \ \ \ \ \ 3\frac{3}{4}\text{ hours}$

6. (1) $7\frac{1}{2}$ Add the hours Paul worked in the morning (see the explanation for Item 4) and the hours he worked in the afternoon (see the explanation for Item 5).

$3\frac{3}{4}$
$\underline{+\ 3\frac{3}{4}}$
$6\frac{6}{4} = 6 + 1\frac{2}{4} = 7\frac{2}{4} = 7\frac{1}{2}$

PAGES 83–85

1. $\frac{3}{8}$ $\ \ \ \frac{15}{16} - \frac{9}{16} = \frac{6}{16} = \frac{3}{8}$

2. $\frac{9}{10}$ $\ \ \ \frac{1}{5} + \frac{7}{10} =$
$\ \ \ \ \ \ \ \ \ \ \frac{2}{10} + \frac{7}{10} = \frac{9}{10}$

3. $5\frac{5}{6}$ $\ \ \ \ \ 8\ \ = \overset{7}{\cancel{8}}\frac{6}{6}$
$\ \ \ \ \ \ \ \ \underline{-\ 2\frac{1}{6} = 2\frac{1}{6}}$
$\ \ \ \ \ \ \ \ \ \ \ \ \ \ \ \ 5\frac{5}{6}$

4. $1\frac{5}{24}$ $\ \ \ \frac{5}{6} + \frac{3}{8} =$
$\ \ \ \ \ \ \ \ \ \frac{20}{24} + \frac{9}{24} = \frac{29}{24} = 1\frac{5}{24}$

5. 8 $\ \ \ \ \ \ 3\frac{7}{9}$
$\ \ \ \ \ \underline{+\ 4\frac{2}{9}}$
$\ \ \ \ \ \ 7\frac{9}{9} = 7 + 1 = 8$

6. $2\frac{3}{5}$ $\ \ \ \ 4\frac{9}{10}$
$\ \ \ \ \ \underline{-\ 2\frac{3}{10}}$
$\ \ \ \ \ \ 2\frac{6}{10} = 2\frac{3}{5}$

7. $5\frac{3}{8}$ $\ \ \ \ 2\frac{5}{8} = 2\frac{5}{8}$
$\ \ \ \ \ \underline{+\ 2\frac{3}{4} = 2\frac{6}{8}}$
$\ \ \ \ \ \ \ \ 4\frac{11}{8} = 4 + 1\frac{3}{8} = 5\frac{3}{8}$

8. $\frac{3}{5}$ $\ \ \ \ 9\frac{1}{5} = \overset{8\ \ 6}{\cancel{9}\frac{1}{5}}$
$\ \ \ \ \ \underline{-\ 8\frac{3}{5} = 8\frac{3}{5}}$
$\ \ \ \ \ \ \ \ \ \ \ \ \ \ \ \frac{3}{5}$

9. $2\frac{1}{8}$ $\ \ \ \ \ 3\ \ = \overset{2}{\cancel{3}}\frac{8}{8}$
$\ \ \ \ \ \ \ \underline{-\ \frac{7}{8} = \frac{7}{8}}$
$\ \ \ \ \ \ \ \ \ \ \ \ \ 2\frac{1}{8}$

10. $3\frac{7}{12}$

$$6\frac{1}{3} = 6\frac{4}{12} = \overset{5}{\cancel{6}}\frac{\overset{16}{\cancel{4}}}{12}$$
$$-\ 2\frac{3}{4} = 2\frac{9}{12} = 2\frac{9}{12}$$
$$\overline{\phantom{-\ 2\frac{3}{4} = 2\frac{9}{12} = }\ 3\frac{7}{12}}$$

11. $6\frac{3}{4}$ **pounds** Subtract the weight loss from the original weight at birth.

$$7\frac{1}{4} = 7\frac{1}{4} = \overset{6}{\cancel{7}}\frac{\overset{5}{\cancel{1}}}{4}$$
$$-\ \frac{1}{2} = \frac{2}{4} = \frac{2}{4}$$
$$\overline{\phantom{-\ \frac{1}{2} = \frac{2}{4} = }\ 6\frac{3}{4}}$$

12. $6\frac{1}{4}$ **cups** Add the amount of each type of flour.

$$2\frac{3}{4} = 2\frac{3}{4}$$
$$+\ 3\frac{1}{2} = 3\frac{2}{4}$$
$$\overline{\phantom{+\ 3\frac{1}{2} = }\ 5\frac{5}{4} = 5 + 1\frac{1}{4} = 6\frac{1}{4}}$$

13. $5\frac{2}{5}$ **inches** Subtract last summer's rainfall from this summer's rainfall.

$$19\frac{1}{10} = \overset{18}{\cancel{19}}\frac{\overset{11}{\cancel{1}}}{10}$$
$$-\ 13\frac{7}{10} = 13\frac{7}{10}$$
$$\overline{\phantom{-\ 13\frac{7}{10} = }\ 5\frac{4}{10} = 5\frac{2}{5}}$$

14. $1\frac{5}{12}$ **feet** Subtract the length needed for the shelf from the total length.

$$6\ \ \ = \overset{5}{\cancel{6}}\frac{12}{12}$$
$$-\ 4\frac{7}{12} = 4\frac{7}{12}$$
$$\overline{\phantom{-\ 4\frac{7}{12} = }\ 1\frac{5}{12}}$$

15. **(3)** $2\frac{1}{2} + 1\frac{1}{2} + \frac{3}{4}$ Add the weight of each type of material collected.

16. **(5)** $3\frac{5}{8}$ Add the weights of each type of nut.

$$2\frac{7}{8} = 2\frac{7}{8}$$
$$+\ \ \frac{3}{4} = \ \ \frac{6}{8}$$
$$\overline{\phantom{+\ \frac{3}{4} = }\ 2\frac{13}{8} = 2 + 1\frac{5}{8} = 3\frac{5}{8}\ \text{pounds}}$$

17. **(2)** $17\frac{1}{2} - 9\frac{1}{4}$ Subtract the number of miles she has jogged already from the total number of miles she wants to jog.

18. **(1)** $3\frac{3}{4}$ Subtract the number of hours spent cleaning the first office from the total number of hours spent cleaning.

$$5\frac{1}{4} = 5\frac{1}{4} = \overset{4}{\cancel{5}}\frac{\overset{5}{\cancel{1}}}{4}$$
$$-\ 1\frac{1}{2} = 1\frac{2}{4} = 1\frac{2}{4}$$
$$\overline{\phantom{-\ 1\frac{1}{2} = 1\frac{2}{4} = }\ 3\frac{3}{4}\ \text{hours}}$$

19. **(3)** $7\frac{1}{8}$ Use the column for size 12. Add the number of yards of fabric in the main color ($5\frac{5}{8}$) and the number of yards of contrasting fabric ($1\frac{1}{2}$) needed for dress B.

$$5\frac{5}{8} = 5\frac{5}{8}$$
$$+\ 1\frac{1}{2} = 1\frac{4}{8}$$
$$\overline{\phantom{+\ 1\frac{1}{2} = }\ 6\frac{9}{8} = 6 + 1\frac{1}{8} = 7\frac{1}{8}\ \text{yards}}$$

20. **(3)** $\frac{3}{8}$ Use the column for size 8. Subtract the number of yards of lace needed for dress B ($2\frac{1}{8}$) from the number of yards of lace needed for dress A ($2\frac{1}{2}$).

$$2\frac{1}{2} = 2\frac{4}{8}$$
$$-\ 2\frac{1}{8} = 2\frac{1}{8}$$
$$\overline{\phantom{-\ 2\frac{1}{8} = }\ \frac{3}{8}\ \text{yard}}$$

21. **(3)** $(5\frac{5}{8} + 1\frac{1}{2}) - 6\frac{3}{8}$ Use the column for size 12. Add the number of yards of main color ($5\frac{5}{8}$) and the number of yards of contrasting color ($1\frac{1}{2}$) needed for dress B. Then subtract the number of yards needed for dress A ($6\frac{3}{8}$).

22. **6 miles** Sundra drives $3\frac{2}{5}$ miles from the courthouse to the art museum, $1\frac{1}{5}$ miles from the art museum to the science museum, and $1\frac{9}{10}$ miles from the science museum to the shopping mall. To estimate the total distance, round each distance and add.

$$3\frac{2}{5}\ \text{rounds to}\ 3$$
$$1\frac{1}{5}\ \text{rounds to}\ 1$$
$$+\ 1\frac{9}{10}\ \text{rounds to}\ 2$$
$$\overline{\phantom{+\ 1\frac{9}{10}\ \text{rounds to}\ }\ 6}$$

23. $6\frac{1}{2}$ **miles** Add each distance to find the total distance. See the explanation for Item 22.

$$3\frac{2}{5} = 3\frac{4}{10}$$
$$1\frac{1}{5} = 1\frac{2}{10}$$
$$+\ 1\frac{9}{10} = 1\frac{9}{10}$$
$$\overline{\phantom{+\ 1\frac{9}{10} = }\ 5\frac{15}{10} = 5 + 1\frac{5}{10} = 6\frac{5}{10} = 6\frac{1}{2}}$$

24. **12 miles** Sundra drives $5\frac{3}{10}$ miles from the bus depot to the library. The entire route is $17\frac{1}{5}$ miles. Round each distance and subtract.

$$17\frac{1}{5}\ \text{rounds to}\ 17$$
$$-\ \ 5\frac{3}{10}\ \text{rounds to}\ \ \ 5$$
$$\overline{\phantom{-\ \ 5\frac{3}{10}\ \text{rounds to}\ \ }\ 12}$$

25. $3\frac{3}{4}$ **hours** Since 24 is close to 30, think of 8:24 as $8\frac{1}{2}$. Since 13 is close to 15, think of 12:13 as $12\frac{1}{4}$. Then subtract.

$$12\frac{1}{4} = 12\frac{1}{4} = \overset{11}{\cancel{12}}\frac{\overset{5}{\cancel{1}}}{4}$$
$$-\ \ 8\frac{1}{2} = \ \ 8\frac{2}{4} = \ \ 8\frac{2}{4}$$
$$\overline{\phantom{-\ \ 8\frac{1}{2} = \ \ 8\frac{2}{4} = }\ 3\frac{3}{4}}$$

26. $4\frac{3}{4}$ **hours** Since 58 is close to 60, think of 12:58 as 1. Since 43 is close to 45, think of 5:43 as $5\frac{3}{4}$. Then subtract.

$$5\frac{3}{4}$$
$$-\ 1$$
$$\overline{\ 4\frac{3}{4}}$$

27. $8\frac{1}{2}$ **hours**   Add the hours Joy worked in the morning (see the explanation for Item 25) and the hours she worked in the afternoon (see the explanation for Item 26).

$$3\frac{3}{4}$$
$$+\ 4\frac{3}{4}$$
$$7\frac{6}{4} = 7 + 1\frac{2}{4} = 8\frac{2}{4} = 8\frac{1}{2}$$

SECTION 7

PAGE 88

1. **(5)** $5\frac{1}{2} \div 3$ Vince wants to make a third of the recipe, so divide the amount of potatoes by 3.
2. **(3)** $7\frac{1}{4} \times \frac{1}{2}$ Kasia wants to make half of the recipe, so multiply the amount of flour by $\frac{1}{2}$.
3. **(4)** $4\frac{2}{3} \div \frac{1}{3}$ Divide the total amount of cocoa by the amount needed for each pound.
4. **(5)** $1\frac{1}{4} \times 2$ Karl is planning to double the recipe, so multiply the amount of milk by 2.
5. **(2)** $\frac{1}{2} \times 3$ Since 18 is 3 times 6, Rosa needs to triple the recipe. Multiply the amount of chilies by 3.
6. **(1)** $1\frac{1}{2} \div 2$ Since 12 is half of 24, Luis needs to make half of the recipe. Divide the amount of cheese by 2.

PAGE 90

2. $\frac{25}{48}$ $\frac{5}{6} \times \frac{5}{8} = \frac{25}{48}$
3. $2\frac{2}{5}$ $3 \times \frac{4}{5} = \frac{3}{1} \times \frac{4}{5} = \frac{12}{5} = 2\frac{2}{5}$
4. $\frac{2}{21}$ $\frac{\overset{1}{\cancel{3}}}{7} \times \frac{2}{\underset{3}{\cancel{9}}} = \frac{2}{21}$
5. $2\frac{1}{4}$ $\frac{3}{8} \times 6 = \frac{3}{8} \times \frac{\overset{3}{\cancel{6}}}{1} = \frac{9}{4} = 2\frac{1}{4}$
6. $11\frac{1}{2}$ $5 \times 2\frac{3}{10} = \frac{\overset{1}{\cancel{5}}}{1} \times \frac{23}{\underset{2}{\cancel{10}}} = \frac{23}{2} = 11\frac{1}{2}$
7. $1\frac{1}{2}$ $\frac{5}{8} \times 2\frac{2}{5} = \frac{\overset{1}{\cancel{5}}}{\underset{2}{\cancel{8}}} \times \frac{\overset{3}{\cancel{12}}}{\underset{1}{\cancel{5}}} = \frac{3}{2} = 1\frac{1}{2}$
8. $3\frac{1}{9}$ $3\frac{1}{2} \times \frac{8}{9} = \frac{7}{2} \times \frac{\overset{4}{\cancel{8}}}{9} = \frac{28}{9} = 3\frac{1}{9}$
9. $3\frac{1}{2}$ $2\frac{1}{3} \times 1\frac{1}{2} = \frac{7}{\cancel{3}} \times \frac{\overset{1}{\cancel{3}}}{2} = \frac{7}{2} = 3\frac{1}{2}$
10. 12 $1\frac{4}{5} \times 6\frac{2}{3} = \frac{\overset{3}{\cancel{9}}}{\underset{1}{\cancel{5}}} \times \frac{\overset{4}{\cancel{20}}}{\underset{3}{\cancel{3}}} = \frac{12}{1} = 12$

PAGE 91

2. $\frac{8}{21}$ $\frac{2}{7} \div \frac{3}{4} = \frac{2}{7} \times \frac{4}{3} = \frac{8}{21}$
3. 5 $4 \div \frac{4}{5} = \frac{4}{1} \div \frac{4}{5} = \frac{\overset{1}{\cancel{4}}}{1} \times \frac{5}{\cancel{4}} = \frac{5}{1} = 5$
4. $\frac{4}{5}$ $\frac{2}{3} \div \frac{5}{6} = \frac{2}{3} \times \frac{\overset{2}{\cancel{6}}}{5} = \frac{4}{5}$
5. $\frac{7}{36}$ $\frac{7}{12} \div 3 = \frac{7}{12} \div \frac{3}{1} = \frac{7}{12} \times \frac{1}{3} = \frac{7}{36}$
6. $1\frac{3}{4}$ $2 \div 1\frac{1}{7} = \frac{2}{1} \div \frac{8}{7} = \frac{\overset{1}{\cancel{2}}}{1} \times \frac{7}{\underset{4}{\cancel{8}}} = \frac{7}{4} = 1\frac{3}{4}$
7. $\frac{15}{44}$ $\frac{5}{8} \div 1\frac{5}{6} = \frac{5}{8} \div \frac{11}{6} = \frac{5}{8} \times \frac{\overset{3}{\cancel{6}}}{11} = \frac{15}{44}$
8. $12\frac{1}{2}$ $3\frac{3}{4} \div \frac{3}{10} = \frac{15}{4} \div \frac{3}{10} = \frac{\overset{5}{\cancel{15}}}{\underset{2}{\cancel{4}}} \times \frac{\overset{5}{\cancel{10}}}{\underset{1}{\cancel{3}}} = \frac{25}{2} = 12\frac{1}{2}$
9. $\frac{28}{45}$ $1\frac{2}{5} \div 2\frac{1}{4} = \frac{7}{5} \div \frac{9}{4} = \frac{7}{5} \times \frac{4}{9} = \frac{28}{45}$
10. $2\frac{5}{6}$ $4\frac{1}{4} \div 1\frac{1}{2} = \frac{17}{4} \div \frac{3}{2} = \frac{17}{\underset{2}{\cancel{4}}} \times \frac{\overset{1}{\cancel{2}}}{3} = \frac{17}{6} = 2\frac{5}{6}$

PAGE 95

1. **(2)** $3\frac{19}{24}$ Since there are 12 inches in a foot, and inches are smaller than feet, divide $45\frac{1}{2}$ by 12.
$$45\frac{1}{2} \div 12 = \frac{91}{2} \div \frac{12}{1} = \frac{91}{2} \times \frac{1}{12} = \frac{91}{24} = 3\frac{19}{24}$$
2. **(4)** 24 Since there are 36 inches in a yard, and yards are larger than inches, multiply $\frac{2}{3}$ times 36.
$$\frac{2}{3} \times 36 = \frac{2}{\underset{1}{\cancel{3}}} \times \frac{\overset{12}{\cancel{36}}}{1} = \frac{24}{1} = 24$$
3. **(3)** $2\frac{1}{2}$ Since there are 3 feet in a yard, and feet are smaller than yards, divide $7\frac{1}{2}$ by 3.
$$7\frac{1}{2} \div 3 = \frac{15}{2} \div \frac{3}{1} = \frac{\overset{5}{\cancel{15}}}{2} \times \frac{1}{\underset{1}{\cancel{3}}} = \frac{5}{2} = 2\frac{1}{2}$$
4. **(2)** $2\frac{3}{16}$ Since there are 12 inches in a foot, and inches are smaller than feet, divide $26\frac{1}{4}$ by 12.
$$26\frac{1}{4} \div 12 = \frac{105}{4} \div \frac{12}{1} = \frac{105}{4} \times \frac{1}{12} = \frac{105}{48} = 2\frac{9}{48} = 2\frac{3}{16}$$
5. 100 Multiply the length of each shelf ($1\frac{2}{3}$ feet) by the number of shelves. Then multiply by 12 to change feet to inches.
$$1\frac{2}{3} \times 5 = \frac{5}{3} \times \frac{5}{1} = \frac{25}{3} = 8\frac{1}{3} \text{ feet}$$
$$8\frac{1}{3} \times 12 = \frac{25}{\underset{1}{\cancel{3}}} \times \frac{\overset{4}{\cancel{12}}}{1} = \frac{100}{1} = 100 \text{ inches}$$

6. 4 cuts

$\frac{3}{16}$"	$\frac{3}{16}$"	$\frac{3}{16}$"	$\frac{3}{16}$" waste	
$1\frac{2}{3}$	$1\frac{2}{3}$	$1\frac{2}{3}$	$1\frac{2}{3}$	$1\frac{2}{3}$	5 shelves
1	2	3	4 cuts	

7. $\frac{3}{4}$ inch   Multiply the waste per cut ($\frac{3}{16}$ inch) by the number of cuts (4; see the diagram for Item 6).

$$\frac{3}{16} \times 4 = \frac{3}{\overset{}{\underset{4}{16}}} \times \frac{\overset{1}{4}}{1} = \frac{3}{4} \text{ inch}$$

8. $100\frac{3}{4}$ inches   Add the total length needed for the shelves (see the explanation for Item 5) and the total waste (see the explanation for Item 7).

$$100 + \frac{3}{4} = 100\frac{3}{4} \text{ inches}$$

PAGE 98

1. 6 lb.   Multiply $\frac{1}{2}$ pound per person by the number of people (12).

$$\frac{1}{2} \times 12 = \frac{1}{\underset{1}{2}} \times \frac{\overset{6}{12}}{1} = \frac{6}{1} = 6$$

2. $4\frac{1}{2}$ lb.   Multiply $\frac{3}{8}$ pound per person by the number of people (12).

$$\frac{3}{8} \times 12 = \frac{3}{\underset{2}{8}} \times \frac{\overset{3}{12}}{1} = \frac{9}{2} = 4\frac{1}{2}$$

3. 3 lb.   Multiply $\frac{1}{4}$ pound per person by the number of people (12).

$$\frac{1}{4} \times 12 = \frac{1}{\underset{1}{4}} \times \frac{\overset{3}{12}}{1} = \frac{3}{1} = 3$$

4. 9 cups   Multiply $\frac{3}{4}$ cup per person by the number of people (12).

$$\frac{3}{4} \times 12 = \frac{3}{\underset{1}{4}} \times \frac{\overset{3}{12}}{1} = \frac{9}{1} = 9$$

5. 8 yd.   Multiply $\frac{1}{2}$ yard per doll by the number of dolls (16).

$$\frac{1}{2} \times 16 = \frac{1}{\underset{1}{2}} \times \frac{\overset{8}{16}}{1} = \frac{8}{1} = 8$$

6. 10 yd.   Multiply $\frac{5}{8}$ yard per doll by the number of dolls (16).

$$\frac{5}{8} \times 16 = \frac{5}{\underset{1}{8}} \times \frac{\overset{2}{16}}{1} = \frac{10}{1} = 10$$

7. 24 yd.   Multiply $1\frac{1}{2}$ yards per doll by the number of dolls (16).

$$1\frac{1}{2} \times 16 = \frac{3}{\underset{1}{2}} \times \frac{\overset{8}{16}}{1} = \frac{24}{1} = 24$$

8. 12 lb.   Multiply $\frac{3}{4}$ pound per doll by the number of dolls (16).

$$\frac{3}{4} \times 16 = \frac{3}{\underset{1}{4}} \times \frac{\overset{4}{16}}{1} = \frac{12}{1} = 12$$

PAGES 99–101

1. $\frac{4}{15}$ $\frac{4}{5} \times \frac{1}{3} = \frac{4}{15}$

2. $2\frac{2}{3}$ $\frac{4}{9} \div \frac{1}{6} = \frac{4}{\underset{3}{9}} \times \frac{\overset{2}{6}}{1} = \frac{8}{3} = 2\frac{2}{3}$

3. $1\frac{1}{24}$ $\frac{5}{8} \div \frac{3}{5} = \frac{5}{8} \times \frac{5}{3} = \frac{25}{24} = 1\frac{1}{24}$

4. $\frac{5}{42}$ $\frac{\overset{1}{2}}{7} \times \frac{5}{\underset{6}{12}} = \frac{5}{42}$

5. 8 $7 \div \frac{7}{8} = \frac{7}{1} \div \frac{7}{8} = \frac{\overset{1}{7}}{1} \times \frac{8}{\underset{1}{7}} = \frac{8}{1} = 8$

6. $4\frac{1}{2}$ $6 \times \frac{3}{4} = \frac{\overset{3}{6}}{1} \times \frac{3}{\underset{2}{4}} = \frac{9}{2} = 4\frac{1}{2}$

7. $\frac{6}{25}$ $\frac{4}{\underset{5}{15}} \times \frac{\overset{3}{9}}{10} = \frac{6}{25}$

8. $\frac{9}{10}$ $\frac{2}{5} \div \frac{4}{9} = \frac{\overset{1}{2}}{5} \times \frac{9}{\underset{2}{4}} = \frac{9}{10}$

9. $7\frac{1}{3}$ $\frac{11}{12} \times 8 = \frac{11}{\underset{3}{12}} \times \frac{\overset{2}{8}}{1} = \frac{22}{3} = 7\frac{1}{3}$

10. $11\frac{1}{3}$ $4 \times 2\frac{5}{6} = \frac{4}{1} \times \frac{17}{\underset{3}{6}} = \frac{34}{3} = 11\frac{1}{3}$

11. $\frac{3}{32}$ $\frac{3}{8} \div 4 = \frac{3}{8} \div \frac{4}{1} = \frac{3}{8} \times \frac{1}{4} = \frac{3}{32}$

12. $4\frac{1}{2}$ $5 \div 1\frac{1}{9} = \frac{5}{1} \div \frac{10}{9} = \frac{\overset{1}{5}}{1} \times \frac{9}{\underset{2}{10}} = \frac{9}{2} = 4\frac{1}{2}$

13. $2\frac{1}{10}$ $\frac{7}{12} \times 3\frac{3}{5} = \frac{7}{\underset{2}{12}} \times \frac{\overset{3}{18}}{5} = \frac{21}{10} = 2\frac{1}{10}$

14. $\frac{1}{3}$ $\frac{5}{6} \div 2\frac{1}{2} = \frac{5}{6} \div \frac{5}{2} = \frac{\overset{1}{5}}{\underset{3}{6}} \times \frac{\overset{1}{2}}{\underset{1}{5}} = \frac{1}{3}$

15. $1\frac{5}{6}$ $2\frac{3}{4} \times \frac{2}{3} = \frac{11}{\underset{2}{4}} \times \frac{\overset{1}{2}}{3} = \frac{11}{6} = 1\frac{5}{6}$

16. $3\frac{3}{4}$ $4\frac{1}{2} \div 1\frac{1}{5} = \frac{9}{2} \div \frac{6}{5} = \frac{\overset{3}{9}}{2} \times \frac{5}{\underset{2}{6}} = \frac{15}{4} = 3\frac{3}{4}$

17. $1\frac{1}{3}$ $3\frac{1}{5} \div 2\frac{2}{5} = \frac{16}{5} \div \frac{12}{5} = \frac{\overset{4}{16}}{\underset{1}{5}} \times \frac{\overset{1}{5}}{\underset{3}{12}} = \frac{4}{3} = 1\frac{1}{3}$

18. $4\frac{1}{7}$ $2\frac{5}{12} \times 1\frac{5}{7} = \frac{29}{12} \times \frac{\overset{1}{12}}{7} = \frac{29}{7} = 4\frac{1}{7}$

19. $3\frac{3}{4}$ $2\frac{6}{7} \times 1\frac{5}{16} = \frac{\overset{5}{20}}{\underset{1}{7}} \times \frac{\overset{3}{21}}{\underset{4}{16}} = \frac{15}{4} = 3\frac{3}{4}$

20. $\frac{4}{5}$ $3\frac{1}{3} \div 4\frac{1}{6} = \frac{10}{3} \div \frac{25}{6} = \frac{\overset{2}{10}}{\underset{1}{3}} \times \frac{\overset{2}{6}}{\underset{5}{25}} = \frac{4}{5}$

21. **24 lots**   Divide the total number of acres by the number of acres for each lot.

$$15 \div \tfrac{5}{8} = \tfrac{15}{1} \div \tfrac{5}{8} = \tfrac{\overset{3}{15}}{1} \times \tfrac{8}{\underset{1}{5}} = \tfrac{24}{1} = 24$$

22. **22 patties**   Divide the total weight of the ground beef by the weight of each patty.

$$5\tfrac{1}{2} \div \tfrac{1}{4} = \tfrac{11}{2} \div \tfrac{1}{4} = \tfrac{11}{2} \times \tfrac{\overset{2}{4}}{\underset{1}{1}} = \tfrac{22}{1} = 22$$

23. **$2\tfrac{1}{2}$ hours**   Multiply the hours worked by the part of the day spent answering the phone.

$$7\tfrac{1}{2} \times \tfrac{1}{3} = \tfrac{\overset{5}{15}}{2} \times \tfrac{1}{\underset{1}{3}} = \tfrac{5}{2} = 2\tfrac{1}{2}$$

24. **18 people**   Multiply the total number of people by the fraction that bought new cars.

$$24 \times \tfrac{3}{4} = \tfrac{\overset{6}{24}}{1} \times \tfrac{3}{\underset{1}{4}} = \tfrac{18}{1} = 18$$

25. **4 dozen plants**   Since $\tfrac{1}{7}$ of the plants were lost, $\tfrac{6}{7}$ survived. Multiply the total number of plants by the fraction that survived.

$$4\tfrac{2}{3} \times \tfrac{6}{7} = \tfrac{\overset{2}{14}}{\underset{1}{3}} \times \tfrac{\overset{2}{6}}{\underset{1}{7}} = \tfrac{4}{1} = 4$$

26. **8 batches**   Divide the total amount of pectin by the amount needed for each batch.

$$14 \div 1\tfrac{3}{4} = \tfrac{14}{1} \div \tfrac{7}{4} = \tfrac{\overset{2}{14}}{1} \times \tfrac{4}{\underset{1}{7}} = \tfrac{8}{1} = 8$$

27. **$5\tfrac{1}{4}$ miles**   Multiply the hourly rate of speed by the hours walked.
$$3\tfrac{1}{2} \times 1\tfrac{1}{2} = \tfrac{7}{2} \times \tfrac{3}{2} = \tfrac{21}{4} = 5\tfrac{1}{4}$$

28. **40 strips**   Divide the total width by the width of each strip.

$$45 \div 1\tfrac{1}{8} = \tfrac{45}{1} \div \tfrac{9}{8} = \tfrac{\overset{5}{45}}{1} \times \tfrac{8}{\underset{1}{9}} = \tfrac{40}{1} = 40$$

29. **(3) $\tfrac{3}{4}$ x 2**   Since Richard is planning to double the recipe, multiply the amount of bread crumbs by 2.

30. **(2) $\tfrac{5}{8}$ cup**   Since 6 is one third of 18, Carla needs to make one third of the recipe. Multiply the amount of mayonnaise by $\tfrac{1}{3}$.

$$1\tfrac{7}{8} \times \tfrac{1}{3} = \tfrac{\overset{5}{15}}{8} \times \tfrac{1}{\underset{1}{3}} = \tfrac{5}{8}$$

31. **(4) $56 \div 12$**   Since there are 12 inches in a foot, and inches are smaller than feet, divide the number of inches by 12.

32. **(5) 126 in.**   Since there are 36 inches in a yard, and yards are larger than inches, multiply the number of yards by 36.

$$3\tfrac{1}{2} \times 36 = \tfrac{7}{2} \times \tfrac{\overset{18}{36}}{\underset{1}{1}} = \tfrac{126}{1} = 126$$

33. **15 lb.**   Multiply $\tfrac{3}{4}$ pound per person times the number of people (20).

$$\tfrac{3}{4} \times 20 = \tfrac{3}{4} \times \tfrac{\overset{5}{20}}{\underset{1}{1}} = \tfrac{15}{1} = 15$$

34. **5 cups**   Multiply $\tfrac{1}{4}$ cup per person by the number of people (20).

$$\tfrac{1}{4} \times 20 = \tfrac{1}{4} \times \tfrac{\overset{5}{20}}{\underset{1}{1}} = \tfrac{5}{1} = 5$$

35. **10 lb.**   Multiply $\tfrac{1}{2}$ pound per person by the number of people (20).

$$\tfrac{1}{2} \times 20 = \tfrac{1}{2} \times \tfrac{\overset{10}{20}}{\underset{1}{1}} = \tfrac{10}{1} = 10$$

36. **$7\tfrac{1}{2}$ lb.**   Multiply $\tfrac{3}{8}$ pound per person by the number of people (20).

$$\tfrac{3}{8} \times 20 = \tfrac{3}{\underset{2}{8}} \times \tfrac{\overset{5}{20}}{1} = \tfrac{15}{2} = 7\tfrac{1}{2}$$

UNIT 2 REVIEW

PAGES 102–103

1. $1\tfrac{7}{12}$
$\tfrac{5}{6} + \tfrac{3}{4} =$
$\tfrac{10}{12} + \tfrac{9}{12} = \tfrac{19}{12} = 1\tfrac{7}{12}$

2. $\tfrac{7}{30}$
$\tfrac{9}{10} - \tfrac{2}{3} =$
$\tfrac{27}{30} - \tfrac{20}{30} = \tfrac{7}{30}$

3. $7\tfrac{5}{24}$
$4\tfrac{7}{8} = 4\tfrac{21}{24}$
$+ 2\tfrac{1}{3} = 2\tfrac{8}{24}$
$\phantom{+ 2\tfrac{1}{3} =} 6\tfrac{29}{24} = 6 + 1\tfrac{5}{24} = 7\tfrac{5}{24}$

4. $1\tfrac{13}{20}$
$3\tfrac{2}{5} = 3\tfrac{8}{20} = \overset{2}{\cancel{3}}\overset{28}{\tfrac{8}{20}}$
$- 1\tfrac{3}{4} = 1\tfrac{15}{20} = 1\tfrac{15}{20}$
$\phantom{- 1\tfrac{3}{4} = 1\tfrac{15}{20} =} 1\tfrac{13}{20}$

5. $\tfrac{14}{15}$
$\tfrac{7}{12} \div \tfrac{5}{8} = \tfrac{7}{\underset{3}{12}} \times \tfrac{\overset{2}{8}}{5} = \tfrac{14}{15}$

6. $\tfrac{5}{6}$
$\tfrac{\overset{5}{15}}{\underset{2}{16}} \times \tfrac{\overset{1}{8}}{\underset{3}{9}} = \tfrac{5}{6}$

7. $8\tfrac{1}{3}$
$3\tfrac{1}{3} \times 2\tfrac{1}{2} = \tfrac{10}{3} \times \tfrac{\overset{5}{5}}{\underset{1}{2}} = \tfrac{25}{3} = 8\tfrac{1}{3}$

8. $\tfrac{15}{16}$
$3\tfrac{3}{8} \div 3\tfrac{3}{5} = \tfrac{27}{8} \div \tfrac{18}{5} = \tfrac{\overset{3}{27}}{8} \times \tfrac{5}{\underset{2}{18}} = \tfrac{15}{16}$

9. $\tfrac{3}{20}$

10. **40 packets**   Divide the weight of a box by the weight of a packet.

$$30 \div \tfrac{3}{4} = \tfrac{30}{1} \div \tfrac{3}{4} = \tfrac{\overset{10}{30}}{1} \times \tfrac{4}{\underset{1}{3}} = \tfrac{40}{1} = 40$$

11. **$4\tfrac{5}{8}$ feet**   Since there are 12 inches in one foot, and inches are smaller than feet, divide the number of inches by 12.

$$55\tfrac{1}{2} \div 12 = \tfrac{111}{2} \div \tfrac{12}{1} = \tfrac{111}{2} \times \tfrac{1}{12} = \tfrac{111}{24} = 4\tfrac{15}{24} = 4\tfrac{5}{8}$$

12. 25 feet   Since there are 3 feet in one yard, and yards are larger than feet, multiply the number of yards by 3.

$$8\tfrac{1}{3} \times 3 = \tfrac{25}{3} \times \tfrac{\overset{1}{\cancel{3}}}{1} = \tfrac{25}{1} = 25$$

13. 5 miles   Henry drives $1\tfrac{3}{10}$ miles from point C to point D, $1\tfrac{1}{5}$ miles from point D to point E, and $2\tfrac{4}{5}$ miles from point E to the garage. To estimate the total distance, round each distance and add.

$1\tfrac{3}{10}$	rounds to	1
$1\tfrac{1}{5}$	rounds to	1
$+\ 2\tfrac{4}{5}$	rounds to	$\underline{\ 3\ }$
		5

14. $7\tfrac{1}{2}$ hours   Find the number of hours Geri worked in the morning. Since 51 is close to 45, think of 8:51 as $8\tfrac{3}{4}$. Since 24 is close to 30, think of 12:24 as $12\tfrac{1}{2}$. Then subtract.

$$12\tfrac{1}{2} = 12\tfrac{2}{4} = \overset{11}{\cancel{12}}\overset{6}{\tfrac{\cancel{2}}{4}}$$
$$\underline{-\ 8\tfrac{3}{4} = \ \ 8\tfrac{3}{4} = \ \ 8\tfrac{3}{4}}$$
$$3\tfrac{3}{4}$$

Find the number of hours Geri worked in the afternoon. Since 8 is close to 15, think of 1:08 as $1\tfrac{1}{4}$. Since 3 is close to zero, think of 5:03 as 5. Then subtract.

$$5 \ = \overset{4}{\cancel{5}}\tfrac{4}{4}$$
$$\underline{-\ 1\tfrac{1}{4} = \ 1\tfrac{1}{4}}$$
$$3\tfrac{3}{4}$$

Add the number of hours Geri worked in the morning and in the afternoon.

$$3\tfrac{3}{4}$$
$$\underline{+\ 3\tfrac{3}{4}}$$
$$6\tfrac{6}{4} = 6 + 1\tfrac{2}{4} = 7\tfrac{2}{4} = 7\tfrac{1}{2}$$

15. (3) $4\tfrac{1}{8}$ yards   Use the column for size 12. Add the number of yards needed for blouse A ($2\tfrac{7}{8}$) and the number of yards needed for the skirt ($1\tfrac{1}{4}$).

$$2\tfrac{7}{8} = 2\tfrac{7}{8}$$
$$\underline{+\ 1\tfrac{1}{4} = \ 1\tfrac{2}{8}}$$
$$3\tfrac{9}{8} = 3 + 1\tfrac{1}{8} = 4\tfrac{1}{8}$$

16. (4) $(3\tfrac{1}{4} + 1\tfrac{5}{8}) - (3 + 1\tfrac{5}{8})$ Use the column for size 14 to find the number of yards needed for blouse B ($3\tfrac{1}{4}$) and the skirt ($1\tfrac{5}{8}$). Add. Use the column for size 14 to find the number of yards needed for blouse A (3) and the skirt ($1\tfrac{5}{8}$). Add. Then subtract the total yards for blouse A and the skirt from the total yards for blouse B and the skirt.

17. (2) $2\tfrac{1}{3} \times 2$ Since 16 is 2 times 8, Clara needs to double the recipe. Multiply the amount of milk ($2\tfrac{1}{3}$ cups) by 2.

CUMULATIVE REVIEW
PAGES 104–105

1. 32,774 > 3,274
32,774 has more digits than 3,274.

2. 948,526 > 948,256   5 is greater than 2.

3. 5

8	−	3 × 2	+	9 ÷ 3		
8	−	6	+	9 ÷ 3		
8	−	6	+	3		
	2		+	3		
			5			

4. 4

6 × (7 − 2)	÷ 10	+ 1		
6 × 5	÷ 10	+ 1		
30	÷ 10	+ 1		
3		+ 1		
	4			

5. $4.54

$$\$\overset{7}{\cancel{8}}\overset{\overset{14}{\cancel{4}}}{.}\overset{12}{\cancel{5}}\overset{}{\cancel{2}}$$
$$\underline{-\ 3.98}$$
$$\$4.54$$

6. 360,558

$$594$$
$$\underline{\times\ 607}$$
$$4\ 158$$
$$\underline{356\ 40\ \ }$$
$$360,558$$

7. 483

$$\overset{8\ 9\ 10}{\cancel{9}\cancel{0}\cancel{0}}$$
$$\underline{-\ 417}$$
$$483$$

8. 206 r15

$$\begin{array}{r} 206\ r15 \\ 38)\overline{7,843} \\ \underline{-\ 7\ 6\ \ \ } \\ 243 \\ \underline{-\ 228} \\ 15 \end{array}$$

9. 976

$$\overset{1\ 1}{}684$$
$$35$$
$$\underline{+\ 257}$$
$$976$$

10. $4.23

$$\begin{array}{r} \$4.23 \\ 9)\overline{\$38.07} \\ \underline{-\ 36\ \ \ \ } \\ 2\ 0 \\ \underline{-\ 1\ 8} \\ 27 \\ \underline{-\ 27} \\ 0 \end{array}$$

11. $1\frac{7}{24}$ $\quad \frac{2}{3} + \frac{5}{8} =$

$\quad\quad\quad \frac{16}{24} + \frac{15}{24} = \frac{31}{24} = 1\frac{7}{24}$

12. $\frac{2}{3}$ $\quad \frac{5}{9} \div \frac{5}{6} = \frac{\overset{1}{\cancel{5}}}{\underset{3}{\cancel{9}}} \times \frac{\overset{2}{\cancel{6}}}{\cancel{5}_{1}} = \frac{2}{3}$

13. $9\frac{2}{15}$ $\quad 3\frac{4}{5} = 3\frac{12}{15}$

$\quad\quad\quad \underline{+ 5\frac{1}{3} = 5\frac{5}{15}}$

$\quad\quad\quad\quad\quad 8\frac{17}{15} = 8 + 1\frac{2}{15} = 9\frac{2}{15}$

14. $3\frac{11}{12}$ $\quad 6\frac{2}{3} = 6\frac{8}{12} = \overset{5\ \ 20}{\cancel{6}\frac{\cancel{8}}{12}}$

$\quad\quad\quad \underline{- 2\frac{3}{4} = 2\frac{9}{12} = 2\frac{9}{12}}$

$\quad\quad\quad\quad\quad\quad\quad\quad\quad\quad 3\frac{11}{12}$

15. $3\frac{3}{4}$ $\quad 6\frac{2}{3} \div 1\frac{7}{9} = \frac{20}{3} \div \frac{16}{9} = \frac{\overset{5}{\cancel{20}}}{\underset{1}{\cancel{3}}} \times \frac{\overset{3}{\cancel{9}}}{\underset{4}{\cancel{16}}} = \frac{15}{4} = 3\frac{3}{4}$

16. $4\frac{1}{2}$ $\quad 2\frac{5}{8} \times 1\frac{5}{7} = \frac{\overset{3}{\cancel{21}}}{\underset{2}{\cancel{8}}} \times \frac{\overset{3}{\cancel{12}}}{\underset{1}{\cancel{7}}} = \frac{9}{2} = 4\frac{1}{2}$

17. 18   Because $18^2 = 324$, the square root of 324 is 18.

18. 5,600,000   5,⑥48,312 The number to the right of 6 is 4. Do not change the circled digit.

19. 1,500 parts   The tallest bar, Thursday, represents the highest production. This bar ends between the *3* and *4* marks and represents 3,500 parts. The smallest bar, Tuesday, represents the lowest production. This bar reaches the *2* mark and represents 2,000 parts. Subtract to find the difference.

$\quad\quad$ 3,500

$\quad\quad \underline{- \ 2,000}$

$\quad\quad$ 1,500

20. 60 feet   Two sides measure 12 feet and two sides measure 18 feet. Add all four sides together to find the perimeter.

$\quad\quad \overset{2}{1}2$

$\quad\quad 12$

$\quad\quad 18$

$\quad\quad \underline{+ \ 18}$

$\quad\quad 60$

21. 3,240 cubic inches $\quad V = l \times w \times h$

$\quad\quad\quad\quad\quad\quad\quad\quad\quad = 18 \times 12 \times 15$

$\quad\quad\quad\quad\quad\quad\quad\quad\quad = 216 \times 15$

$\quad\quad\quad\quad\quad\quad\quad\quad\quad = 3,240$

22. (4) $36 + $15   Add the amount Lupe paid for the overalls and the amount he paid to hold the jacket. You do not need the total cost of the jacket.

23. (3) 200   Add to find a total. Round the three numbers to the nearest ten and add to estimate the total.

$\quad\quad$ 63   rounds to   60

$\quad\quad$ 89   rounds to   90

$\quad\quad \underline{+ \ 45}$ rounds to $\underline{50}$

$\quad\quad\quad\quad\quad\quad\quad\quad\quad\quad 200$

24. (2) $54\frac{3}{4} \div 12$ Since there are 12 inches in one foot and inches are smaller than feet, divide the number of inches by 12.

UNIT 3: DECIMALS

SECTION 8

PAGE 109

2. seven tenths
3. one thousandth
4. three tenths
5. six ten thousandths
6. zero hundredths
8. two hundred fifty-six thousandths
9. two and nine hundredths
10. six and eight hundred five thousandths

PAGE 110

2. **0.43 > 0.09**
   0.4̲3   0.0̲9 4 is greater than 0.
3. **0.73 > 0.542**
   Add a zero: 0.7̲30   0.5̲42
   Then compare: 7 is greater than 5.
4. **8.058 < 8.58**
   Add a zero: 8.0̲58   8.5̲80
   Then compare: 0 is less than 5.
5. **2.58 = 2.580**
   Add a zero: 2.580   2.580
   The numbers are the same.
6. **53.005 > 52.008**
   53̲.005 52̲.008 3 is greater than 2.
8. **8**   ⑧.276 Since 2 is less than 5, do not
   change the circled digit.
9. **46.4**   46.③5̲18 The number to the right of 3
   is 5; add 1 to the circled digit.
10. **71.048**   71.04⑧3̲ Since 3 is less than 5, do
    not change the circled digit.

PAGE 112

1. **(4) 5.8 + 5.8 + 2.7 + 2.7**   To find the
   perimeter, add the lengths of all four sides.
2. **(2) 2.7 − 0.7**   Find the difference between
   the length of the side and the opening.
3. **(3) 60.2 + 3.1 + 3.1**   Add the lengths of
   the three sides that do not touch the side of
   the building.

4. **(3) 60.2 − 15.8**   Find the difference between
   the length of the side and the length of the
   ornamental fencing.
5. **9.6 + 9.6 + 3.2 + 3.2**   To find the
   perimeter, add the lengths of all four sides.

PAGE 114

2. **8.953**
$$\begin{array}{r} \overset{0\ 16\ 13}{1\cancel{7}.\cancel{8}68} \\ -\ \ 8.415 \\ \hline 8.953 \end{array}$$

3. **10.58**
$$\begin{array}{r} \overset{3\ 12}{2\cancel{4}.\cancel{2}8} \\ -\ 13.70 \\ \hline 10.58 \end{array}$$

4. **65.757**
$$\begin{array}{r} \overset{1\quad\ 1}{28.467} \\ +\ 37.290 \\ \hline 65.757 \end{array}$$

5. **5.25**
$$\begin{array}{r} \overset{0\ 11\ 10}{1\cancel{2}.\cancel{0}5} \\ -\ \ 6.80 \\ \hline 5.25 \end{array}$$

6. **77.04**
$$\begin{array}{r} \overset{1}{35.20} \\ +\ 41.84 \\ \hline 77.04 \end{array}$$

7. **22.88**
$$\begin{array}{r} \overset{3\ 1210}{7\cancel{4}.\cancel{3}\cancel{0}} \\ -\ 51.42 \\ \hline 22.88 \end{array}$$

8. **78.924**
$$\begin{array}{r} \overset{8\ 12\ 12\ 5\ 10}{\cancel{9}\cancel{3}.\cancel{2}\cancel{6}\cancel{0}} \\ -\ 14.336 \\ \hline 78.924 \end{array}$$

9. **20.825**
$$\begin{array}{r} \overset{1\ 1\ 1}{15.930} \\ +\ \ 4.895 \\ \hline 20.825 \end{array}$$

10. **23.766**
$$\begin{array}{r} \overset{1}{\ \ 8.450} \\ +\ 15.316 \\ \hline 23.766 \end{array}$$

11. **20.24**
$$\begin{array}{r} \overset{1\ 1}{\ \ 3.70} \\ 14.24 \\ +\ \ 2.30 \\ \hline 20.24 \end{array}$$

12. 88.784

$$
\begin{array}{r}
\overset{1\ 1}{24.810} \\
35.700 \\
+\ 28.274 \\
\hline
88.784
\end{array}
$$

13. 8.09

$$
\begin{array}{r}
\overset{3\ 10}{8.4\cancel{0}} \\
-\ 0.31 \\
\hline
8.09
\end{array}
$$

14. 8.047

$$
\begin{array}{r}
\overset{0\ 14\ \ 7\ 9\ 10}{\cancel{14.800}} \\
-\ 6.753 \\
\hline
8.047
\end{array}
$$

15. 17.88

$$
\begin{array}{r}
12.00 \\
+\ 5.88 \\
\hline
17.88
\end{array}
$$

16. 6.18

$$
\begin{array}{r}
\overset{1\ \ 1}{2.43} \\
0.57 \\
+\ 3.18 \\
\hline
6.18
\end{array}
$$

17. 17.484

$$
\begin{array}{r}
\overset{5\ 16\ \ 121010}{\cancel{67.310}} \\
-\ 49.826 \\
\hline
17.484
\end{array}
$$

18. 27.93

$$
\begin{array}{r}
\overset{4\ 16\ 14}{\cancel{57.43}} \\
-\ 29.50 \\
\hline
27.93
\end{array}
$$

19. 25.208

$$
\begin{array}{r}
\overset{1}{0.300} \\
21.508 \\
+\ 3.400 \\
\hline
25.208
\end{array}
$$

20. 17.75

$$
\begin{array}{r}
\overset{1}{4.26} \\
5.10 \\
+\ 8.39 \\
\hline
17.75
\end{array}
$$

21. 3.703

$$
\begin{array}{r}
\overset{0\ 11\ 15\ 9\ 10}{\cancel{12.600}} \\
-\ 8.897 \\
\hline
3.703
\end{array}
$$

22. 30.637

$$
\begin{array}{r}
\overset{1\ 1\ 1}{14.560} \\
3.800 \\
+\ 12.277 \\
\hline
30.637
\end{array}
$$

23. 42.817

$$
\begin{array}{r}
\overset{1\ 1\ 1}{2.800} \\
34.337 \\
+\ 5.680 \\
\hline
42.817
\end{array}
$$

24. 20.36

$$
\begin{array}{r}
\overset{3\ 10}{36.4\cancel{0}} \\
-\ 16.04 \\
\hline
20.36
\end{array}
$$

25. 0.188

$$
\begin{array}{r}
\overset{6\ 910}{0.7\cancel{00}} \\
-\ 0.512 \\
\hline
0.188
\end{array}
$$

PAGE 117

1. **$60** Round the cost of the jeans and the cost of the sweat shirt and add.

$$
\begin{array}{llr}
\$34.95 & \text{rounds to} & \overset{1}{\$35} \\
+\ \ 24.50 & \text{rounds to} & +\ 25 \\
\hline
& & \$60
\end{array}
$$

2. **$59.45** Add the cost of the jeans and the cost of the sweat shirt.

$$
\begin{array}{r}
\overset{1}{\$34.95} \\
+\ 24.50 \\
\hline
\$59.45
\end{array}
$$

3. **$62.42** Add the tax to the subtotal (see the explanation for Item 2).

$$
\begin{array}{r}
\overset{1\ 1\ 1}{\$59.45} \\
+\ \ 2.97 \\
\hline
\$62.42
\end{array}
$$

4. **$7.58** Subtract the total (see the explanation for Item 3) from the amount Mr. Simon gives Ervin.

$$
\begin{array}{r}
\overset{6\ 9\ \ 9\ 10}{\$\cancel{70.00}} \\
-\ \ 62.42 \\
\hline
\$\ 7.58
\end{array}
$$

5. **(5) $158.25** Add the costs of both coats.

$$
\begin{array}{r}
\overset{1}{\$76.50} \\
+\ 81.75 \\
\hline
\$158.25
\end{array}
$$

6. **(3) $167.74** Add the tax to the subtotal (see the explanation for Item 5).

$$
\begin{array}{r}
\overset{1\ \ 1}{\$158.25} \\
+\ \ \ 9.49 \\
\hline
\$167.74
\end{array}
$$

7. (4) $123 Round the total of the sale (see the explanation for Item 6) and the amount Mrs. Wilson paid. Then subtract.

$167.74   rounds to $168
−   45.00   rounds to   45
                                $123

8. (1) $122.74 Subtract the amount Mrs. Wilson paid from the total of the sale (see the explanation for Item 6).

$167.74
−   45.00
$122.74

PAGE 120

1. **(2) 2.9** The point for week 4 is at the ninth small line above 2 on the scale.
2. **(3) from week 3 to week 4** The steepest part of the graph is between the points for week 3 and week 4.
3. **(2) 2.5** Subtract the number of miles Ahmad walked each day during week 1 (1.3) from the number of miles he walked each day during week 6 (3.8).

   3.8
− 1.3
   2.5

4. **$2.6 million** The point for 1987 is at the sixth small line above 2 on the scale.
5. **$6.5 million** Add the total sales for 1990 ($3.1 million) and the total sales for 1991 ($3.4 million).

   $3.1 million
+   3.4 million
   $6.5 million

6. **$2.6 million** Sales were greatest in 1989: $3.7 million. Sales were lowest in 1986: $1.1 million. Subtract to find the difference.

   $3.7 million
−   1.1 million
   $2.6 million

PAGES 121–123

1. **seven hundredths**
2. **two ten thousandths**
3. **0.759 < 0.795**
0.7<u>5</u>95   0.7<u>9</u>5
5 is less than 9.
4. **0.326 < 0.54**
Add a zero: 0.<u>3</u>26   0.<u>5</u>40
Then compare: 3 is less than 5.
5. **3.20** 3.1⑨6 Since 6 is greater than 5, add 1 to the circled digit.

6. **6.5** 6.④<u>5</u>3 The number to the right of 4 is 5; add 1 to the circled digit.
7. **1** ⓪.<u>7</u>24 Since 7 is greater than 5, add 1 to the circled digit.

8. **8.207**
$$\begin{array}{r} {}^{11} \\ 4.260 \\ + \ 3.947 \\ \hline 8.207 \end{array}$$

9. **6.899**
$$\begin{array}{r} {}^{6\ \ 1218} \\ 7.\cancel{389} \\ - \ 0.490 \\ \hline 6.899 \end{array}$$

10. **1.12**
$$\begin{array}{r} {}^{8\ 10} \\ 5.\cancel{00} \\ - \ 4.78 \\ \hline 1.12 \end{array}$$

11. **21.673**
$$\begin{array}{r} {}^{1\ 1} \\ 3.810 \\ 12.463 \\ + \ \ 5.400 \\ \hline 21.673 \end{array}$$

12. **2.899**
$$\begin{array}{r} {}^{0\ 11\ 1216\ 12} \\ \cancel{12.372} \\ - \ 9.473 \\ \hline 2.899 \end{array}$$

13. **1.477**
$$\begin{array}{r} {}^{6\ 1216\ 10} \\ \cancel{7.370} \\ - \ 5.893 \\ \hline 1.477 \end{array}$$

14. **20.78**
$$\begin{array}{r} {}^{1} \\ 8.25 \\ 9.47 \\ + \ 3.06 \\ \hline 20.78 \end{array}$$

15. **22.146**
$$\begin{array}{r} {}^{1\ 2} \\ 15.430 \\ 2.900 \\ + \ \ 3.816 \\ \hline 22.146 \end{array}$$

16. **9.015**
$$\begin{array}{r} {}^{2\ \ 1} \\ 4.245 \\ 1.970 \\ + \ 2.800 \\ \hline 9.015 \end{array}$$

17. **1.876**
$$\begin{array}{r} {}^{2\ 17\ 910} \\ \cancel{3.800} \\ - \ 1.924 \\ \hline 1.876 \end{array}$$

18. **(2) 0.016**

19. **(4) 5.2 + 5.2 + 3.4 + 3.4** To find the perimeter, add the lengths of all four sides.

20. **(1) 1.5 meters** Subtract the number of meters of fabric Calvin used from the number of meters of fabric he had.

$$\begin{array}{r} \overset{3}{\cancel{4}}.\overset{12}{\cancel{2}} \\ -\ 2.7 \\ \hline 1.5 \end{array}$$

21. **(3) $11** Estimate the cost of each battery, then subtract.

$65.49	rounds to	$65.00
− 53.99	rounds to	54.00
		$11.00

22. **1.54 centimeters** Subtract this June's rainfall from the average rainfall.

$$\begin{array}{r} \overset{3}{1}\overset{12}{4}.\overset{10}{\cancel{3}}\cancel{0} \\ -\ 12.76 \\ \hline 1.54 \end{array}$$

23. **Brand A** The box that weighs more is the better buy. To compare the number of kilograms in each box, add a zero. 3.420 > 3.059 since 4 > 0.

24. **6.06 meters** Add the lengths of both pieces of lumber.

$$\begin{array}{r} \overset{1}{2}.90 \\ +\ 3.16 \\ \hline 6.06 \end{array}$$

25. **2.12 meters** Two sides are 0.6 meter long and two sides are 0.46 meter long. To find the perimeter, add the lengths of all four sides.

$$\begin{array}{r} \overset{2}{0}.\overset{1}{6}0 \\ 0.60 \\ 0.46 \\ +\ 0.46 \\ \hline 2.12 \end{array}$$

26. **$44** Round the cost of the tape player and the cost of the tape and add.

$36.90	rounds to	$\overset{1}{3}7$
+ 7.49	rounds to	+ 7
		$44

27. **$44.39** Add the cost of the tape player and the cost of the tape.

$$\begin{array}{r} \overset{1}{\$}\overset{1}{3}6.90 \\ +\ 7.49 \\ \hline \$44.39 \end{array}$$

28. **$47.06** Add the tax to the subtotal (see the explanation for Item 27).

$$\begin{array}{r} \overset{1}{\$}4\overset{1}{4}.39 \\ +\ 2.67 \\ \hline \$47.06 \end{array}$$

29. **$2.94** Subtract the total (see the explanation for Item 28) from the amount Mrs. McDonald gave George.

$$\begin{array}{r} \$\overset{4}{\cancel{5}}\overset{9}{\cancel{0}}.\overset{9}{\cancel{0}}\overset{10}{\cancel{0}} \\ -\ 47.06 \\ \hline \$2.94 \end{array}$$

30. **(2) 2.3 thousand** The point for 1987 is at the third small line above 2 on the scale.

31. **(5) increase from 1989 to 1990** The steepest part of the graph is between the points for 1989 and 1990. This part of the graph slants upward, indicating an increase.

32. **(1) 1.3 thousand** Subtract the number of students enrolled in 1986 (1.7 thousand) from the number enrolled in 1991 (3.0 thousand).

$$\begin{array}{r} \overset{2}{\cancel{3}}.\overset{10}{\cancel{0}}\ \text{thousand} \\ -\ 1.7\ \text{thousand} \\ \hline 1.3\ \text{thousand} \end{array}$$

SECTION 9

PAGES 125–126

1. **(4) $8.50 x 4** Find the total cost by multiplying the unit cost ($8.50) by the number of pizzas (4).

2. **(3) $14.95 ÷ 5** Find the unit cost by dividing the total cost ($14.95) by the number of tapes (5).

3. **(1) $9.00 ÷ 6** Find the unit cost by dividing the total cost ($9.00) by the number of pairs of socks (6).

4. **(5) $0.05 x 25** Find the total cost by multiplying the unit cost ($0.05) by the number of pencils (25).

5. **(2) $2.19 x 3** Find the total cost by multiplying the unit cost ($2.19) by the number of pounds (3).

6. **(3) $2.00 ÷ 5** Find the unit cost by dividing the total cost ($2.00) by the number of cans (5).

7. **(1) $5.40 ÷ 3** Find the unit cost by dividing the total cost ($5.40) by the number of bottles (3).

8. **(5) Not enough information is given.** You need to know the number of pounds of bananas to find the total cost.

9. **(2) $0.69 × 25** Find the total cost by multiplying the unit cost ($0.69) by the number of rolls (25).

10. **(4) $0.90 ÷ 6** Find the unit cost by dividing the total cost ($0.90) by the number of cans (6).

PAGE 127

2. **72.8**

$$
\begin{array}{r}
9.1 \\
\times\ 8 \\
\hline
72.8
\end{array}
$$

3. **6.15**

$$
\begin{array}{r}
12.3 \\
\times\ 0.5 \\
\hline
6.15
\end{array}
$$

4. **0.0728**

$$
\begin{array}{r}
1.04 \\
\times\ 0.07 \\
\hline
0.0728
\end{array}
$$

5. **8.25**

$$
\begin{array}{r}
0.75 \\
\times\ 11 \\
\hline
75 \\
+\ 7\,5 \\
\hline
8.25
\end{array}
$$

6. **0.816**

$$
\begin{array}{r}
136 \\
\times\ 0.006 \\
\hline
0.816
\end{array}
$$

7. **25.6**

$$
\begin{array}{r}
128 \\
\times\ 0.2 \\
\hline
25.6
\end{array}
$$

8. **27.68**

$$
\begin{array}{r}
17.3 \\
\times\ 1.6 \\
\hline
10\,38 \\
+\ 17\,3 \\
\hline
27.68
\end{array}
$$

9. **0.0126**

$$
\begin{array}{r}
0.42 \\
\times\ 0.03 \\
\hline
0.0126
\end{array}
$$

10. **1.845**

$$
\begin{array}{r}
2.05 \\
\times\ 0.9 \\
\hline
1.845
\end{array}
$$

PAGE 129

2. **0.63**

$$
\begin{array}{r}
0.63 \\
9)\overline{5.67} \\
-\ 5\,4 \\
\hline
27 \\
-\ 27 \\
\hline
0
\end{array}
$$

3. **5.9**

$$
\begin{array}{r}
5.9 \\
7)\overline{41.3} \\
-\ 35 \\
\hline
6\,3 \\
-\ 6\,3 \\
\hline
0
\end{array}
$$

4. **2.8**

$$
\begin{array}{r}
2.8 \\
12)\overline{33.6} \\
-\ 24 \\
\hline
9\,6 \\
-\ 9\,6 \\
\hline
0
\end{array}
$$

5. **8.5**

$$
\begin{array}{r}
8.5 \\
13)\overline{110.5} \\
-\ 104 \\
\hline
6\,5 \\
-\ 6\,5 \\
\hline
0
\end{array}
$$

6. **0.306**

$$
\begin{array}{r}
0.306 \\
4)\overline{1.224} \\
-\ 1\,2 \\
\hline
24 \\
-\ 24 \\
\hline
0
\end{array}
$$

7. **0.042**

$$
\begin{array}{r}
0.042 \\
21)\overline{0.882} \\
-\ 84 \\
\hline
42 \\
-\ 42 \\
\hline
0
\end{array}
$$

8. **0.002**

$$
\begin{array}{r}
0.002 \\
0.5)\overline{0.0.010} \\
-\ 10 \\
\hline
0
\end{array}
$$

9. **0.31**

$$0.08.\overline{)0.02.48}$$
$$\underline{-24}$$
$$8$$
$$\underline{-8}$$
$$0$$

10. **8.53**

$$0.12.\overline{)1.02.36}$$
$$\underline{-96}$$
$$63$$
$$\underline{-60}$$
$$36$$
$$\underline{-36}$$
$$0$$

11. **1.75**

$$0.06.\overline{)0.10.50}$$
$$\underline{-6}$$
$$45$$
$$\underline{-42}$$
$$30$$
$$\underline{-30}$$
$$0$$

12. **42.5**

$$0.012.\overline{)0.510.0}$$
$$\underline{-48}$$
$$30$$
$$\underline{-24}$$
$$60$$
$$\underline{-60}$$
$$0$$

PAGE 132

1. **50,000 grams** Multiply by 1,000 to convert kilograms to grams.
$50 \times 1,000 = 50.000. = 50,000$

2. **0.6 liters** Divide by 1,000 to convert milliliters to liters.
$600 \div 1,000 = 0.600. = 0.6$

3. **40,000 meters** Multiply by 1,000 to convert kilometers to meters.
$40 \times 1,000 = 40.000. = 40,000$

4. **240 centimeters** Multiply by 100 to convert meters to centimeters.
$2.4 \times 100 = 2.40. = 240$

5. **32 centimeters** Divide by 10 to convert millimeters to centimeters.
$320 \div 10 = 32.0. = 32$

6. **4,500 grams** Multiply by 1,000 to convert kilograms to grams.
$4.5 \times 1,000 = 4.500. = 4,500$

7. **(5) 1,750 cm** Multiply by 100 to convert meters to centimeters.
$17.5 \times 100 = 17.50. = 1,750$

8. **(4) 5,500 mg** Multiply by 1,000 to convert grams to milligrams.
$5.5 \times 1,000 = 5.500. = 5,500$

9. **(2) 160 cm** First multiply 0.4 by 4 to find the perimeter of the square.
$0.4 \times 4 = 1.6$ m
Then multiply by 100 to convert meters to centimeters.
$1.6 \times 100 = 1.60. = 160$ cm

10. **(3) 0.1 L** Divide by 1,000 to convert milliliters to liters.
$100 \div 1,000 = 0.100. = 0.1$ L

PAGE 135

1. **Mean: 411; (Median: 367)** To find the mean, first find the total of the numbers in the set.
$672 + 256 + 410 + 350 + 367 = 2,055$
Then divide the total by the number of items in the set.
$2,055 \div 5 = 411$
To find the median, arrange the numbers in order. Then find the middle number.
256, 350, <u>367</u>, 410, 672
The median is more typical because the unusual number (672) throws off the mean.

2. **Mean: 224; (Median: 257)** To find the mean, first find the total of the numbers in the set.
$260 + 254 + 102 + 280 = 896$
Then divide the total by the number of items in the set.
$896 \div 4 = 224$
To find the median, arrange the numbers in order. Then find the middle numbers.
102, <u>254</u>, <u>260</u>, 280
Then find the mean of the middle numbers.
$254 + 260 = 514; 514 \div 2 = 257$
The median is more typical because the unusual number (102) throws off the mean.

3. **(Mean: 8.7); Median: 8.6** To find the mean, first find the total of the numbers in the set.
$8 + 8.5 + 8.7 + 9 + 8 + 10 = 52.2$
Then divide the total by the number of items in the set.
$52.2 \div 6 = 8.7$
To find the median, arrange the numbers in order. Find the middle numbers.
8, 8, <u>8.5</u>, <u>8.7</u>, 9, 10
Then find the mean of the middle numbers.
$8.5 + 8.7 = 17.2; 17.2 \div 2 = 8.6$
The mean is more typical because there are no unusual numbers to throw off the mean.

4. Mean: 2,350; Median: 2,430 To find the mean, first find the total of the numbers in the set.
2,450 + 2,100 + 1,970 + 2,430 + 2,840 + 1,800 + 2,860 = 16,450
Then divide the total by the number of items in the set.
16,450 ÷ 7 = 2,350
To find the median, arrange the numbers in order. Then find the middle number.
1,800; 1,970; 2,100; 2,430; 2,450; 2,840; 2,860
The mean is more typical because there is no unusual number to throw off the mean.

5. (4) $425 To find the average rent, find the mean of the amounts.
$450 + $395 + $430 = $1,275
$1,275 ÷ 3 = $425

6. (3) 42 Arrange the numbers in order. Then find the middle number.
25, 27, 37, 38, 42, 45, 46, 86, 102

7. (5) 478 Arrange the numbers in order, and find the middle numbers.
147, 425, 454, 502, 504, 518
Then find the mean of the middle numbers.
454 + 502 = 956; 956 ÷ 2 = 478

8. (3) 425 First, find the total of the numbers in the set.
502 + 147 + 425 + 454 + 518 + 504 = 2,550
Then divide the total by the number of items in the set.
2,550 ÷ 6 = 425

PAGES 136–137

1. 19.2
$$\begin{array}{r} 3.2 \\ \times\ \ 6 \\ \hline 19.2 \end{array}$$

2. 0.0824
$$\begin{array}{r} 2.06 \\ \times\ 0.04 \\ \hline 0.0824 \end{array}$$

3. 1.251
$$\begin{array}{r} 4.17 \\ \times\ \ 0.3 \\ \hline 1.251 \end{array}$$

4. 33.48
$$\begin{array}{r} 12.4 \\ \times\ \ 2.7 \\ \hline 8\ 68 \\ +\ 24\ 8 \\ \hline 33.48 \end{array}$$

5. 0.13536
$$\begin{array}{r} 0.752 \\ \times\ 0.18 \\ \hline 6016 \\ +\ \ 752 \\ \hline 0.13536 \end{array}$$

6. 0.76
$$\begin{array}{r} 0.76 \\ 6)\overline{4.56} \\ -\ 4\ 2 \\ \hline 36 \\ -\ 36 \\ \hline 0 \end{array}$$

7. 0.825
$$\begin{array}{r} 0.825 \\ 4)\overline{3.300} \\ -\ 3\ 2 \\ \hline 10 \\ -\ \ 8 \\ \hline 20 \\ -\ 20 \\ \hline 0 \end{array}$$

8. 3.87
$$\begin{array}{r} 3.87 \\ 0.5.)\overline{1.9.35} \\ -\ 1.5 \\ \hline 4\ 3 \\ -\ 4\ 0 \\ \hline 35 \\ -\ 35 \\ \hline 0 \end{array}$$

9. 67.75
$$\begin{array}{r} 67.75 \\ 0.08.)\overline{5.42.00} \\ -\ 4.8 \\ \hline 62 \\ -\ 56 \\ \hline 6\ 0 \\ -\ 5\ 6 \\ \hline 40 \\ -\ 40 \\ \hline 0 \end{array}$$

10. 9.3
$$\begin{array}{r} 9.3 \\ 1.5.)\overline{13.9.5} \\ -\ 13.5 \\ \hline 4\ 5 \\ -\ 4\ 5 \\ \hline 0 \end{array}$$

11. **0.00504**

$$\begin{array}{r} 0.56 \\ \times\ 0.009 \\ \hline 0.00504 \end{array}$$

12. **235**

$$0.16\overbrace{)}\,\underset{\smile}{2\,35}\;37.60.$$
$$\begin{array}{r} -32 \\ \hline 5\,6 \\ -4\,8 \\ \hline 80 \\ -80 \\ \hline 0 \end{array}$$

13. **12,500 milligrams** Multiply by 1,000 to convert grams to milligrams.
$12.5 \times 1,000 = 12.500. = 12,500$

14. **14.9 miles** Divide the total distance by the number of days.
$74.5 \div 5 = 14.9$

15. **$2.96** Multiply the cost of each pound by the number of pounds.
$\$1.85 \times 1.6 = \$2.96$

16. **$23.76** To find the average sale, find the mean of the amounts.
$\$24.50 + \$31.75 + \$18.41 + \$20.38 = \$95.04$
$\$95.04 \div 4 = \$23.76$

17. **(2) $197.00 ÷ 4** Find the unit cost by dividing the total cost ($197.00) by the number of tires (4).

18. **(3) $1.12** Multiply the cost of each pound by the number of pounds.
$\$0.28 \times 4 = \$1.12$

19. **(3) 78 inches** Find the total of the numbers in the set.
$80 + 76 + 75 + 80 + 79 = 390$
Then divide the total by the number of items in the set.
$390 \div 5 = 78$

20. **(4) $1.29 x 3** Find the total cost by multiplying the unit cost ($1.29) by the number of notebooks (3).

21. **(1) 5 ÷ 1.2** Divide the total length (5 meters) by the length of each piece (1.2 meters).

22. **(5) Not enough information is given.**
You need to know the number of doses in each bottle to find the total amount.

23. **(2) 3.98 meters** Divide by 100 to convert centimeters to meters.
$398 \div 100 = 3.98$

24. **(4) 24.3 miles per gallon** Divide the total miles by the number of gallons of gas.
$291.6 \div 12 = 24.3$

UNIT 3 REVIEW

PAGES 138–139

1. **six ten thousandths**
2. **eight hundredths**
3. **0.25 > 0.025** Add a zero: 0.250 0.025
   Then compare: 2 is greater than 0.
4. **0.97 = 0.970** Add a zero: 0.970 0.970
   Then compare: 0.970 and 0.970 are the same.
5. **5.36** 5.3⑥2 Since 2 is less than 5, do not change the circled digit.
6. **7.4** 7.③51 The number to the right of 3 is 5; add 1 to the circled digit.

7. **11.785**
$$\begin{array}{r} \overset{1}{}3.925 \\ 4.600 \\ +\ 3.260 \\ \hline 11.785 \end{array}$$

8. **7.86**
$$\begin{array}{r} \overset{1\ 14\ 13}{2\cancel{5}.\cancel{3}6} \\ -\ 17.50 \\ \hline 7.86 \end{array}$$

9. **5.143**
$$\begin{array}{r} \overset{3\ 9\,10}{8.\cancel{4}\cancel{0}\cancel{0}} \\ -\ 3.257 \\ \hline 5.143 \end{array}$$

10. **9.4**
$$\begin{array}{r} 9.4 \\ 4\,)\overline{37.6} \\ -36 \\ \hline 1\,6 \\ -1\,6 \\ \hline 0 \end{array}$$

11. **50.4**
$$\begin{array}{r} 6.3 \\ \times\ 8 \\ \hline 50.4 \end{array}$$

12. **2.286**
$$\begin{array}{r} 2.54 \\ \times\ 0.9 \\ \hline 2.286 \end{array}$$

13. **45**
$$0.06\,\underset{\smile}{)}\,\underset{\smile}{2.70.}\quad 45.$$
$$\begin{array}{r} -2\,4 \\ \hline 30 \\ -30 \\ \hline 0 \end{array}$$

14. 468

$$0.016\overline{\smash{\big)}\,7.488.}$$
$$\;\underline{-\;6\,4}$$
$$108$$
$$\underline{-\;96}$$
$$128$$
$$\underline{-\;128}$$
$$0$$

15. 15.56

$$\begin{array}{r} 1\;1\;\\ 3.54\\ 6.83\\ +\;5.19\\ \hline 15.56 \end{array}$$

16. 0.51

$$0.07\overline{\smash{\big)}\,0.03.57}$$
$$\;0.51$$
$$\underline{-\;3\,5}$$
$$07$$
$$\underline{-\;7}$$
$$0$$

17. 42.48

$$\begin{array}{r} {\scriptstyle 4\;13\;10}\\ 4\cancel{5}.\cancel{4}\cancel{0}\\ -\;2.92\\ \hline 42.48 \end{array}$$

18. 0.0285

$$\begin{array}{r} 0.57\\ \times\;0.05\\ \hline 0.0285 \end{array}$$

19. 8.996

$$\begin{array}{r} 1\\ 4.380\\ 2.700\\ +\;1.916\\ \hline 8.996 \end{array}$$

20. 44.28

$$\begin{array}{r} 16.4\\ \times\;2.7\\ \hline 114\,8\\ +\;328\\ \hline 44.28 \end{array}$$

21. **$5.51** Add the cost of the shoes and the socks to find the subtotal. Then add the tax to find the total. Finally, subtract the total from the amount Bryant gave the clerk.

$$\begin{array}{r} {\scriptstyle 1\;1\;1}\\ \$64.95\\ +\;\;5.99\\ \hline \$70.94 \end{array} \qquad \begin{array}{r} {\scriptstyle 1}\\ \$70.94\\ +\;\;3.55\\ \hline \$74.49 \end{array} \qquad \begin{array}{r} {\scriptstyle 7\;9\;\;9\;10}\\ \$\cancel{8}\cancel{0}.\cancel{0}\cancel{0}\\ -\;74.49\\ \hline \$\;5.51 \end{array}$$

22. **190 centimeters** Multiply by 100 to convert meters to centimeters.
$1.9 \times 100 = 1.90. = 190$

23. **55.2 miles** To find the mean, first find the total of the numbers in the set.
$62 + 28 + 57 + 66 + 63 = 276$
Then divide the total by the number of items in the set. $276 \div 5 = 55.2$

24. **62 miles** To find the median, arrange the numbers in order. Find the middle value.
28, 57, <u>62</u>, 63, 66

25. **The median** is more typical because the number 28 is unusual and throws off the mean.

26. **(5) 6.8 + 6.8 + 2.4 + 2.4** To find the perimeter, add the lengths of all four sides.

27. **(4) $42.50 x 4** Find the total cost by multiplying the unit cost ($42.50) by the number of tires (4).

28. **(5) 6.1 thousand** Add the number of parts produced in November (3.2 thousand) and the number produced in December (2.9 thousand).

$$\begin{array}{r} {\scriptstyle 1}\\ 3.2\;\text{thousand}\\ +\;2.9\;\text{thousand}\\ \hline 6.1\;\text{thousand} \end{array}$$

CUMULATIVE REVIEW

PAGES 140–141

1. **two ten thousands**
2. **seven million**
3. **three tenths**
4. **four thousandths**

5. 348

$$\begin{array}{r} {\scriptstyle 6\;9\;10}\\ \cancel{7}\cancel{0}\cancel{0}\\ -\;352\\ \hline 348 \end{array}$$

6. 200,438

$$\begin{array}{r} 973\\ \times\;206\\ \hline 5\,838\\ +\;194\,60\\ \hline 200{,}438 \end{array}$$

7. 208 r24

$$\begin{array}{r} 208\;\text{r}24\\ 42\overline{\smash{\big)}\,8{,}760}\\ \underline{-\;8\,4}\\ 360\\ \underline{-\;336}\\ 24 \end{array}$$

8. 15

$$2.4\overline{\smash{\big)}\,36.0.}$$
$$\;1\,5$$
$$\underline{-\;24}$$
$$12\,0$$
$$\underline{-\;12\,0}$$
$$0$$

9. $6\frac{3}{8}$

$$2\frac{3}{4} = 2\frac{6}{8}$$
$$+\ 3\frac{5}{8} = 3\frac{5}{8}$$
$$5\frac{11}{8} = 5 + 1\frac{3}{8} = 6\frac{3}{8}$$

10. $4\frac{11}{15}$

$$8\frac{2}{5} = 8\frac{6}{15} = 8\overset{7\ \ 21}{\cancel{8}\cancel{\frac{6}{15}}}$$
$$-\ 3\frac{2}{3} = 3\frac{10}{15} = 3\frac{10}{15}$$
$$4\frac{11}{15}$$

11. 453

$$\overset{1\ 2}{28}$$
$$376$$
$$+\ \ 49$$
$$453$$

12. \$5.46

$$\overset{8\ \ 9\,15}{\$9.\cancel{0}\cancel{5}}$$
$$-\ 3.59$$
$$\$5.46$$

13. $2\frac{5}{12}$ $3\frac{5}{8} \div 1\frac{1}{2} = \frac{29}{8} \div \frac{3}{2} = \frac{29}{\underset{4}{8}} \times \frac{\overset{1}{2}}{3} = \frac{29}{12} = 2\frac{5}{12}$

14. 21.758

$$\overset{4\ 15\,9\,10}{2\cancel{5}.\cancel{6}\cancel{0}\cancel{0}}$$
$$-\ \ 3.842$$
$$21.758$$

15. 729 $9^3 = 9 \times 9 \times 9 = 729$

16. 42.5

$$0.04.\overline{)\,1.70.0}\quad 42.5$$
$$-\ 1.6$$
$$10$$
$$-\ 8$$
$$2\ 0$$
$$-\ 2\ 0$$
$$0$$

17. $14\frac{2}{5}$ $5\frac{1}{3} \times 2\frac{7}{10} = \frac{\overset{8}{16}}{\underset{1}{3}} \times \frac{\overset{9}{27}}{\underset{5}{10}} = \frac{72}{5} = 14\frac{2}{5}$

18. 67.141

$$\overset{1\ 1\ 1}{3.270}$$
$$54.800$$
$$+\ \ 9.071$$
$$67.141$$

19. 0.0441

$$0.063$$
$$\times\ \ \ 0.7$$
$$0.0441$$

20. 6   Because $6^2 = 36$, the square root of 36 is 6.

21. **8 miles**   Monica drives $2\frac{1}{5}$ miles from the dry cleaner to point A, $2\frac{1}{10}$ miles from point A to point B, and $3\frac{7}{10}$ miles from point B to point C. Round each distance and add.

$2\frac{1}{5}$	rounds to	2
$2\frac{1}{10}$	rounds to	2
$+\ 3\frac{7}{10}$	rounds to	$+\ 4$
		8

22. $18\frac{2}{5}$ **miles**   Subtract the distance from point E to the cleaners ($6\frac{3}{5}$ miles) from the total length of the route.

$$25\ \ = \overset{24}{2\cancel{5}\frac{5}{5}}$$
$$-\ \ 6\frac{3}{5} = \ \ 6\frac{3}{5}$$
$$18\frac{2}{5}$$

23. **(4) 480 sq. ft.**   To find the area, multiply the length times the width.

$$24$$
$$\times\ 20$$
$$480$$

24. **(3)** $\frac{2}{3}$ **x 3**   Rosa is planning to triple the recipe, so multiply the amount of cheese by 3.

25. **(5)** $8\frac{1}{4}$ **hours**   First find the number of hours Mike worked in the morning. Since 28 is close to 30, think of 8:28 as $8\frac{1}{2}$. Since 21 is close to 15, think of 12:21 as $12\frac{1}{4}$. Then subtract.

$$12\frac{1}{4} = 12\frac{1}{4} = \overset{11\ \ 5}{\cancel{12}\frac{\cancel{1}}{4}}$$
$$-\ \ 8\frac{1}{2} = \ \ 8\frac{2}{4} = \ \ 8\frac{2}{4}$$
$$3\frac{3}{4}$$

Then find the number of hours Mike worked in the afternoon. Since 6 is close to zero, think of 1:06 as 1. Since 36 is close to 30, think of 5:36 as $5\frac{1}{2}$. Then subtract.

$$5\frac{1}{2}$$
$$-\ 1$$
$$4\frac{1}{2}$$

Finally, add the number of hours Mike worked in the morning and in the afternoon.

$$3\frac{3}{4} = 3\frac{3}{4}$$
$$+\ 4\frac{1}{2} = 4\frac{2}{4}$$
$$7\frac{5}{4} = 7 + 1\frac{1}{4} = 8\frac{1}{4}$$

26. **(3)** $\frac{4}{7}$ Write a fraction for the number of hours Mario worked overtime and reduce to lowest terms.

$$\frac{12}{21} = \frac{12 \div 3}{21 \div 3} = \frac{4}{7}$$

UNIT 4: RATIO, PROPORTION, AND PERCENT

SECTION 10

PAGE 148

1. (3) $\frac{10}{\$22.50} = \frac{6}{?}$ Both ratios are in the same order. The first ratio means that 10 reams cost $22.50. The second ratio means that 6 reams cost an unknown amount.

2. (4) $\frac{12}{\$3.96} = \frac{18}{?}$ Both ratios are in the same order. The first ratio means that 12 pads cost $3.96. The second ratio means that 18 pads cost an unknown amount.

3. (5) $\frac{3}{\$2.49} = \frac{4}{?}$ Both ratios are in the same order. The first ratio means that 3 bottles cost $2.49. The second ratio means that 4 bottles cost an unknown amount.

4. (2) $\frac{2}{\$1.28} = \frac{5}{?}$ Both ratios are in the same order. The first ratio means that 2 heads cost $1.28. The second ratio means that 5 heads cost an unknown amount.

5. (4) $\frac{3}{\$1.22} = \frac{2}{?}$ Both ratios are in the same order. The first ratio means that 3 bags cost $1.22. The second ratio means that 2 bags cost an unknown amount.

6. (2) $\frac{5}{\$3.15} = \frac{?}{\$4.41}$ Both ratios are in the same order. The first ratio means that 5 pounds cost $3.15. The second ratio means that an unknown number of pounds cost $4.41.

PAGES 149–150

2. $\frac{2}{3}$

$$\frac{12 \text{ won}}{18 \text{ played}} = \frac{12 \div 6}{18 \div 6} = \frac{2}{3}$$

3. $\frac{5}{2}$

$$\frac{35 \text{ cars}}{14 \text{ vans}} = \frac{35 \div 7}{14 \div 7} = \frac{5}{2}$$

4. $\frac{23}{1}$

$$\frac{230 \text{ miles}}{10 \text{ gallons}} = \frac{230 \div 10}{10 \div 10} = \frac{23}{1}$$

5. $\frac{3}{5}$

$$\frac{15 \text{ cash}}{25 \text{ charge}} = \frac{15 \div 5}{25 \div 5} = \frac{3}{5}$$

6. $\frac{\$6}{1}$

$$\frac{\$42}{7 \text{ hours}} = \frac{\$42 \div 7}{7 \div 7} = \frac{\$6}{1}$$

PAGE 151

2. 6 $4 \times 18 = 72; 72 \div 12 = 6$

3. 6 $18 \times 10 = 180; 180 \div 30 = 6$

4. 2 $7 \times 4 = 28; 28 \div 14 = 2$

5. 55 $20 \times 11 = 220; 220 \div 4 = 55$

6. 25 $30 \times 10 = 300; 300 \div 12 = 25$

7. 35 $42 \times 10 = 420; 420 \div 12 = 35$

8. $19\frac{1}{5}$ $24 \times 4 = 96$ $5\overline{)96} = 19\frac{1}{5}$

9. 25 $5 \times 40 = 200; 200 \div 8 = 25$

10. $16\frac{2}{3}$ $15 \times 10 = 150;$ $9\overline{)150} = 16\frac{6}{9} = 16\frac{2}{3}$

PAGES 154–155

1. (5) 1,200   Multiply the number of symbols in the row for nonfiction books (6) times the value of one symbol (200).
$6 \times 200 = 1,200$

2. (2) 200   The shortest row is labeled *Records & Tapes*. That row has one symbol with a value of 200.

3. (4) 600   The row for fiction books has 3 more symbols than the row for reference materials. Multiply 3 times the value of one symbol (200).
$3 \times 200 = 600$

4. (5) 1,600   Together the rows for nonfiction and reference materials have 8 symbols. Multiply 8 times the value of one symbol (200).
$8 \times 200 = 1,600$

5. (4) $\frac{6}{5}$

$\dfrac{6 \text{ symbols for nonfiction}}{5 \text{ symbols for fiction}}$

This ratio cannot be reduced.

6. (2) $\frac{1}{14}$

$\dfrac{1 \text{ symbol for records and tapes}}{14 \text{ symbols for all materials}}$

This ratio cannot be reduced.

7. 4,500 students   Multiply the number of symbols in the row for students (3) times the value of one symbol (1,500).
$3 \times 1,500 = 4,500$

8. 9,000 people   The longest row is labeled *Adults*. Multiply the number of symbols in that row (6) times the value of one symbol (1,500).
$6 \times 1,500 = 9,000$

9. 3,750 more senior citizens   The row for senior citizens has $2\frac{1}{2}$ more symbols than the row for preschoolers. Multiply $2\frac{1}{2}$ times the value of one symbol (1,500).

$2\frac{1}{2} \times 1,500 = \frac{5}{2} \times \frac{\overset{750}{1,500}}{\underset{1}{1}} = \frac{3,750}{1} = 3,750$

10. **21,750 people**   There are $14\frac{1}{2}$ symbols in the graph. Multiply $14\frac{1}{2}$ times the value of one symbol (1,500).

$$14\frac{1}{2} \times 1,500 = \frac{29}{2} \times \frac{\overset{750}{\cancel{1,500}}}{1} = \frac{21,750}{1} = 21,750$$

11. $\frac{2}{1}$

$$\frac{6 \text{ symbols for adults}}{3 \text{ symbols for students}} = \frac{6 \div 3}{3 \div 3} = \frac{2}{1}$$

12. $\frac{4}{14\frac{1}{2}}$

$$\frac{4 \text{ symbols for senior citizens}}{14\frac{1}{2} \text{ symbols for all categories}}$$

This ratio cannot be reduced.

PAGE 158

1. **(3) 20**   The distance on the map from Riverton to Plainview is 1 inch.

$\dfrac{2 \text{ in.}}{40 \text{ mi.}} = \dfrac{1 \text{ in.}}{? \text{ mi.}}$ $40 \times 1 = 40$
$40 \div 2 = 20$

2. **(2) 55**   The distance on the map from Plainview to Rock Falls is $2\frac{3}{4}$ inches.

$\dfrac{2 \text{ in.}}{40 \text{ mi.}} = \dfrac{2\frac{3}{4} \text{ in.}}{? \text{ mi.}}$ $40 \times 2\frac{3}{4} = 110$
$110 \div 2 = 55$

3. **(3) 3**

$\dfrac{2 \text{ in.}}{40 \text{ mi.}} = \dfrac{? \text{ in.}}{60 \text{ mi.}}$ $2 \times 60 = 120$
$120 \div 40 = 3$

4. $7\frac{1}{2}$ **miles**   The distance on the map from Mesa to Canyon City is $1\frac{1}{2}$ inches.

$\dfrac{3 \text{ in.}}{15 \text{ mi.}} = \dfrac{1\frac{1}{2} \text{ in.}}{? \text{ mi.}}$ $15 \times 1\frac{1}{2} = 22\frac{1}{2}$
$22\frac{1}{2} \div 3 = 7\frac{1}{2}$

5. $11\frac{1}{4}$ **miles**   The distance on the map from Bluffton to Canyon City is $2\frac{1}{4}$ inches.

$\dfrac{3 \text{ in.}}{15 \text{ mi.}} = \dfrac{2\frac{1}{4} \text{ in.}}{? \text{ mi.}}$ $15 \times 2\frac{1}{4} = 33\frac{3}{4}$
$33\frac{3}{4} \div 3 = 11\frac{1}{4}$

6. **7 inches**

$\dfrac{3 \text{ in.}}{15 \text{ mi.}} = \dfrac{? \text{ mi.}}{35 \text{ mi.}}$ $3 \times 35 = 105$
$105 \div 15 = 7$

PAGES 159–161

1. $\frac{5}{7}$

$$\frac{20 \text{ in office}}{28 \text{ in warehouse}} = \frac{20 \div 4}{28 \div 4} = \frac{5}{7}$$

2. $\frac{5}{12}$

$$\frac{15 \text{ with field goals}}{36 \text{ total points}} = \frac{15 \div 3}{36 \div 3} = \frac{5}{12}$$

3. **36** $6 \times 42 = 252; 252 \div 7 = 36$

4. **20** $8 \times 30 = 240; 240 \div 12 = 20$

5. **35** $77 \times 5 = 385; 385 \div 11 = 35$

6. **25** $10 \times 40 = 400; 400 \div 16 = 25$

7. **(4) $1.65**

$\dfrac{3}{\$0.99} = \dfrac{5}{?}$ $\$0.99 \times 5 = \$4.95$
$\$4.95 \div 3 = \$1.65$

8. **265 miles**

$\dfrac{106 \text{ miles}}{2 \text{ hours}} = \dfrac{? \text{ mile}}{5 \text{ hours}}$ $106 \times 5 = 530$
$530 \div 2 = 265$

9. $7\frac{1}{2}$ **gallons**

$\dfrac{3 \text{ parts blue}}{4 \text{ parts gray}} = \dfrac{? \text{ gallons blue}}{10 \text{ gallons gray}}$
$3 \times 10 = 30$
$30 \div 4 = 7\frac{1}{2}$

10. **12 parts**

$\dfrac{400 \text{ total parts}}{3 \text{ defective parts}} = \dfrac{1,600 \text{ total parts}}{? \text{ defective parts}}$
$3 \times 1,600 = 4,800$
$4,800 \div 400 = 12$

11. **240 females**

$\dfrac{5 \text{ females}}{9 \text{ employees}} = \dfrac{? \text{ females}}{432 \text{ employees}}$
$5 \times 432 = 2,160$
$2,160 \div 9 = 240$

12. $6\frac{2}{5}$ **hours**

$\dfrac{2 \text{ hours}}{5 \text{ pictures}} = \dfrac{? \text{ hours}}{16 \text{ pictures}}$ $2 \times 16 = 32$
$32 \div 5 = 6\frac{2}{5}$

13. **400 miles**

$\dfrac{300 \text{ miles}}{12 \text{ gallons}} = \dfrac{? \text{ miles}}{16 \text{ gallons}}$ $300 \times 16 = 4,800$
$4,800 \div 12 = 400$

14. **15 cups**

$\dfrac{3 \text{ cups}}{16 \text{ people}} = \dfrac{? \text{ cups}}{80 \text{ people}}$ $3 \times 80 = 240$
$240 \div 16 = 15$

15. **$210**

$\dfrac{40 \text{ hours}}{\$240} = \dfrac{35 \text{ hours}}{?}$
$\$240 \times 35 = \$8,400$
$\$8,400 \div 40 = \$210$

16. $10\frac{1}{2}$ **miles**   The distance on the map from Mountainview to Somerset is $1\frac{3}{4}$ inches.

$\dfrac{2 \text{ in.}}{12 \text{ mi.}} = \dfrac{1\frac{3}{4} \text{ in.}}{? \text{ mi.}}$ $12 \times 1\frac{3}{4} = 21$
$21 \div 2 = 10\frac{1}{2}$

17. **21 miles**   The distance on the map from Somerset to Princeton is $3\frac{1}{2}$ inches.

$\dfrac{2 \text{ in.}}{12 \text{ mi.}} = \dfrac{3\frac{1}{2} \text{ in.}}{? \text{ mi.}}$ $12 \times 3\frac{1}{2} = 42$
$42 \div 2 = 21$

18. **5 inches**

$\dfrac{2 \text{ in.}}{12 \text{ mi.}} = \dfrac{? \text{ in.}}{30 \text{ mi.}}$ $2 \times 30 = 60$
$60 \div 12 = 5$

19. **(5) 120**   The longest row is labeled *Rock*. Multiply the number of symbols in that row (6) times the value of one symbol (20).
$6 \times 20 = 120$

20. **(3) 40** The row for country has 2 more symbols than the row for jazz. Multiply 2 times the value of one symbol (20).
$2 \times 20 = 40$

21. **(5) 310** There are $15\frac{1}{2}$ symbols on the graph. Multiply $15\frac{1}{2}$ times the value of one symbol (20).

$$15\frac{1}{2} \times 20 = \frac{31}{2} \times \frac{\overset{10}{\cancel{20}}}{1} = \frac{310}{1} = 310$$
$$\phantom{15\frac{1}{2} \times 20 = \frac{31}{\cancel{2}}}_{1}$$

SECTION 11

PAGE 163

2. $\frac{3}{4}$, **0.75, 75%** 75 of 100 parts are shaded.
$\frac{75}{100}$ reduces to $\frac{3}{4}$.
$\frac{75 \div 25}{100 \div 25} = \frac{3}{4}$; $\qquad \frac{75}{100} = 0.75$;
$\frac{75}{100}$ is the same as 75%.

3. $\frac{3}{10}$, **0.3, 30%** 30 of 100 parts are shaded.
$\frac{30}{100}$ reduces to $\frac{3}{10}$.
$\frac{30 \div 10}{100 \div 10} = \frac{3}{10}$; $\qquad \frac{30}{100} = 0.3$;
$\frac{30}{100}$ is the same as 30%.

4. $\frac{1}{5}$, **0.2, 20%** 20 of 100 parts are shaded.
$\frac{20}{100}$ reduces to $\frac{1}{5}$.
$\frac{20 \div 20}{100 \div 20} = \frac{1}{5}$; $\qquad \frac{20}{100} = 0.2$;
$\frac{20}{100}$ is the same as 20%.

5. $\frac{9}{10}$, **0.9, 90%** 90 of 100 parts are shaded.
$\frac{90}{100}$ reduces to $\frac{9}{10}$.
$\frac{9 \div 10}{100 \div 10} = \frac{9}{10}$; $\qquad \frac{90}{100} = 0.9$;
$\frac{90}{100}$ is the same as 90%.

6. $\frac{1}{100}$, **0.01, 1%** 1 of 100 parts is shaded.
$\frac{1}{100}$ is in lowest terms. $\frac{1}{100} = 0.01$
$\frac{1}{100}$ is the same as 1%.

PAGE 166

1. **0.37** $37\% = {}_{\curvearrowleft}37 = 0.37$

2. **0.04** $4\% = {}_{\curvearrowleft}04 = 0.04$

3. **2.25** $225\% = 2{\underset{\curvearrowright}{.}}25 = 2.25$

4. **0.065** $6\frac{1}{2}\% = 6.5\% = {}_{\curvearrowleft}06.5 = 0.065$

5. **46%** $0.46 = 0{\underset{\curvearrowright}{.}}46 = 46\%$

6. **8%** $0.08 = 0{\underset{\curvearrowright}{.}}08 = 8\%$

7. **250%** $2.5 = 2{\underset{\curvearrowright}{.}}50 = 250\%$

8. **37.5%** $0.375 = 0{\underset{\curvearrowright}{.}}37 5 = 37.5\%$

9. $\frac{1}{2}$ $\quad 50\% = \frac{50}{100} = \frac{50 \div 50}{100 \div 50} = \frac{1}{2}$

10. $\frac{2}{5}$ $\quad 40\% = \frac{40}{100} = \frac{40 \div 20}{100 \div 20} = \frac{2}{5}$

11. $\frac{1}{4}$ $\quad 25\% = \frac{25}{100} = \frac{25 \div 25}{100 \div 25} = \frac{1}{4}$

12. $\frac{9}{10}$ $\quad 90\% = \frac{90}{100} = \frac{90 \div 10}{100 \div 10} = \frac{9}{10}$

13. **70%**
$$\begin{array}{r} 0.7 \\ 10\overline{)7.0} \end{array} \quad 0.7 = 0{\underset{\curvearrowright}{.}}70 = 70\%$$

14. **75%**
$$\begin{array}{r} 0.75 \\ 4\overline{)3.00} \end{array} \quad 0.75 = 0{\underset{\curvearrowright}{.}}75 = 75\%$$

15. **80%**
$$\begin{array}{r} 0.8 \\ 5\overline{)4.0} \end{array} \quad 0.8 = 0{\underset{\curvearrowright}{.}}80 = 80\%$$

16. **87.5%**
$$\begin{array}{r} 0.875 \\ 8\overline{)7.000} \end{array} \quad 0.875 = 0{\underset{\curvearrowright}{.}}87.5$$
$$= 87.5\%$$

SECTION 12

PAGE 170

1. **(2) 6 x 20%** Multiply the base (6) times the rate (20%) to find the part.

2. **(4) 25% + 20% + 15%** Add the rates for all jobs except food preparation.

3. **(1) 6 x (40% + 15%)** Multiply the base (6) times the total rate for food preparation (40%) and stockroom duties (15%).

4. **(3) 8 x 5%** Multiply the base (8) times the rate (5%) to find the part.

5. **(5) 8 x (60% to 20%)** Multiply the base (8) times the total rate for data entry (60%) and for copying and collating (20%).

6. **(2) 8 x (60% – 15%)** Subtract the rate for mail distribution (15%) from the rate for data entry (60%). Multiply the base (8) times the difference in rates.

PAGE 172

2. **$18** $\quad 40\% = 0.4$
$$\begin{array}{r} \$45 \\ \times\ 0.4 \\ \hline \$18.0 \end{array}$$

3. **1.28** $\quad 8\% = 0.08$
$$\begin{array}{r} 16 \\ \times\ 0.08 \\ \hline 1.28 \end{array}$$

4. **24** $\quad 75\% = 0.75$
$$\begin{array}{r} 32 \\ \times\ 0.75 \\ \hline 24.00 \end{array}$$

5. **$225** $\quad 300\% = 3$
$$\begin{array}{r} \$75 \\ \times\ \ 3 \\ \hline \$225 \end{array}$$

6. **120** $\quad 250\% = 2.5$
$$\begin{array}{r} 48 \\ \times\ 2.5 \\ \hline 120.0 \end{array}$$

7. **$2.25** $\quad 4\frac{1}{2}\% = 0.045$
$$\begin{array}{r} \$50 \\ \times\ 0.045 \\ \hline 2.2500 \end{array}$$

8. **10.44** $\quad 7\frac{1}{4}\% = 0.0725$
$$\begin{array}{r} 144 \\ \times\ 0.0725 \\ \hline 10.4400 \end{array}$$

9. **$8** Multiply the base ($32) times the rate (25%).
$25\% = 0.25$
$$\begin{array}{r} \$32 \\ \times\ 0.25 \\ \hline \$8.00 \end{array}$$

10. **400 people** Multiply the base (8,000) times the rate (5%).

5% = 0.05

$$\begin{array}{r} 8,000 \\ \times\ 0.05 \\ \hline 400.00 \end{array}$$

11. **12 games** Multiply the base (15) times the rate (80%).

80% = 0.8

$$\begin{array}{r} 15 \\ \times\ 0.8 \\ \hline 12.0 \end{array}$$

12. **108 kitchen appliances** Multiply the base (240) times the rate (45%).

45% = 0.45

$$\begin{array}{r} 240 \\ \times\ 0.45 \\ \hline 12\ 00 \\ +\ 96\ 0 \\ \hline 108.00 \end{array}$$

PAGE 175

1. **$78**   interest = principal × rate × time
= $650 × 0.12 × 1
= $78

2. **$75.60** $i = p \times r \times t$
= $420 × 0.18 × 1
= $75.60

3. **$210.80** $i = p \times r \times t$
= $1,240 × 0.085 × 2
= $210.80

4. **$672** $i = p \times r \times t$
= $1,600 × 0.14 × 3
= $672

5. **$541.20**   Subtract the down payment from the cost to find the principal.
$560 − $150 = $410
Use the formula to find the interest.
$i = p \times r \times t$
= $410 × 0.16 × 2
= $131.20
Add the principal and interest to find the amount to be paid back.
$410 + $131.20 = $541.20

6. **$641.20**   Subtract the down payment from the cost to find the principal.
$675 − $115 = $560
Use the formula to find the interest.
$i = p \times r \times t$
= $560 × 0.145 × 1
= $81.20
Add the principal and interest to find the amount to be paid back.
$560 + $81.20 = $641.20

7. **$196**   Use the formula to find the interest.
$i = p \times r \times t$
= $2,100 × 0.12 × 1
= $252
Add the principal and interest to find the amount to be paid back.
$2,100 + $252 = $2,352
Divide the amount to be paid back by the number of monthly payments.
$2,352 ÷ 12 = $196

8. **$195**   Subtract the down payment from the cost to find the principal.
$4,000 − $400 = $3,600
Use the formula to find the interest.
$i = p \times r \times$
= $3,600 × 0.15 × 2
= $1,080
Add the principal and interest to find the amount to be paid back.
$3,600 + $1,080 = $4,680
Divide the amount to be paid back by the number of monthly payments.
$4,680 ÷ 24 = $195

PAGE 178

1. To find the degrees in each section, multiply the base (360°) times the rate for each item.

Federal income tax	360° × 0.5	= **180°**
State income tax	360° × 0.2	= **72°**
Health insurance	360° × 0.15	= **54°**
Credit union	360° × 0.1	= **36°**
Retirement fund	360° × 0.05	= **18°**

2. **(1) federal income tax**   The largest section of the graph represents federal income tax.

3. **(3) $18.00**   Multiply the base ($120) times the rate (15%).
$120 × 0.15 = $18.00

4. To find the degrees in each section, multiply the base (360°) times the rate for each item.

Heating	360° × 0.4	= **144°**
Refrigerator	360° × 0.2	= **72°**
Water heater	360° × 0.1	= **36°**
Cooking	360° × 0.05	= **18°**
Other	360° × 0.25	= **90°**

5. **Cooking**   The smallest section of the graph represents electricity used for cooking.

6. **$25.60**   Multiply the base ($64) times the rate (40%).
$64 × 0.4 = $25.60

PAGES 179–181

1. **192**   64% = 0.64

$$\begin{array}{r} 300 \\ \times\ 0.64 \\ \hline 192.00 \end{array}$$

2. 4.32

6% = 0.06

$$\begin{array}{r} 72 \\ \times\ 0.06 \\ \hline 4.32 \end{array}$$

3. $86.40

90% = 0.9

$$\begin{array}{r} \$96 \\ \times\ \ 0.9 \\ \hline \$86.40 \end{array}$$

4. $224

400% = 4

$$\begin{array}{r} \$56 \\ \times\ \ 4 \\ \hline \$224 \end{array}$$

5. 45

125% = 1.25

$$\begin{array}{r} 1.25 \\ \times\ 36 \\ \hline 45.00 \end{array}$$

6. 5.25

$3\frac{1}{2}\%$ = 0.035

$$\begin{array}{r} 150 \\ \times\ 0.035 \\ \hline 5.250 \end{array}$$

7. $116 Multiply the base ($145) times the rate (80%).

80% = 0.8

$$\begin{array}{r} \$145 \\ \times\ \ 0.8 \\ \hline \$116.0 \end{array}$$

8. $41.25 Multiply the base ($125) times the rate (33%).

33% = 0.33

$$\begin{array}{r} \$125 \\ \times\ 0.33 \\ \hline 3\ 75 \\ +\ 37\ 5 \\ \hline \$41.25 \end{array}$$

9. 1,650 Multiply the base (3,000) times the rate (55%).

55% = 0.55

$$\begin{array}{r} 3,000 \\ \times\ \ 0.55 \\ \hline 1,650.00 \end{array}$$

10. $37.20 Multiply the base ($310) times the rate (12%).

12% = 0.12

$$\begin{array}{r} \$310 \\ \times\ 0.12 \\ \hline \$37.20 \end{array}$$

11. $127.50

$i = p \times r \times t$
$= \$1,500 \times 0.085 \times 1$
$= \$127.50$

12. $560

$i = p \times r \times t$
$= \$2,000 \times 0.14 \times 2$
$= \$560.00$

13. $150

$i = p \times r \times t$
$= \$1,200 \times 0.125 \times 1$
$= \$150$

14. $2,040 Subtract the down payment from the cost to find the principal.
$1,750 − $250 = $1,500
Use the formula to find the interest.
$i = p \times r \times t$
$= \$1,500 \times 0.18 \times 2$
$= \$540$
Add the principal and interest to find the amount to be paid back.
$1,500 + $540 = $2,040

15. $1,950 Use the formula to find the interest.
$i = p \times r \times t$
$= \$1,500 \times 0.15 \times 2$
$= \$450$
Add the principal and the interest to find the amount to be paid back.
$1,500 + $450 = $1,950

16. $56.10 Use the formula to find the interest.
$i = p \times r \times t$
$= \$990 \times 0.18 \times 2$
$= \$356.40$
Add the principal and interest to find the amount to be paid back.
$990 + $356.40 = $1,346.40
Divide the amount to be paid back by the number of monthly payments.
$1,346.40 ÷ 24 = $56.10

17. $14,960 The principal is $9,350.
Use the formula to find the interest.
$i = p \times r \times t$
$= \$9,350 \times 0.12 \times 5$
$= \$5,610$
Add the principal and interest to find the amount to be paid back.
$9,350 + $5,610 = $14,960

18. $97.15 Add the cost of both appliances.
$475 + $680 = $1,155
Subtract the down payment from the cost to find the principal.
$1,155 − $150 = $1,005
Use the formula to find the interest.
$i = p \times r \times t$
$= \$1,005 \times 0.16 \times 1$
$= \$160.80$
Add the principal and interest to find the amount to be paid back.
$1,005 + $160.80 = $1,165.80
Divide the amount to be paid back by the number of monthly payments.
$1,165.80 ÷ 12 = $97.15

19. (4) 40 x 15% Multiply the base (40) times the rate (15%) to find the part.

20. (2) 40% + 25% Add the rates for supervising (40%) and planning (25%).

21. **(1) 8** Multiply the base (40) times the rate (20%).
20% = 0.2   40 × 0.2 = 8

22. To find the degrees in each section, multiply the base (360°) times the rate for each item.
Rent and utilities   360° × 0.35 = **126°**
Food   360° × 0.25 = **90°**
Transportation   360° × 0.2 = **72°**
Clothes   360° × 0.15 = **54°**
Other   360° × 0.05 = **18°**

23. **(5) Other** The smallest section of the graph represents *other*.

24. **(5) $770** Multiply the base ($2,200) times the rate (35%).
$2,200 × 0.35 = $770

SECTION 13

PAGE 185

1. **(2) $30.00 ÷ $600.00** Divide the part deducted for health insurance ($30.00) by the base ($600.00) to find the rate.

2. **(1) ($84.00 + $12.60) ÷ $600.00** Add the deductions for federal ($84.00) and state ($12.60) income taxes to find the part. Then divide the part by the base ($600.00) to find the rate.

3. **(3) $600.00 x 3%** Multiply the base ($600.00) times the rate (3%) to find the part.

4. **(3) $143.75 ÷ $1,250.00** Divide the part deducted for federal income tax ($143.75) by the base ($1,250.00) to find the rate.

5. **(4) $1,250.00 x 5%** Multiply the base ($1,250.00) times the rate (5%) to find the part.

6. **(2) ($62.50 + $25.00) ÷ $1,250.00** Add the deductions for the retirement fund ($62.50) and insurance ($25.00) to find the part. Then divide the part by the base ($1,250.00) to find the rate.

PAGE 187

2. **10%**   0.1   0.1 = 10%
              360) 36.0

3. **400%**   4   4 = 400%
               45) 180

4. **60%**   0.6   0.6 = 60%
               95) 57.0

5. **2%**   0.02   0.02 = 2%
              200) 4.00

6. **250%**   2.5   2.5 = 250%
                6) 15.0

7. **83%**   0.833   0.833 rounds to 0.83
               84) 70.000   0.83 = 83%

8. **63%**   0.625   0.625 rounds to 0.63
               64) 40.000   0.63 = 63%

9. **80%** Divide the part (32) by the base (40) to find the rate.
        0.8   0.8 = 80%
   40) 32.0

10. **57%** Divide the part (42) by the base (74) to find the rate.
        0.567   0.567 rounds to 0.57
   74) 42.000   0.57 = 57%

11. **25%** Divide the part ($9) by the base ($36) to find the rate.
         0.25   0.25 = 25%
   $36) $9.00

12. **16%** Divide the part ($41.60) by the base ($260) to find the rate.
          0.16   0.16 = 16%
   $260) $41.60

PAGE 191

1. **9**   1 gram × 9 = 9 calories
    4.5% $\frac{Part}{Base} = \frac{Rate}{100}$

             $\frac{9}{200} = \frac{?}{100}$ 9 × 100 = 900
                            900 ÷ 200 = 4.5

2. **117**   13 grams × 9 = 117 calories
    39% $\frac{117}{300} = \frac{?}{100}$ 117 × 100 = 11,700
                            11,700 ÷ 300 = 39

3. **18**   2 grams × 9 = 18 calories
    15% $\frac{18}{120} = \frac{?}{100}$ 18 × 100 = 1,800
                            1,800 ÷ 120 = 15

4. **45**   5 grams × 9 = 45 calories
    90% $\frac{45}{50} = \frac{?}{100}$ 45 × 100 = 4,500
                            4,500 ÷ 50 = 90

5. **macaroni and cheese and light mayonnaise**
In macaroni and cheese, 39% of the calories come from fat, and in light mayonnaise, 90% of the calories come from fat.

PAGE 194

1. **(4) $1,600** Add the amounts on the graph to find the total.
     $ 600
        300
        250
        350
   +   100
     $1,600

2. **(3) 38%** Divide the part ($600) by the base ($1,600; see the explanation for Item 1) to find the rate.

$$1,600\overline{)600.000} = 0.375 \qquad 0.375 \text{ rounds to } 0.38.$$
$$0.38 = 38\%$$

3. **(3) 28%** Add the amounts budgeted for personal expenses ($350) and other ($100). $350 + $100 = $450.
Then divide the part ($450) by the base ($1,600; see the explanation for Item 1) to find the rate.

$$1,600\overline{)450.000} = 0.281 \qquad 0.281 \text{ rounds to } 0.28.$$
$$0.28 = 28\%$$

4. **$200,000** Add the amounts on the graph to find the total. Then multiply by 1,000 because the key says *$ in thousands*.

$$
\begin{array}{r}
\$\ 50 \\
85 \\
30 \\
20 \\
+\ \ 15 \\
\hline
\$200
\end{array}
\qquad
\begin{array}{r}
\$200 \\
\times\ 1,000 \\
\hline
\$200,000
\end{array}
$$

5. **68%** Add the sales from T-shirts ($50,000) and from sweat shirts ($85,000).
$50,000 + $85,000 = $135,000
Then divide the part ($135,000) by the base ($200,000; see the explanation for Item 4) to find the rate.

$$\$200\overline{)\$135.000} = 0.675 \qquad 0.675 \text{ rounds to } 0.68.$$
$$0.68 = 68\%$$

6. **5%** Subtract the sales from caps ($20,000) from the sales from jackets ($30,000).
$30,000 − $20,000 = $10,000
Then divide the part ($10,000) by the base ($200,000; see the explanation for Item 4) to find the rate.

$$\$200\overline{)\$10.00} = 0.05 \qquad 0.05 = 5\%$$

PAGES 195–197

1. **160%**
$$10\overline{)16.0} = 1.6 \qquad 1.6 = 160\%$$

2. **75%**
$$72\overline{)54.00} = 0.75 \qquad 0.75 = 75\%$$

3. **4%**
$$300\overline{)12.00} = 0.04 \qquad 0.04 = 4\%$$

4. **500%**
$$15\overline{)75} = 5 \qquad 5 = 500\%$$

5. **31%**
$$80\overline{)25.000} = 0.312 \qquad 0.312 \text{ rounds to } 0.31.$$
$$0.31 = 31\%$$

6. **37%**
$$90\overline{)33.000} = 0.366 \qquad 0.366 \text{ rounds to } 0.37.$$
$$0.37 = 37\%$$

7. **40%** Divide the part (240) by the base (600) to find the rate.
$$600\overline{)240.0} = 0.4 \qquad 0.4 = 40\%$$

8. **80%** Divide the part (360) by the base (450) to find the rate.
$$450\overline{)360.0} = 0.8 \qquad 0.8 = 80\%$$

9. **83%** Divide the part ($80) by the base ($96) to find the rate.
$$\$96\overline{)\$80.000} = 0.833 \qquad 0.833 \text{ rounds to } 0.83.$$
$$0.83 = 83\%$$

10. **6%** Divide the part ($500) by the base ($8,000) to find the rate.
$$\$8,000\overline{)\$500.000} = 0.062 \qquad 0.062 \text{ rounds to } 0.06.$$
$$0.06 = 6\%$$

11. **(2) 125 ÷ 220** Divide the part (125) by the base (220) to find the rate.

12. **(3) 800 x 52%** Multiply the base (800) times the rate (52%) to find the part.

13. **(4) 30%** Divide the part (12) by the base (40) to find the rate.
$$40\overline{)12.0} = 0.3 \qquad 0.3 = 30\%$$

14. **(4) $30.00** Multiply the base ($200) times the rate (15%) to find the part.
$$
\begin{array}{r}
\$200 \\
\times\ 0.15 \\
\hline
\$30.00
\end{array}
$$

15. **(2) $25.00 ÷ $500.00** Divide the part deducted for the credit union account ($25.00) by the base ($500.00).

16. **(3) 14%** Add the deductions for federal ($63.40) and state ($6.60) income taxes to find the part.
$$
\begin{array}{r}
\$63.40 \\
+\ \ 6.60 \\
\hline
\$70.00
\end{array}
$$
Then divide the part by the base ($500.00) to find the rate.
$$\$500\overline{)\$70.00} = 0.14 \qquad 0.14 = 14\%$$

17. **(2) $20.00** Multiply the base ($500.00) times the rate (4%).
$$4\% = 0.04$$
$$
\begin{array}{r}
\$500.00 \\
\times\ \ 0.04 \\
\hline
\$20.0000
\end{array}
$$

18. **9 calories**
10%
1 gram × 9 = 9 calories
$$\frac{9}{90} = \frac{?}{100} \qquad 9 \times 100 = 900$$
$$900 \div 90 = 10$$

19. **45 calories**
25%
5 grams × 9 = 45 calories
$$\frac{45}{180} = \frac{?}{100} \qquad 45 \times 100 = 4,500$$
$$4,500 \div 180 = 25$$

20. 20,000 Add the amounts on the graph to find the total. Then multiply by 1,000.
$$7 + 2 + 5 + 4 + 2 = 20$$
$$20 \times 1,000 = 20,000$$

21. 25% Divide the part (5,000) by the base (20,000; see the explanation for Item 20) to find the rate.

$$20,000\overline{)5,000.00}^{\,0.25} \qquad 0.25 = 25\%$$

22. 45% Add the amounts for coffee (7,000) and tea (2,000) to find the part.
$$7,000 + 2,000 = 9,000$$
Then divide the part by the base (20,000; see the explanation for Item 20) to find the rate.

$$20,000\overline{)9,000.00}^{\,0.45} \qquad 0.45 = 45\%$$

SECTION 14

PAGE 201

1. **(2) $7.20 ÷ 30%** Divide the part ($7.20) by the rate (30%) to find the base (regular price).

2. **(3) $54.00 ÷ 45%** Divide the part ($54.00) by the rate (45%) to find the base (regular price).

3. **(5) $36.00 – $12.60** Subtract the amount you save ($12.60) from the regular price ($36.00) to find the sale price.

4. **(2) $5.60 ÷ 40%** Divide the part ($5.60) by the rate (40%) to find the base (regular price).

5. **(2) $64.00 x 25%** Multiply the base ($64.00) times the rate (25%) to find the part (savings).

6. **(2) $6.50 ÷ $32.50** Divide the part ($6.50) by the base ($32.50) to find the rate (discount rate).

PAGE 203

2. **90** $40\% = 0.4$ $0.4\overline{)36.0}^{\,90.}$

3. **$12** $75\% = 0.75$ $0.75\overline{)\$9.00}^{\,\$12.}$

4. **19** $300\% = 3$ $3\overline{)57}^{\,19}$

5. **500** $8\% = 0.08$ $0.08\overline{)40.00}^{\,5\,00.}$

6. **50** $32\% = 0.32$ $0.32\overline{)16.00}^{\,50.}$

7. **$82.50** $80\% = 0.8$ $0.8\overline{)66.0.00}^{\,\$82.50}$

8. **20** $175\% = 1.75$ $1.75\overline{)35.00}^{\,20.}$

9. **$75** Divide the part ($22.50) by the rate (30%) to find the base.
$30\% = 0.3$ $0.3\overline{)\$22.5.0}^{\,\$75.}$

10. **20** Divide the part (14) by the rate (70%) to find the base.
$70\% = 0.7$ $0.7\overline{)14.0}^{\,20.}$

11. **$1,400** Divide the part ($490) by the rate (35%) to find the base.
$35\% = 0.35$ $0.35\overline{)\$490.00}^{\,\$1400.}$

12. **$685** Divide the part ($34.25) by the rate (5%) to find the base.
$5\% = 0.05$ $0.05\overline{)\$34.25.}^{\,\$685.}$

PAGE 206

1. **(3) $316.80** Multiply the base ($1,320.00) times the rate (24%) to find the part.
$24\% = 0.24$
$$\begin{array}{r} \$1,320 \\ \times\quad 0.24 \\ \hline 52\ 80 \\ +\ 264\ 0 \\ \hline \$316.80 \end{array}$$

2. **(4) $2,125.00** Divide the part ($425.00) by the rate (20%) to find the base.
$20\% = .20$ $0.20\overline{)\$425.00}^{\,\$21\ 25.}$

3. **(1) 22%** Divide the part ($290.40) by the base ($1,320.00) to find the rate.
$$\$1,320\overline{)\$290.40}^{\,0.22} \qquad 0.22 = 22\%$$

Salesperson	Base (Profit)	Rate	Part (Commission)
4. L. Morgan	$4,350.00	**20%**	$870.00
5. B.Whitefeather	**$7,564.00**	25%	$1,891.00
6. S. Chapa	$5,427.00	23%	**$1,248.21**

L. Morgan: Divide the part ($870.00) by the base ($4,350.00) to find the rate.
$$\$4,350\overline{)\$870.0}^{\,0.2} \qquad 0.2 = 20\%$$

B. Whitefeather: Divide the part ($1,891.00) by the rate (25%) to find the base.
$25\% = 0.25$ $0.25\overline{)\$1,891.00}^{\,\$7564.}$

S. Chapa: Multiply the base ($5,427.00) times the rate (23%) to find the part.
$23\% = 0.23$
$$\begin{array}{r} \$5,427 \\ \times\quad 0.23 \\ \hline \$1,248.21 \end{array}$$

1. **90**   30% = 0.3

$$0.3\overline{)27.0.}\quad\frac{90.}{}$$

2. **2,000**   3% = 0.03

$$0.03\overline{)60.00.}\quad\frac{2000.}{}$$

3. **$60**   68% = 0.68

$$0.68\overline{)\$40.80.}\quad\frac{\$60.}{}$$

4. **20**   20% = 0.2

$$0.2\overline{)4.0.}\quad\frac{20.}{}$$

5. **$28**   125% = 1.25

$$1.25\overline{)\$35.00.}\quad\frac{\$28.}{}$$

6. **48**   75% = 0.75

$$0.75\overline{)36.00.}\quad\frac{48.}{}$$

7. **18**   350% = 3.5

$$3.5\overline{)63.0.}\quad\frac{18.}{}$$

8. **$42.50**   8% = 0.08

$$0.08\overline{)\$3.40.00}\quad\frac{\$42.50}{}$$

9. **(5) $120 ÷ 80%**   Divide the part ($120) by the rate (80%) to find the base.

10. **(3) 9,610 ÷ 62%**   Divide the part (9,610) by the rate (62%) to find the base.

11. **$14.40**   Divide the part ($3.60) by the rate (25%) to find the base.
25% = 0.25

$$0.25\overline{)3.60.00}\quad\frac{\$14.40}{}$$

12. **$10.80**   Subtract the amount you save ($3.60) from the regular price (see the explanation for Item 11).

$$\begin{array}{r}{}^{3\ 14}\\ \$1\cancel{4}.\cancel{4}0\\ -\ \ 3.60\\ \hline \$10.80\end{array}$$

13. **$17.40**   Multiply the base ($58.00) times the rate (30%) to find the part.
30% = 0.3

$$\begin{array}{r}\$58.00\\ \times\ \ \ \ 0.3\\ \hline \$17.400\end{array}$$

14. **$40.60**   Subtract the amount you save (see the explanation for Item 13) from the regular price ($58.00).

$$\begin{array}{r}{}^{7\ 10}\\ \$5\cancel{8}.\cancel{0}0\\ -\ 17.40\\ \hline \$40.60\end{array}$$

15. **25 questions**   Divide the part (22) by the rate (88%) to find the base.
88% = 0.88

$$0.88\overline{)22.00.}\quad\frac{25.}{}$$

16. **$292**   Divide the part ($17.52) by the rate (6%) to find the base.
6% = 0.06

$$0.06\overline{)\$17.52.}\quad\frac{\$292.}{}$$

17. **270 sales**   Multiply the base (360) times the rate (75%) to find the part.
75% = 0.75

$$\begin{array}{r}360\\ \times\ 0.75\\ \hline 270.00\end{array}$$

18. **14,830**   Divide the part (16,313) by the rate (110%) to find the base.
110% = 1.1

$$1.1\overline{)16,313.0.}\quad\frac{14,830.}{}$$

19. **(2) 18**   Multiply the base (40) times the rate (45%) to find the part.
45% = 0.45

$$\begin{array}{r}40\\ \times\ 0.45\\ \hline 18.00\end{array}$$

20. **(4) 425**   Divide the part (85) by the rate (20%) to find the base.
20% = 0.2

$$0.2\overline{)85.0.}\quad\frac{425.}{}$$

21. **(4) 86%**   Divide the part (129) by the base (150) to find the rate.

$$150\overline{)129.00}\quad\frac{0.86}{}\qquad 0.86 = 86\%$$

22. **(5) $7,600**   Divide the part ($2,356) by the rate (31%) to find the base.
31% = 0.31

$$0.31\overline{)\$2,356.00.}\quad\frac{\$7600.}{}$$

	Salesperson	Base (Profit)	Rate	Part (Commission)
23.	V. Murphy	$6,352.00	22%	**$1,397.44**
24.	S. Santino	**$4,163.00**	21%	$874.23
25.	D. Hill	$5,240.00	**25%**	$1,310.00
26.	P. Moreno	$6,500.00	24%	**$1,560.00**

V. Murphy: Multiply the base ($6,352.00) times the rate (22%) to find the part.
22% = 0.22

$$\begin{array}{r}\$6,352\\ \times\ \ \ \ 0.22\\ \hline \$1,397.44\end{array}$$

S. Santino: Divide the part ($874.23) by the rate (21%) to find the base.
21% = 0.21

$$0.21\overline{)\$874.23.}\quad\frac{\$4163.}{}$$

D. Hill: Divide the part ($1,310.00) by the base ($5,240.00) to find the rate.

$$\$5,240\overline{)\$1,310.00}\quad\frac{0.25}{}\qquad 0.25 = 25\%$$

P. Moreno: Multiply the profit on each sale ($3,250.00) times the number of sales (2). Then multiply the base (total profit) times the rate (24%) to find the part.

$$\begin{array}{r}\$3,520\\ \times\ \ \ \ \ \ 2\\ \hline \$6,500\end{array}\qquad 24\% = 0.24\qquad \begin{array}{r}\$6,500\\ \times\ \ \ 0.24\\ \hline \$1,560.00\end{array}$$

SECTION 15

PAGE 212

1. **(4) ($6.21 − $5.75) ÷ $5.75** Subtract Tanya's current wage from her new wage to find the amount of change. Then divide by the original amount, her current wage.

2. **(5) ($5.40 − $5.13) ÷ $5.40** Subtract the new wage from Tony's current wage to find the amount of change. Then divide by the original amount, his current wage.

3. **(3) $12.19 − $11.50** Subtract Carla's current wage from her new wage to find the amount of change.

4. **(5) ($6.40 − $6.20) ÷ $6.40** Subtract Laura's new wage from the current wage to find the amount of change. Then divide by the original amount, her current wage.

5. **(1) $1.06 ÷ $13.25** Divide the amount of change (raise) by the original amount (Ike's current wage).

6. **(3) ($7.24 − $6.95) ÷ $7.24** Subtract the new wage from Marcus's current wage to find the amount of change. Then divide by the original amount, his current wage.

PAGE 215

2. **25%**

$$\begin{array}{r} \$8.80 \\ -\ 6.60 \\ \hline \$2.20 \end{array} \qquad \begin{array}{r} 0.25 \\ \$8.80.\overline{)\$2.20.00} \end{array} \quad 0.25 = 25\%$$

3. **40%**

$$\begin{array}{r} 25 \\ -\ 15 \\ \hline 10 \end{array} \qquad \begin{array}{r} 0.4 \\ 25\overline{)10.0} \end{array} \quad 0.4 = 40\%$$

4. **12%**

$$\begin{array}{r} \overset{4\ \ 13}{5{,}376} \\ -\ 4{,}800 \\ \hline 576 \end{array} \qquad \begin{array}{r} 0.12 \\ 4{,}800\overline{)576.00} \end{array} \quad 0.12 = 12\%$$

5. **10%**

$$\begin{array}{r} 70 \\ -\ 63 \\ \hline 7 \end{array} \qquad \begin{array}{r} 0.1 \\ 70\overline{)7.0} \end{array} \quad 0.1 = 10\%$$

6. **6%**

$$\begin{array}{r} \overset{3\ \ 9\,10}{\$24.00} \\ -\ 22.56 \\ \hline \$1.44 \end{array} \qquad \begin{array}{r} 0.06 \\ \$24.00.\overline{)\$1.44.00} \end{array} \quad 0.06 = 6\%$$

7. **50%** Subtract the original premium ($750.00) from the new premium ($1,125.00). Then divide by the original premium.

$$\begin{array}{r} \overset{0\ \ 10\,12}{\$1{,}125.00} \\ -\quad 750.00 \\ \hline \$375.00 \end{array} \qquad \begin{array}{r} 0.50 \\ \$750\overline{)\$375.00} \end{array} \quad 0.50 = 50\%$$

8. **15%** Subtract the new fare ($23.80) from the original fare ($28.00). Then divide by the original fare.

$$\begin{array}{r} \overset{7\ \ 10}{\$28.00} \\ -\ 23.00 \\ \hline \$4.20 \end{array} \qquad \begin{array}{r} 0.15 \\ \$28\overline{)\$4.20} \end{array} \quad 0.15 = 15\%$$

PAGE 218

1. **(3) 30** The shaded bar for dinner in September reaches halfway between the marks for *140* and *160*. So, the number of customers in September was 150. The number of dinner customers in August was 120. Subtract to find the difference.
$$150 − 120 = 30$$

2. **(3) 25%** Divide the change in the number of dinner customers (30; see the explanation for Item 1) by the number of dinner customers in August (120).

$$\begin{array}{r} 0.25 \\ 120\overline{)30.00} \end{array} \quad 0.25 = 25\%$$

3. **18%** Add the number of customers for breakfast (60), lunch (130), and dinner (150) in September. Then divide the part (number of breakfast customers, 60) by the base (total customers) to find the rate.

$$\begin{array}{r} 60 \\ 130 \\ +\ 150 \\ \hline 340 \end{array} \qquad \begin{array}{r} 0.176 \\ 340\overline{)60.000} \end{array} \quad \begin{array}{l} 0.176 \text{ rounds to } 0.18. \\ 0.18 = 18\% \end{array}$$

4. **20%** Subtract the number of customers for breakfast in August (50) from the number of customers for breakfast in September (60). Then divide by the number of customers in August.

$$\begin{array}{r} 60 \\ -\ 50 \\ \hline 10 \end{array} \qquad \begin{array}{r} 0.2 \\ 50\overline{)10.0} \end{array} \quad 0.2 = 20\%$$

5. **7%** Subtract the number of customers for lunch in September (130) from the number of customers for lunch in August (140). Then divide by the number in August.

$$\begin{array}{r} 140 \\ -\ 130 \\ \hline 10 \end{array} \qquad \begin{array}{r} 0.071 \\ 140\overline{)10.000} \end{array} \quad \begin{array}{l} 0.071 \text{ rounds to } 0.07. \\ 0.07 = 7\% \end{array}$$

6. 10% Add the number of customers for breakfast (50), lunch (140), and dinner (120) in August. Then add the number of customers for breakfast (60), lunch (130), and dinner (150) in September. Subtract the total for August from the total for September. Then divide by the total for August.

$$
\begin{array}{r}
1 \\
50 \\
140 \\
+\ 120 \\
\hline
310
\end{array}
\qquad
\begin{array}{r}
1 \\
60 \\
130 \\
+\ 150 \\
\hline
340
\end{array}
\qquad
\begin{array}{r}
340 \\
-\ 310 \\
\hline
30
\end{array}
\qquad
310\overline{)\,30.000}\ \ 0.096
$$

0.096 rounds to 0.10
0.10 = 10%

PAGE 221

1. (4) 11% Subtract Vanessa's current weight (142 lb.) from her original weight (160 lb.). Then divide by her original weight.

$$
\begin{array}{r}
510 \\
16\cancel{0} \\
-\ 142 \\
\hline
18
\end{array}
\qquad
160\overline{)\,18.000}\ \ 0.112
\qquad
\begin{array}{l}
0.112 \text{ rounds to } 0.11 \\
0.11 = 11\%
\end{array}
$$

2. (2) 6% Subtract Vanessa's current weight (142 lb.) from her ideal weight (150 lb.). Then divide by her current weight.

$$
\begin{array}{r}
410 \\
15\cancel{0} \\
-\ 142 \\
\hline
8
\end{array}
\qquad
142\overline{)\,8.000}\ \ 0.056
\qquad
\begin{array}{l}
0.056 \text{ rounds to } 0.06 \\
0.06 = 6\%.
\end{array}
$$

3. (3) 23% Subtract John's ideal weight (185 lb.) from his original weight (240 lb.). Then divide by his original weight.

$$
\begin{array}{r}
11310 \\
2\cancel{40} \\
-\ 185 \\
\hline
55
\end{array}
\qquad
240\overline{)\,55.000}\ \ 0.229
\qquad
\begin{array}{l}
0.229 \text{ rounds to } 0.23 \\
0.23 = 23\%
\end{array}
$$

4. (2) 6% Subtract John's current weight (225 lb.) from his weight two months ago (240 lb.). Then divide by his weight two months ago.

$$
\begin{array}{r}
310 \\
2\cancel{40} \\
-\ 225 \\
\hline
15
\end{array}
\qquad
240\overline{)\,15.000}\ \ 0.062
\qquad
\begin{array}{l}
0.062 \text{ rounds to } 0.06 \\
0.06 = 6\%
\end{array}
$$

5. 14% Subtract Toya's original weight (95 lb.) from her current weight (108 lb.). Then divide by her original weight.

$$
\begin{array}{r}
108 \\
-\ 95 \\
\hline
13
\end{array}
\qquad
95\overline{)\,13.000}\ \ 0.136
\qquad
\begin{array}{l}
0.136 \text{ rounds to } 0.14 \\
0.14 = 14\%
\end{array}
$$

6. 11% Subtract Toya's current weight (108 lb.) from her ideal weight (120 lb.). Then divide by her current weight.

$$
\begin{array}{r}
110 \\
12\cancel{0} \\
-\ 108 \\
\hline
12
\end{array}
\qquad
108\overline{)\,12.000}\ \ 0.111
\qquad
\begin{array}{l}
0.111 \text{ rounds to } 0.11 \\
0.11 = 11\%
\end{array}
$$

PAGES 222–223

1. (5) ($5.76 − $5.40) ÷ $5.76 Subtract Willis' current wage from his old wage to find the amount of change. Then divide by the original amount, his old wage.

2. (2) 8% Subtract the original premium ($216.00) from the new premium ($233.28). Then divide by the original premium.

$$
\begin{array}{r}
213 \\
\$23\cancel{3}.28 \\
-\ 216.00 \\
\hline
\$17.28
\end{array}
\qquad
\$216\overline{)\,\$17.28}\ \ 0.08
\qquad
0.08 = 8\%
$$

3. (3) 10% Subtract Stan's current wage ($6.50) from his new wage ($7.15). Then divide by his current wage.

$$
\begin{array}{r}
6\ 11 \\
\$7.\cancel{15} \\
-\ 6.50 \\
\hline
\$0.65
\end{array}
\qquad
\$6.50.\overline{)\,\$0.65.0}\ \ 0.1
\qquad
0.1 = 10\%
$$

4. (4) ($550,000 − $526,000) ÷ $526,000 Subtract the amount of last year's sales ($526,000) from this year's sales ($550,000). Then divide by the amount of last year's sales.

5. 4% Subtract Jan's original weight (150 lb.) from her weight just before starting the program (156 lb.). Then divide by her original weight.

$$
\begin{array}{r}
156 \\
-\ 150 \\
\hline
6
\end{array}
\qquad
150\overline{)\,6.00}\ \ 0.04
\qquad
0.04 = 4\%
$$

6. 6% Subtract Jan's current weight (146 lb.) from her weight one month ago (156 lb.). Then divide by her weight one month ago.

$$
\begin{array}{r}
156 \\
-\ 146 \\
\hline
10
\end{array}
\qquad
156\overline{)\,10.000}\ \ 0.064
\qquad
\begin{array}{l}
0.064 \text{ rounds to } 0.06 \\
0.06 = 6\%
\end{array}
$$

7. 18% Subtract Jan's ideal weight (128 lb.) from her weight one month ago (156 lb.). Then divide by her weight one month ago.

$$
\begin{array}{r}
4\ 16 \\
15\cancel{6} \\
-\ 128 \\
\hline
28
\end{array}
\qquad
156\overline{)\,28.000}\ \ 0.179
\qquad
\begin{array}{l}
0.179 \text{ rounds to } 0.18. \\
0.18 = 18\%
\end{array}
$$

8. 75% Subtract the later attendance (245) from the opening night attendance (980). Then divide by the opening night attendance.

$$\begin{array}{r} \overset{7\,10}{9\cancel{8}\cancel{0}} \\ -\ 245 \\ \hline 735 \end{array}$$

$$\begin{array}{r} 0.75 \\ 980\overline{)735.00} \end{array}$$ 0.75 = 75%

9. 4% Subtract last year's fare ($450) from the current fare ($470). Then divide by last year's fare.

$$\begin{array}{r} \$470 \\ -\ 450 \\ \hline \$20 \end{array}$$

$$\begin{array}{r} 0.044 \\ \$450\overline{)\$20.000} \end{array}$$ 0.044 rounds to 0.04 0.04 = 4%

10. 64% Subtract the old car's mileage (15 mpg) from the new car's mileage (24.6 mpg). Then divide by the old car's mileage.

$$\begin{array}{r} \overset{1\,14}{2\cancel{4}.6} \\ -\ 15.0 \\ \hline 9.6 \end{array}$$

$$\begin{array}{r} 0.64 \\ 15\overline{)9.60} \end{array}$$ 0.64 = 64%

11. 9% Subtract the current number of employees (320) from the original number of employees (350). Then divide by the original number.

$$\begin{array}{r} 350 \\ -\ 320 \\ \hline 30 \end{array}$$

$$\begin{array}{r} 0.085 \\ 350\overline{)30.000} \end{array}$$ 0.085 rounds to 0.09 0.09 = 9%

12. 89% Subtract the amount of July's gas bill ($10) from January's gas bill ($95). Then divide by the amount of January's gas bill.

$$\begin{array}{r} \$95 \\ -\ 10 \\ \hline \$85 \end{array}$$

$$\begin{array}{r} 0.894 \\ \$95\overline{)\$85.000} \end{array}$$ 0.894 rounds to 0.89 0.89 = 89%

13. 88% Subtract the amount of January's electric bill ($40) from July's electric bill ($75). Then divide by the amount of January's electric bill.

$$\begin{array}{r} \$75 \\ -\ 40 \\ \hline \$35 \end{array}$$

$$\begin{array}{r} 0.875 \\ \$40\overline{)\$35.000} \end{array}$$ 0.875 rounds to 0.88 0.88 = 88%

14. 33% Subtract the amount of January's water bill ($15) from July's water bill ($20). Then divide by the amount of January's water bill.

$$\begin{array}{r} \$20 \\ -\ 15 \\ \hline \$5 \end{array}$$

$$\begin{array}{r} 0.333 \\ \$15\overline{)\$5.000} \end{array}$$ 0.333 rounds to 0.33 0.33 = 33%

UNIT 4 REVIEW

PAGES 224–225

1. 14 $8 \times 35 = 280; 280 \div 20 = 14$

2. 324 $450\% = 4.5$

$$\begin{array}{r} 72 \\ \times\ 4.5 \\ \hline 324.0 \end{array}$$

3. 2.5%

$$\begin{array}{r} 0.025 \\ 320\overline{)8.000} \end{array}$$ 0.025 = 2.5%

4. $45

$$\begin{array}{r} \$45. \\ 0.09.\overline{)\$4.05.} \end{array}$$ 9% = 0.09

5. 40%

$$\begin{array}{r} \$17.50 \\ -\ 12.50 \\ \hline \$5.00 \end{array}$$

$$\begin{array}{r} 0.4 \\ \$12.50.\overline{)\$5.00.0} \end{array}$$ 0.4 = 40%

6. $151.20 Subtract the down payment from the cost to find the principal.
$520 − $100 = $420.
Use the formula to find the interest.
$i = p \times r \times t$
= $420 \times 0.18 \times 2$
= $151.20

7. $23.80 Add the principal and interest (see the explanation for Item 6) to find the amount to be paid back.
$420 + $151.20 = $571.20
Divide the amount to be paid back by the number of monthly payments. (2 years = 24 months)
$571.20 ÷ 24 = $23.80

8. $7.60

$$\frac{3}{\$2.85} = \frac{8}{?}$$ $2.85 \times 8 = $22.80
$22.80 ÷ 3 = $7.60

9. 5% Subtract Carlos' current weight (237 lb.) from his original weight (250 lb.). Then divide by his original weight.

$$\begin{array}{r} 250 \\ -\ 237 \\ \hline 13 \end{array}$$

$$\begin{array}{r} 0.052 \\ 250\overline{)13.000} \end{array}$$ 0.052 rounds to 0.05 0.05 = 5%

10. (2) $40.80 ÷ $340.00 Divide the part deducted for federal income tax ($40.80) by the base ($340.00) to find the rate.

11. (4) $25.60 Divide the part ($6.40) by the rate (25%) to find the base (regular price).
25% = 0.25 $6.40 ÷ 0.25 = $25.60

12. (3) 108° Multiply the base (360° in a circle) times the rate (30%) to find the part.
30% = 0.3

$$\begin{array}{r} 360 \\ \times\ 0.3 \\ \hline 108.0 \end{array}$$

13. (4) ($8.84 − $8.50) ÷ $8.50 Subtract Wanda's current wage from the new wage to find the amount of change. Then divide by the original amount, the current wage.

14. 18 The distance on the map from Riverview to Mesa is $2\frac{1}{4}$ inches.

$$\frac{2 \text{ in.}}{16 \text{ mi.}} = \frac{2\frac{1}{4} \text{ in.}}{? \text{ mi.}}$$ $16 \times 2\frac{1}{4} = 36$
36 ÷ 2 = 18

15. **2,500**   Add the amounts on the graph to find the total. Then multiply by 100.
$6 + 4 + 5 + 7 + 3 = 25$
$25 \times 100 = 2,500$

16. **28%**   Divide the part (700) by the base (2,500; see the explanation for Item 15) to find the rate.
$700 \div 2,500 = 0.28$
$0.28 = 28\%$

CUMULATIVE REVIEW

PAGES 226–227

1. **six million, thirty thousand, seventeen**
2. **seven and ninety-six thousandths**
3. **$54,2\underline{7}7 > 54,2\underline{2}7$**   7 is greater than 2.
4. **$0.083 < 0.83$**
Add a zero: $0.\underline{0}83$
$0.\underline{8}30$
Then compare: 0 is less than 8.
5. **$5.10 = 5.1$**
6. **$9\frac{5}{12}$**
$5\frac{2}{3} = 5\frac{8}{12}$
$\underline{+ 3\frac{3}{4} = 3\frac{9}{12}}$
$8\frac{17}{12} = 8 + 1\frac{5}{12} = 9\frac{5}{12}$
7. **$2\frac{11}{30}$**
$7\frac{1}{6} = 7\frac{5}{30} = 7\overset{6\;35}{\frac{5}{30}}$
$\underline{-4\frac{4}{5} = 4\frac{24}{30} = 4\frac{24}{30}}$
$2\frac{11}{30}$
8. **21**
$5 \times 4 - 2 + 9 \div 3$
$20 - 2 + 9 \div 3$
$20 - 2 + 3$
$18 + 3$
21
9. **5** $5 \times 5 = 25$, so $\sqrt{25} = 5$
10. **31.25**
11. **$3.04**
12. **4,560**
13. **0.00485**
14. **1,108**
15. **$5.52**
16. **$11\frac{1}{4}$** $3\frac{3}{8} \times 3\frac{1}{3} = \frac{\overset{9}{27}}{\underset{4}{8}} \times \frac{\overset{5}{10}}{\underset{1}{3}} = \frac{45}{4} = 11\frac{1}{4}$
17. **$\frac{10}{13}$** $2\frac{1}{2} \div 3\frac{1}{4} = \frac{5}{2} \div \frac{13}{4} = \frac{5}{2} \times \frac{\overset{2}{4}}{\underset{1}{13}} = \frac{10}{13}$
18. **59.048**
19. **4.674**
20. **(5) $4.3 + 4.3 + 2.5 + 2.5$**   To find the perimeter, add the lengths of all four sides.

21. **(4) 15%**   2 grams $\times$ 9 = 18
$\frac{\text{part}}{\text{base}} = \frac{?}{100}$
$\frac{18}{120} = \frac{?}{100}$ $18 \times 100 = 1,800$
$\phantom{\frac{18}{120} = \frac{?}{100}}$ $1,800 \div 120 = 15$
$\frac{15}{100} = 15\%$

22. **(4) $62.80**   Multiply the cost of a 2-day pass for children ($11.95) times the number of children (3). Then add the cost of one 2-day pass for adults.
 \$11.95 \$35.85
$\underline{\times 3}$ $\underline{+ 26.95}$
 \$35.85 \$62.80

23. **41**   To find the mean, first find the total of the numbers of the set of data.
$46 + 39.5 + 41.5 + 38.5 + 39 + 41.5 = 246$
Then divide the total by the number of items in the set.
$246 \div 6 = 41$

24. **40.5**   To find the median, arrange the numbers in order. Find the middle numbers.
38.5, 39, $\underline{39.5}$, $\underline{41.5}$, 41.5, 46
Then find the mean of the middle numbers.
$39.5 + 41.5 = 81$; $81 \div 2 = 40.5$

25. **150**   The bar for Friday is the tallest. It reaches the *4* and represents 400 deliveries. The bar for Tuesday is the smallest. It ends between *2* and *3* and represents 250 deliveries. Subtract to find the difference.
$400 - 250 = 150$

UNIT 5: SPECIAL TOPICS

SECTION 16

PAGE 231

1. $\frac{1}{6}$; $16\frac{2}{3}\%$

   $\dfrac{\text{number of ways you can roll a 4}}{\text{number of possible outcomes}} = \dfrac{1}{6}$ or $16\frac{2}{3}\%$

   $1 \div 6 = 0.16\frac{2}{3} = 16\frac{2}{3}\%$

2. **0; 0%** The numbers on a die are 1 to 6, so you cannot roll a 9. The probability of rolling a 9 is 0 or 0%.

3. **1; 100%** All of the possible rolls of a die are numbers less than 7. So the probability of rolling a number less than 7 is 1 or 100%.

4. $\frac{1}{2}$; **50%**

   $\dfrac{\substack{\text{number of ways to roll}\\ \text{an even number}}}{\substack{\text{number of possible}\\ \text{outcomes}}} = \dfrac{3}{6} = \dfrac{1}{2}$ or 50%

5. **1; 100%** All of the marbles you can choose are colored. So the probability of choosing a colored marble is 1 or 100%.

6. $\frac{1}{5}$; **20%**

   $\dfrac{\substack{\text{number of ways you can}\\ \text{choose a blue marble}}}{\text{number of marbles}} = \dfrac{1}{5}$ or 20%

PAGE 233

1. **(2) $\frac{3}{10}$ or 30%**

   $\dfrac{\text{number of shaded sections}}{\text{number of sections}} = \dfrac{3}{10}$ or 30%

2. **(3) $\frac{1}{2}$ or 50%** There are 5 even numbers on the wheel.

   $\dfrac{\substack{\text{number of sections}\\ \text{with even numbers}}}{\text{number of sections}} = \dfrac{5}{10} = \dfrac{1}{2}$ or 50%

3. **(5) $\frac{3}{5}$ or 60%** The numbers on the wheel that are greater than 4 are 5, 6, 7, 8, 9, and 10.

   $\dfrac{\substack{\text{number of sections}\\ \text{greater than 4}}}{\text{number of sections}} = \dfrac{6}{10} = \dfrac{3}{5}$ or 60%

4. **(5) 1 or 100%** All of the numbers on the wheel are less than 12. So the probability of the wheel stopping on a number less than 12 is 1 or 100%.

5. $\frac{3}{8}$ **or 37.5%**

   $\dfrac{\text{number of gray marbles}}{\text{number of marbles}} = \dfrac{3}{8}$ or 37.5%

   $3 \div 8 = 0.375 = 37.5\%$

6. $\frac{3}{4}$ **or 75%**

   $\dfrac{\substack{\text{number of marbles that}\\ \text{are black or gray}}}{\text{number of marbles}} = \dfrac{6}{8} = \dfrac{3}{4}$ or 75%

7. $\frac{5}{8}$ **or 62.5%**

   $\dfrac{\substack{\text{number of marbles}\\ \text{that are not black}}}{\text{number of marbles}} = \dfrac{5}{8}$ or 62.5%

   $5 \div 8 = 0.625 = 62.5\%$

PAGE 235

1. **(1) $\frac{1}{5}$ or 20%**

   $\dfrac{\text{number of cards with } Drive}{\text{number of cards}} = \dfrac{1}{5}$ or 20%

2. **(2) $\frac{1}{4}$ or 25%** After a blank card is drawn, there are 4 cards left, *Drive* and 3 blanks.

   $\dfrac{\text{number of cards with } Drive}{\text{number of cards}} = \dfrac{1}{4}$ or 25%

3. **(4) $\frac{3}{4}$ or 75%** After a blank card is drawn, there are 4 cards left, *Drive* and 3 blanks.

   $\dfrac{\text{number of blank cards}}{\text{number of cards}} = \dfrac{3}{4}$ or 75%

4. $\frac{1}{3}$ **or $33\frac{1}{3}\%$**

   $\dfrac{\text{number of \$100 bills}}{\text{number of bills}} = \dfrac{3}{9} = \dfrac{1}{3}$ or $33\frac{1}{3}\%$

5. $\frac{1}{4}$ **or 25%** After a \$100 bill is drawn, there are 8 bills left, 6 \$20 bills and 2 \$100 bills.

   $\dfrac{\text{number of \$100 bills}}{\text{number of bills}} = \dfrac{2}{8} = \dfrac{1}{4}$ or 25%

6. $\frac{3}{8}$ **or 37.5%** After a \$20 bill is drawn, there are 8 bills left, 5 \$20 bills and 3 \$100 bills.

   $\dfrac{\text{number of \$100 bills}}{\text{number of bills}} = \dfrac{3}{8}$ or 37.5%

   $3 \div 8 = 0.375 = 37.5\%$

PAGE 236

1. **(2) $\frac{3}{5}$ or 60%**

$$\frac{\text{number of black marbles}}{\text{number of marbles}} = \frac{6}{10} = \frac{3}{5} \text{ or } 60\%$$

2. **(1) 0 or 0%** There are no green marbles in the box, so there is no possibility of choosing one.

3. **(2) $\frac{1}{10}$ or 10%**

$$\frac{\text{number of gray marbles}}{\text{number of marbles}} = \frac{1}{10} \text{ or } 10\%$$

4. **(5) $\frac{7}{10}$ or 70%**

$$\frac{\begin{array}{c}\text{number of marbles}\\ \text{that are not white}\end{array}}{\text{number of marbles}} = \frac{7}{10} \text{ or } 70\%$$

5. **$\frac{1}{3}$ or $33\frac{1}{3}$%** After the gray marble is drawn, there are 9 marbles left: 6 black and 3 white.

$$\frac{\text{number of white marbles}}{\text{number of marbles}} = \frac{3}{9} = \frac{1}{3} \text{ or } 33\frac{1}{3}\%$$

6. **0 or 0%** After the gray marble is drawn, there are 9 marbles left: 6 black and 3 white. Since there are no gray marbles left, there is no possibility of choosing one.

7. **$\frac{2}{3}$ or $66\frac{2}{3}$%** After a white marble is drawn, there are 9 marbles left: 6 black, 1 gray, and 2 white.

$$\frac{\text{number of black marbles}}{\text{number of marbles}} = \frac{6}{9} = \frac{2}{3} \text{ or } 66\frac{2}{3}\%$$

8. **$\frac{1}{8}$ or 12.5%** After 2 white marbles are drawn, there are 8 marbles left: 6 black, 1 gray, and 1 white.

$$\frac{\text{number of white marbles}}{\text{number of marbles}} = \frac{1}{8} \text{ or } 12.5\%$$

SECTION 17

PAGE 237

1. **acute; isosceles** Each angle measures less than 90°, and two sides have the same length.

2. **right; isosceles** One angle is a right angle, and each side has a different length.

3. **acute; equilateral** Each angle measures less than 90°, and all sides have the same length.

4. **isosceles** Two sides have the same length.

5. **acute** Each angle measures less than 90°, and each side has a different length.

6. **right; isosceles** One angle is a right angle, and two sides have the same length.

PAGE 239

1. **47 inches**

$$\begin{aligned} C &= \pi d \\ &= 3.14 \times 15 \\ &= 47.1 \text{ inches} \end{aligned}$$

47.1 inches rounds to 47 inches.

2. **19 feet** Multiply the radius (3 ft.) by 2 to find the diameter ($3 \times 2 = 6$ ft.).

$$\begin{aligned} C &= \pi d \\ &= 3.14 \times 6 \\ &= 18.84 \text{ feet} \end{aligned}$$

18.84 feet rounds to 19 feet.

3. **38 feet**

$$\begin{aligned} C &= \pi d \\ &= 3.14 \times 12 \\ &= 37.68 \text{ feet} \end{aligned}$$

37.68 feet rounds to 38 feet.

4. **75 feet**

$$\begin{aligned} C &= \pi d \\ &= 3.14 \times 24 \\ &= 75.36 \text{ feet} \end{aligned}$$

75.36 feet rounds to 75 feet.

5. **201 inches** Multiply the radius (32 in.) by 2 to find the diameter ($32 \times 2 = 64$ in.).

$$\begin{aligned} C &= \pi d \\ &= 3.14 \times 64 \\ &= 200.96 \text{ inches} \end{aligned}$$

200.96 inches rounds to 201 inches.

PAGE 240

1. **50 square inches**

$$\begin{aligned} A &= \pi r^2 \\ &= 3.14 \times 4 \times 4 \\ &= 3.14 \times 16 \\ &= 50.24 \text{ square inches} \end{aligned}$$

50.24 square inches rounds to 50 square inches.

2. **79 square feet** Divide the diameter (10 ft.) by 2 to find the radius ($10 \div 2 = 5$).

$$\begin{aligned} A &= \pi r^2 \\ &= 3.14 \times 5 \times 5 \\ &= 3.14 \times 25 \\ &= 78.5 \text{ square feet} \end{aligned}$$

78.5 square feet rounds to 79 square feet.

3. **64 square feet** Divide the diameter (9 ft.) by 2 to find the radius ($9 \div 2 = 4.5$).

$$\begin{aligned} A &= \pi r^2 \\ &= 3.14 \times 4.5 \times 4.5 \\ &= 3.14 \times 20.25 \\ &= 63.585 \text{ square feet} \end{aligned}$$

63.585 square feet rounds to 64 square feet.

4. 254 square feet   Divide the diameter (18 ft.) by 2 to find the radius (18 ÷ 2 = 9).

$A = \pi r^2$
$= 3.14 \times 9 \times 9$
$= 3.14 \times 81$
$= 254.34$ square feet

254.34 square feet rounds to 254 square feet.

5. 154 square yards

$A = \pi r^2$
$= 3.14 \times 7 \times 7$
$= 3.14 \times 49$
$= 153.86$ square yards

153.86 square yards rounds to 154 square yards.

PAGE 241

1. 50 feet; 201 square feet

$C = \pi d$
$= 3.14 \times 16$
$= 50.24$ feet

50.24 feet rounds to 50 feet.

Divide the diameter (16 ft.) by 2 to find the radius (16 ÷ 2 = 8).

$A = \pi r^2$
$= 3.14 \times 8 \times 8$
$= 3.14 \times 64$
$= 200.96$ square feet

200.96 square feet rounds to 201 square feet.

2. 63 yards; 314 square yards

Multiply the radius (10 yd.) by 2 to find the diameter (10 × 2 = 20).

$C = \pi d$
$= 3.14 \times 20$
$= 62.8$ yards

62.8 yards rounds to 63 yards.

$A = \pi r^2$
$= 3.14 \times 10 \times 10$
$= 3.14 \times 100$
$= 314$ square yards

3. 44 inches; 154 square inches   Multiply the radius (7 in.) by 2 to find the diameter (7 × 2 = 14).

$C = \pi d$
$= 3.14 \times 14$
$= 43.96$ inches

43.96 inches rounds to 44 inches.

$A = \pi r^2$
$= 3.14 \times 7 \times 7$
$= 3.14 \times 49$
$= 153.86$ square yards

153.86 square yards rounds to 154 square yards.

4. (2) acute; isosceles   Each angle measures less than 90° so it is an acute triangle. Two of its sides have the same length, which describes an isosceles triangle.

5. (3) 6 x 3   An equilateral triangle has three sides of the same length. To find the perimeter, multiply the length of one side (6 ft.) by 3.

6. 82 feet   Multiply the radius (13 ft.) by 2 to find the diameter (13 × 2 = 26).

$C = \pi d$
$= 3.14 \times 26$
$= 81.64$ feet

81.64 feet rounds to 82 feet.

7. 254 square inches

$A = \pi r^2$
$= 3.14 \times 9 \times 9$
$= 3.14 \times 81$
$= 254.34$ square inches

254.34 square inches rounds to 254 square inches.

SECTION 18

PAGE 243

1. ⁻3 degrees   Start at ⁺6 on the number line and count 9 units to the left.

2. ⁺2 degrees   Start at ⁻6 on the number line and count 8 units to the right.

3. ⁻1 degree   Start at ⁻5 on the number line and count 4 units to the right.

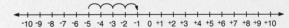

4. ⁻5 degrees   Start at ⁻2 on the number line and count 3 units to the left.

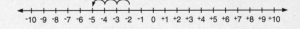

UNIT 5 REVIEW

PAGES 244–245

1. **(2) $\frac{1}{4}$ or 25%**

   $$\frac{\text{number of sections}}{\text{number of sections}} = \frac{2}{8} = \frac{1}{4} \text{ or } 25\%$$

2. **(5) 1 or 100%**   All sections on the wheel have a number less than 5. So the probability of stopping on a number less than 5 is 1 or 100%.

3. **(3) $\frac{3}{5}$ or 60%**   After a black marble is chosen, there are 5 marbles left; 3 black and 2 white.

   $$\frac{\text{number of black marbles}}{\text{number of marbles}} = \frac{3}{5} \text{ or } 60\%$$

4. **(4) acute; equilateral**   Each angle measures less than 90°, and all sides have the same length.

5. **(2) 38** $C = \pi d$
   $$= 3.14 \times 12$$
   $$= 37.68$$
   37.68 rounds to 38.

6. **(3) 113**   Divide the diameter by 2 to find the radius ($12 \div 2 = 6$).
   $A = \pi r^2$
   $$= 3.14 \times 6 \times 6$$
   $$= 3.14 \times 36$$
   $$= 113.04$$
   113.04 rounds to 113.

7. **(5) 18 + 18 + 7**   Because an isosceles triangle has two sides of the same length, the missing length is 18 inches. Add the lengths of all three sides to find the perimeter.

8. **⁻4 degrees**   Start at ⁺3 on the number line.

   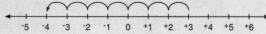

   Count 7 units to the left.

9. **⁺3 degrees**   Start at ⁻5 on the number line.

   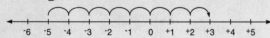

   Count 8 units to the right.

10. **0 or 0%**   You cannot roll an 8 with a die. So the probability of rolling an 8 is 0 or 0%.

11. **154 square feet**
    $A = \pi r^2$
    $$= 3.14 \times 7 \times 7$$
    $$= 3.14 \times 49$$
    $$= 153.86 \text{ square feet}$$
    153.86 square feet rounds to 154 square feet.

12. **188 inches**   Multiply the radius by 2 to find the diameter ($30 \times 2 = 60$ in.).
    $C = \pi d$
    $$= 3.14 \times 60$$
    $$= 188.4 \text{ inches}$$
    188.4 inches rounds to 188 inches.

13. **$\frac{3}{5}$ or 60%**

    $$\frac{\text{number of nickels}}{\text{number of coins}} = \frac{3}{5} \text{ or } 60\%$$

14. **$\frac{1}{2}$ or 50%**   After a nickel has been chosen, there are 4 coins left: 2 nickels and 2 dimes.

    $$\frac{\text{number of nickels}}{\text{number of coins}} = \frac{2}{4} = \frac{1}{2} \text{ or } 50\%$$

15. **$\frac{3}{4}$ or 75%**   After a dime has been chosen, there are 4 coins left: 3 nickels and 1 dime.

    $$\frac{\text{number of nickels}}{\text{number of coins}} = \frac{3}{4} \text{ or } 75\%$$

16. **$\frac{2}{5}$ or 40%**   After a woman's name has been chosen, there are 5 names left: 3 women's names and 2 men's names.

    $$\frac{\text{number of men's names}}{\text{number of names}} = \frac{2}{5} \text{ or } 40\%$$

CUMULATIVE REVIEW

PAGES 246–247

1. **537**

2. **206 r6**

3. **2.713**

4. **0.00288**

5. **$4\frac{3}{8}$** $\quad 8 = 8\frac{8}{8}$
   $\quad\quad\quad -3\frac{5}{8} = 3\frac{5}{8}$
   $\quad\quad\quad\quad\quad\quad 4\frac{3}{8}$

6. **$7\frac{1}{2}$** $\quad 2\frac{2}{5} \times 3\frac{1}{8} = \frac{12}{5} \times \frac{25}{8} = \frac{15}{2} = 7\frac{1}{2}$

7. **81** $\quad 9^2 = 9 \times 9 = 81$

8. **30** $\quad 9 \times 40 = 360; \ 360 \div 12 = 30$

9. **125%** $\quad 40 \div 32 = 1.25 \quad 1.25 = 125\%$

10. **190,512**

11. **643**

12. **612.534**

13. **43.75**

14. **$6\frac{7}{12}$** $\qquad 2\frac{5}{6} = 2\frac{10}{12}$
$$+\ 3\frac{3}{4} = 3\frac{9}{12}$$
$$5\frac{19}{12} = 5 + 1\frac{7}{12} = 6\frac{7}{12}$$

15. **$\frac{2}{3}$** $\qquad 4\frac{1}{2} \div 6\frac{3}{4} = \frac{9}{2} \div \frac{27}{4} = \frac{\overset{1}{\cancel{9}}}{\underset{1}{\cancel{2}}} \times \frac{\overset{2}{\cancel{4}}}{\underset{3}{\cancel{27}}} = \frac{2}{3}$

16. **125** $\qquad 5^3 = 5 \times 5 \times 5 = 125$

17. **\$12** $\qquad 5\% = 0.05 \qquad \$240 \times 0.05 = \$12.00$

18. **60** $\qquad 30\% = 0.3 \qquad 18.0 \div 0.3 = 60$
$$0.3\overline{)18.0.}\ \ ^{60}$$

19. **(4) 90 + 90 + 100 + 100** To find the perimeter, add the lengths of all four sides.

20. **(3) 175–185** Round each number to the nearest ten and add to estimate the total.

63	rounds to	60
78	rounds to	80
+ 35	rounds to	+ 40
		180

21. **(4) (\$6.60 – \$6.20) ÷ \$6.20** Subtract Latrice's current wage from her new wage to find the amount of change. Then divide by the original amount, her current wage.

22. **(4) \$2,352.00** $\qquad i = p \times r \times t$
$$= \$5,600 \times 0.14 \times 3$$
$$= \$2,352$$

23. **$3\frac{1}{2}$ cups** John will double the recipe, so multiply the amount of dates ($1\frac{3}{4}$ cups) by 2.

$1\frac{3}{4} \times 2 = \frac{7}{4} \times \frac{\overset{1}{\cancel{2}}}{\underset{2}{1}} = \frac{7}{2} = 3\frac{1}{2}$

24. **\$28** Divide the part (\$9.80) by the rate (35%) to find the base.
$$35\% = 0.35 \qquad 0.35\overline{)\$9.80.}\ \ ^{\$28.}$$

25. **198 centimeters** Multiply by 100 to convert meters to centimeters.
$$1.98 \times 100 = 1.98. = 198$$

26. **28 square feet** Divide the diameter (6 feet) by 2 to find the radius ($6 \div 2 = 3$). Use the formula:
$A = \pi r^2$
$\quad = 3.14 \times 3 \times 3$
$\quad = 28.26$ rounds to 28.

POSTTEST

PAGES 248–253

1. **two million**
2. **five hundredths**
3. **25,744 > 25,447**
   7 is greater than 4.
4. **0.83 > 0.083**
   Add a zero: 0.830   0.083   Then compare.
   830 is greater than 83.
5. **421,000**
   42⓪,536 The number to the right of 0 is 5;
   add 1 to the circled digit.
6. **7.8**
   7.⑧39 The number to the right of 8 is less
   than 5. Do not change the circled digit.
7. **$1\frac{5}{6}$**   Each figure is divided into 6 equal parts.
   One figure is completely shaded, and 5 of the
   6 parts of the last figure are shaded.
8. **$3.17**
9. **4.646**
10. **292,878**
11. **208 r21**

    $$208 \text{ r } 21$$
    $$38\overline{)7{,}972}$$
    $$\underline{-76}$$
    $$325$$
    $$\underline{-304}$$
    $$21$$

12. **$9\frac{11}{20}$**

    $$3\frac{3}{4} = 3\frac{15}{20}$$
    $$+5\frac{4}{5} = 5\frac{16}{20}$$
    $$8\frac{31}{20} = 8 + 1\frac{11}{20} = 9\frac{11}{20}$$

13. **$3\frac{19}{24}$**

    $$7\frac{1}{6} = 7\frac{4}{24} = 7\overset{6\ 28}{\frac{4}{24}}$$
    $$-3\frac{3}{8} = 3\frac{9}{24} = 3\frac{9}{24}$$
    $$3\frac{19}{24}$$

14. **14**

    $$8 + 2 \times 9 \div (7-4)$$
    $$8 + 2 \times 9 \div \quad 3$$
    $$8 + \quad 18 \quad \div \quad 3$$
    $$8 + \quad\quad 6$$
    $$14$$

15. **563**
16. **40.196**
17. **384**
18. **0.00536**
19. **$5\frac{3}{5}$** $2\frac{2}{3} \times 2\frac{1}{10} = \frac{\overset{4}{8}}{\underset{1}{3}} \times \frac{\overset{7}{21}}{\underset{5}{10}} = \frac{28}{5} = 5\frac{3}{5}$
20. **$3.46**
21. **62.5**

22. **$1\frac{1}{5}$** $6\frac{2}{5} \div 5\frac{1}{3} = \frac{32}{5} \div \frac{16}{3} = \frac{\overset{2}{32}}{\underset{}{2}} \times \frac{3}{\underset{1}{16}} = \frac{6}{5} = 1\frac{1}{5}$
23. **216** $6^3 = 6 \times 6 \times 6 = 216$
24. **0.035** $3\frac{1}{2}\% = 3.5\% = .03.5 = 0.035$
25. **650%** $6.5 = 6.50. = 650\%$
26. **$\frac{3}{4}$** $75\% = \frac{75}{100} = \frac{75 \div 25}{100 \div 25} = \frac{3}{4}$
27. **60%** $3.0 \div 5 = 0.6$ $0.6 = 60\%$
28. **$14.40** $40\% = 0.4$ $36 \times 0.4 = 14.40
29. **125%** $20 \div 16 = 1.25$ $1.25 = 125\%$
30. **400** $2\% = 0.02$ $8.00 \div 0.02 = 400$
31. **30** $40 \times 9 = 360; 360 \div 12 = 30$
32. **(2) 563**   Add the number of seventh graders
    (276) and the number of eighth graders (287)
    enrolled to find the total enrollment. You do
    not need the number attending on the first
    day.

    $$\overset{1\ 1}{276}$$
    $$\underline{+\ 287}$$
    $$563$$

33. **(4) 4.8 + 4.8 + 2.3 + 2.3**   Two sides
    measure 4.8 meters, and two sides measure
    2.3 meters. Add all four measurements to find
    the perimeter.
34. **(4) 144**   To find the area, multiply the
    length (18 feet) times the width (8 feet).
    $18 \times 8 = 144$
35. **(3) 60**   Compare the number of cash
    customers (63) with the total number of
    customers (121). Round the numbers to the
    nearest ten and subtract to find the difference.

    $$121 \quad \text{rounds to} \quad 120$$
    $$\underline{-\ 63} \quad \text{rounds to} \quad \underline{-\ 60}$$
    $$60$$

36. **(5) 36 ÷ 4**   To separate an amount into
    equal parts, divide the number of chairs in the
    order (36) by the number of chairs that can be
    packed in each box (4).
37. **(2) $\frac{2}{5}$ or 40%**
    $\dfrac{\text{number of white marbles}}{\text{number of marbles}} = \dfrac{4}{10} = \dfrac{2}{5}$ or 40%
38. **(4) $2\frac{1}{2}$ x 2**   To double the recipe, multiply
    the amount of milk by 2.
39. **(1) acute; equilateral**   Each angle
    measures less than 90°, and all sides have the
    same length.

40. **(2) 2**   Multiply the base (8) times the rate (25%) $8 \times 0.25 = 2.00$

41. **(2) 0.46**   Divide 100 to change centimeters to meters.
$46 \div 100 = .46. = 0.46$

42. **(5) $25.98 ÷ 3**   To find the unit cost, divide the total cost ($25.98) by the number of shirts (3).

43. **(2) $75.40 ÷ $1,200.00**   Divide the part ($75.40) by the base ($1,200.00) to find the rate.

44. **(4) $17.00**   Divide the part ($6.80) by the rate (40%) to find the base.
$6.80 \div 0.40 = 17.00$

45. **(4)** $\frac{6}{\$4.98} = \frac{10}{?}$ Both ratios are in the same order. The first ratio means that 6 pairs cost $4.98. The second ratio means that 10 pairs cost an unknown amount.

46. **(4) ($8.60 – $8.30) ÷ $8.60**   Subtract the new wage ($8.30) from Marge's current wage ($8.60) to find the amount of change. Then divide by the original amount, her current wage.

47. **2,400 cubic inches**
$$V = l \times w \times h$$
$$= 20 \times 10 \times 12$$
$$= 2,400$$

48. **7 miles**   Round each distance and add to find the total.

$2\frac{1}{5}$	rounds to	2
$3\frac{9}{10}$	rounds to	4
$+ 1\frac{3}{10}$	rounds to	$+ 1$
		7

49. **63 tables**   Divide the number of reservations for Saturday in the ballroom (504) by the number that can be seated at each table (8).
$504 \div 8 = 63$

50. **83 feet**   Since there are 3 feet in a yard and yards are larger than feet, multiply $27\frac{2}{3}$ by 3.
$27\frac{2}{3} \times 3 = \frac{83}{3} \times \frac{\overset{1}{\cancel{3}}}{1} = \frac{83}{1} = 83$

51. **$3\frac{3}{4}$ hours**   Since 27 is close to 30, think of 1:27 as $1\frac{1}{2}$. Since 9 is close to 15, think of 5:09 as $5\frac{1}{4}$. Then subtract.
$$5\frac{1}{4} = 5\frac{1}{4} = \overset{4\ \ 5}{\cancel{5}\frac{\cancel{1}}{4}}$$
$$- 1\frac{1}{2} = 1\frac{2}{4} = 1\frac{2}{4}$$
$$3\frac{3}{4}$$

52. **154 square feet**
$$A = \pi r^2$$
$$= 3.14 \times 7 \times 7$$
$$= 3.14 \times 49$$
$$= 153.86$$
153.86 square feet rounds to 154 square feet.

53. **$5.02**   Add the cost of the paint and the brush to find the subtotal. Add the tax to find the total. Then subtract the total from the amount of cash the customer gave George.

$\overset{1\ \ 1}{\$11.37}$	$14.26	$\overset{19\ \ 9\,10}{\$20.00}$
$+ \ \ 2.89$	$+ \ \ 0.72$	$- \ 14.98$
$14.26	$14.98	$5.02

54. **3.5 inches**   Add the number of inches for August (0.9) and the number of inches for September (2.6).
$$\overset{1}{0.9}$$
$$+ \ 2.6$$
$$3.5$$

55. **126 inches**   Multiply the radius (20 in.) by 2 to find the diameter ($20 \times 2 = 40$ in.)
$$C = \pi d$$
$$= 3.14 \times 40$$
$$= 125.6$$
125.6 inches rounds to 126 inches.

56. **32**   Find the total of the numbers in the set.
$42 + 36 + 19 + 31 = 128$
Then divide by the number of items in the set.
$128 \div 4 = 32$

57. $\frac{3}{2}$
$$\frac{18 \text{ warehouse employees}}{12 \text{ drivers}} = \frac{18 \div 6}{12 \div 6} = \frac{3}{2}$$

58. **15%**   Add the amounts on the graph to find the total. Multiply by 100.
$6 + $4 + $4 + $3 + $3 = $20;
$20 \times 100 = $2,000
Divide the part ($300) by the base ($2,000) to find the rate.
$300 \div $2000 = 0.15 \qquad 0.15 = 15\%$

59. **$3,212**
$$\textit{interest} = \textit{principal} \times \textit{rate} \times \textit{time}$$
$$= \$7,300 \times 0.11 \times 4$$
$$= \$3,212$$

60. **⁺3 degrees**   Start at ⁻3 on the number line. Count 6 units to the right.

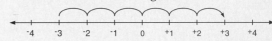

Steck-Vaughn Pre-GED Mathematics
Correlation to Mathematics Skill Books

Section	Skill	Mathematics Skill Book: Pages
1	Whole Number Theory	5500: pp. 2 – 3, 30
2	Add/Subtract Whole Numbers	5500: pp. 4 –15, 30 8800: pp. 2 –7, 19, 21
3	Multiply/Divide Whole Numbers	5500: pp. 16 – 29, 30 8800: pp. 2 –7, 21– 22
4	Squares, Cubes, and Square Roots	8800: p. 23
5	Fraction Theory	6600: pp. 2 – 5
6	Add/Subtract Fractions	6600: pp. 6 –19 8800: pp. 8 –11
7	Multiply/Divide Fractions	6600: pp. 20 – 30 8800: pp. 8 –11
8	Add/Subtract Decimals	7700: pp. 2 –7, 15, 30 8800: pp. 2 –7, 20
9	Multiply/Divide Decimals	7700: pp. 8 –13, 15, 30 8800: pp. 2 –7
10	Ratio and Proportion	8800: p. 27
11	Percent Theory	7700: pp. 16 –19, 29
12	Solving for the Part	7700: pp. 20 – 21, 28 – 30 8800: pp. 12 –14, 19
13	Solving for the Rate	7700: pp. 24 – 25, 29 – 30 8800: pp. 12 –14, 19
14	Solving for the Base	7700: pp. 26 – 27, 29 – 30
15	Percent of Change	7700: pp. 22 – 23 8800: pp. 12 –14
16	Probability Theory	
17	Triangles and Circles	8800: pp. 21– 22
18	Integers	8800: p. 24

Index

Fractions, 58–62
    adding, 73–74
    changing percents to, 165
    changing to decimals, 165
    changing to percents, 165
    cross-multiplying, 64
    decimals and, 106
    dividing, 90–91
    equal, 64
    improper, 61–62, 63–64
    like, 73
    multiplying, 89–90
    percents and, 162–163
    proper, 61–62
    raising to higher terms,
        66–67
    reducing to lowest terms,
        65–66
    subtracting, 75–76
    unlike, 73

G

Geometry (see Measurement
    and geometry)
Grams, 130
Graphs
    bar, 24–26
    circle, 176–178, 192–194
    double bar, 216–218
    line, 118–120
    pictograph, 152–155
Greater than sign, 12

I

Improper fractions, 61–64
Integers, 229, 242–243
Interest, 173
    simple, 173–175
Interest rate, 173
Inverting, dividing fractions
    and, 90
Isosceles triangle, 237

K

Key, in bar graph, 24
Kilograms, 130

L

Less than sign, 12
Like fractions, 73
Line graphs, 118–120
Liter, 131

M

Maps, 77–79, 156–158
Map scale, 156–158
Mathematical expression, 14
Mean, 133–135
Measurement and geometry
    area of rectangle, 41–43
    area of square, 41–43, 46–48
    measuring length, 92–95
    perimeter, 18–20
    time, 168–170
    using maps, 77–79
    using map scales, 156–158
    using metrics, 111–112,
        130–132
    using proportions to solve
        percent problems, 188–191
    weight changes, 219–221
Median, 133–135
Mental math, 130–132
Meter, 111
Metric system, 111–112,
    130–132
Milliliter, 131
Mixed numbers, 58–59, 61–64
Multiplication sign, 14, 35
Multiplying
    cross-multiplying, 64, 145
    decimals, 127
    fractions, 89–90
    whole numbers, 35–36
Multi-step problems, 115–117,
    133–135

N

Negative numbers, 242
New amount, 213
Number line, 229, 242
Numerator, 60–61

O

Operations, 41–43
Order of operations, 14
Original amount, 213
Outcome, 230
    dependent probability and,
        234–235
    more than one chance for,
        232–233
    probability of, 231

P

Part
    percent and, 167, 213
    solving for, 171–172
Percent, 143, 162–163
    changing decimal to, 164
    changing fraction to, 165
    changing to decimal, 164
    changing to fraction, 165
    of decrease, 214–215
    fractions and decimals and,
        162–165
    of increase, 213
    using proportions to solve
        percent problems, 188–191
Percent formula, 167
    solving for base, 198, 202–203
    solving for part, 167, 171–172
    solving for rate, 182, 186–187
Percent sign, 162
Perimeter, 18–20
Pictograph, 152–155
Place holder, 11, 109, 130
Place value, 9–10, 108–109
Plus sign, 14
Positive numbers, 242
Powers of ten, 130–132
Principal, 173–175
Probability, 228, 230
    dependent, 234–235
    of outcomes, 231–233
Problem-solving strategies
    choosing the operation, 41–43
    drawing diagrams, 92–95
    making charts, 204–206
    multi-step problems,
        115–117, 133–135
    reading scales, 156–158